NEW PERSPECTIVES
OF MAN IN ACTION

NEW PERSPECTIVES

OF MAN IN ACTION

Edited by

ROSCOE C. BROWN, JR.
New York University

BRYANT J. CRATTY
University of California

PRENTICE-HALL, INC.
Englewood Cliffs, New Jersey

10/1972
Loc

© 1969 by PRENTICE-HALL, INC., *Englewood Cliffs, New Jersey*

Library of Congress Catalog Card No. 69-10723
Printed in the United States of America

Current printing (last digit):
10 9 8 7 6 5 4 3 2 1

PRENTICE-HALL INTERNATIONAL, INC., *London*
PRENTICE-HALL OF AUSTRALIA, PTY. LTD., *Sydney*
PRENTICE-HALL OF CANADA, LTD., *Toronto*
PRENTICE-HALL OF INDIA PRIVATE LTD., *New Delhi*
PRENTICE-HALL OF JAPAN, INC., *Tokyo*

Contents

NEW PERSPECTIVES
OF MAN IN ACTION

Introduction

For centuries man has been interested in the workings of his own body. Galen, Hippocrates and Leonardo da Vinci were some of the first to investigate man in action. As the task of understanding man became more complex in the centuries that followed, scholars began to narrow their focus. Some were interested in anatomy and physiology; others in the more macroscopic components of human action. Galvani explained nerve impulse transmission; Harvey discovered blood circulation; others investigated strength and endurance.

Toward the end of the 19th century, German scientists became intrigued with perception. Breaking away from philosophers, who had continued to speculate upon the workings of the mind, they began to investigate scientifically the way man organizes his experience. In the beginning of the 20th century, American psychologists became concerned with human and animal behavior. Soon, essays dealing with the interaction of more than one man aroused an interest in man's social behaviors, and sociology was born.

During this same time, various "methods," purporting to improve man's ability on the athletic fields, began to appear in the educational programs of Europe. These methods, when they claimed a scientific base, were derived from physiology and the medical profession. In a sense this was a logical amalgamation since strength and endurance depended on respiration and circulation.

American physical educators in the 19th and early 20th century advanced the emerging profession by measuring the various bodily changes their programs seemed to be eliciting. This approach often gained support from the medical community, and several physicians were early leaders in American physical education.

In the 1920's and 1930's Hetherington, Nash, and Williams were asking and answering questions about the role of physical education in society. In addition to the exercise physiologists and the strength builders were some who inqured about the *why's* of physical activity, in order to provide a rationale for physical education programs.

Others during the first 60 years of the 20th century posed a different but related question. Scholars were beginning to demand scientific proof for the evangelical claims of activity programs. Fortunately, Henry, McCloy, Karpovich, Clarke, Dill, and others were also beginning to supply evidence from research laboratories which supported or refuted some of the exaggerated claims for physical activity which had been voiced during past decades.

If self-criticism is one of the criteria for a profession, physical educators were on the threshold of bringing themselves up from their vocational beginnings. More efficient ways were found to produce strength and endurance; some of the psychological variables were examined with increased sophistication; and a subdiscipline concerned with the social correlates of physical activity emerged, spurred on by Cassidy, Cowell, and others.

By the 1950's and 1960's, however, even more demands were made on the emerging profession. Members of other departments within colleges and universities began to ask, and then to demand, that physical educators present a rationale for their existence. School administrators insisted on seeing evidence justifying the educational worth of programs of vigorous activity.

As readers of Hans Selye know, stress may elicit helpful change or may break down the organism, depending on the hardiness of the individual, previous exposure to stress, and the severity of the stressful event. It is now becoming apparent that the organism we call the profession of physical education is beginning to adapt reasonably well to the stresses imposed on it. Signs that suggest struggle and adaptation are appearing within elementary and secondary schools, and in the institutions that produce teachers for these programs. To an increasing degree, the universities are staffing their physical education departments with men and women who have obtained penetrating backgrounds in established disciplines from which knowledge is obtained about man in action. Teachers on the playground and in the gymnasium are becoming more sophisticated about the new practices they advise and sometimes engage in library research to justify modifications they may wish to adopt. Some evaluate their efforts by measuring the behavior changes in the children they teach. Members of the profession who deal with the more global aspects of kinetic man are renewing their attempts to formulate sound theoretical and philosophical frameworks to serve as rationales for research and practice.

It is believed that this book provides examples of the present struggle and partial successes that the profession of physical education is experiencing. In general, these articles were written by younger members of departments of physical education throughout the country.[1]

These writings point to the multifaceted approach that should be employed if physical education is to be considered an academic discipline focused on the nature of man in action. Thus some of these articles deal with the organization of relevant facts, theories, and techniques. The chapters by Locke, Ismail, Liba, and Brown exemplify this multilevel approach.

Other selections focus on the formulation of subdisciplines and the relationships between them. The sections written by Loy and Malina, for example, deal with sport sociology and anthropology.

Some of the articles deal with other problems of formulating disciplinary guidelines. Those by Lamb, Williams, and Smith suggest that to incorporate the components of human movement into a valid whole, we must inspect carefully the various "pieces" that have been discussed in the past. Their discussions of biochemical changes during exercise, kinesthesis, and visual-motor coordination not only organize helpful information on these subjects, but point to directions for further research.

Eckert and Ismail present guidelines for working with young children. Cratty, Lamb, and Williams point to inherent or early acquired experience that may frustrate the efforts of the most gifted teacher.

The writers thus suggest that members of the profession should continue to search for relevant facts from the research laboratories and from within well-controlled action situations in the schools. From these facts they further recommend that various theoretical frameworks be examined, refined, and when necessary created to fit the knowledge obtained. As theories become more coherent, various subdisciplines, dealing with the intellectually manageable components of man's action patterns, should be formed. Finally, it is implied that a total and comprehensive discipline of man in action might emerge, drawing knowledge from other academic areas but at the same time having its own unique components. The strength of such a discipline, they seem to say, may be tested by the quality of the evidence it rests on, the worth of the theories that guide it, and the philosophical tenets that delineate its boundaries.

Furthermore our writers outline specific guidelines for action for

[1]Three of the chapters were written while their authors were still graduate students.

members of the profession, for our writers are people of action. They have chosen a profession whose main business is vigorous activity, and they are productive researchers, writers, and teacher educators.

The perspectives they outline for us have implications for the university researcher, the teacher educator, and the physical education instructor. Since the interpretation of each of the selections will depend on each reader's interest and experience, we urge him to formulate implications for his own professional activity as he reads.

One may not agree with many of the statements made and may consider other theories and ideas. If this occurs one purpose of the editors will have been met, for this is the type of intellectual confrontation that was intended. Intellectual progress thrives on disagreement, discussion, and confrontation.

Some of the articles may later be expanded into a book or monograph. One of the main purposes for including them in a single text was to give the reader some comprehension of the range and variety of issues and subject areas within the study of kinetic man. After this awareness is developed, the real challenge is to integrate the many ideas and approaches into unifying theories. And hopefully, from these theories, a scholarly discipline might emerge.

The initial chapter by Brown presents a survey of some of the various relationships between social, psychological, and intellectual aspects of the human personality as they may or may not influence motor performance. The failure of his data to support some of the widely accepted relationships provides a cautious and scholarly beginning to the discussions which follow.

Lamb next outlines the known complexities of the biochemical changes that occur during vigorous action. His helpful guidelines for further research delineate areas of future study which require academic backgrounds usually not found in physical education departments today. Lamb, however, aids us even further by suggesting a curriculum for further workers on these elusive and complex topics.

The next chapters point to emerging trends in the interaction of perception and movement. Smith analyzes the mechanisms that regulate the movement sense and presents a "feedback model" for the reader's consideration. Williams discusses the neurological bases of visual-motor activity and suggests areas of further research. Cratty next outlines a hypothesis that relates the concept of imprinting to the modification of perceptual-motor behaviors in the human.

Ryan discusses two perceptual types. He explains the need for educators to consider those individuals who apparently augment stimuli as against those who block out stimuli and prefer to simply act. The questions he poses contain implications for classroom teachers as well as for physical educators.

Ismail reviews research which relates motor activity to various intellectual measures. The factor analysis model that he uses for the components of the human personality is also found in the chapters by Kenyon and Brown. Liba and Safrit then discuss the ways in which factor analysis studies, exemplified in this book by the work of Brown, Kenyon, and Ismail, can be improved by utilizing new developments in that field.

The chapters by Malina, Kenyon, and Loy contain material which treats sport and physical activity within a broad sociocultural context. The discussion by Malina shows how the physical and cultural anthropologist may illuminate our understanding of man in action. Kenyon discusses the criteria and the content of the emerging subdiscipline of sport sociology. The implications he presents should be considered by anyone trying to define a new body of knowledge. Loy outlines the manner in which two theoretical systems may be integrated to form a model for the roles of sport in the resolution of problems as the individual adjusts to cultural demands.

In the concluding chapter, Locke formulates guidelines for the consideration and evaluation of movement education. He cautions against the type of reaction that is sometimes seen as teachers try to grasp and to apply a new theory. At the same time, positive guides for action are presented.

The editors are indebted to the authors for their scholarly contributions, as well as to the publishers for their patience and aid during the compilation of this text. If the content in some way encourages a student to reflect at greater length upon the directions he is taking, provides questions which may be tested by the researcher, or suggests to teachers more meaningful ways to work with children and youth, the editors' purposes have been realized.

ROSCOE C. BROWN, JR.*

The Contribution of Physical Activity
to the Integrated Development of Man

The concept of man as an integrated being dates back at least to the ancient Greeks. The idea of "mens sana in corpore sano" was expressed both in word and deed in the Golden Age of Pericles in Athens and in the Greco-Roman period that followed. The origin of the word *gymnasium* is Greece, where the gymnasium was a place to develop both the mind and the body (24). The asceticism of the Dark Ages was based in part on a philosophy that saw the mind and body as separate entities and led to the view that the body needed both moral and social discipline. The humanistic movement of the 15th and 16th centuries and the general intellectual and social awakening during the Renaissance revived the concept of man as an integrated being (24). This ideal is currently expressed in the mind-body-spirit trilogy that forms the goals of many contemporary educational organizations.

The literature in physical education has been filled with references to the development of one's physical, mental, social, and emotional well being (26). During the 1930's and 1940's references to these objectives were cited so frequently in articles and textbooks that one would have thought that there was considerable evidence to support the generalizations that were made. In all fairness, it might be noted that during this

*Department of Physical Education, Health and Recreation, School of Education, New York University.

time physical education was striving to achieve educational respectability and thus might have exaggerated its contribution to the well being of man. Physical education, however, has not been alone in extolling the contribution of physical activity to the total development of man. Many psychologists have emphasized the role of man's interaction with the environment in his total development. The Gestalt psychologists have contributed some valuable insights to this idea (25). Psychologists have often studied voluntary movement to discover some general principles about how man learns.

Within the past two decades efforts to obtain more evidence about the relationship of physical growth and physical performance to the intellectual, social, and emotional development of man have increased. Most of these efforts have centered on school children, partly because the population of school children is more accessible for research purposes, and partly because it is during the period of childhood and adolescence that the relationships of physical growth and performance may be most significant. A number of longitudinal studies have been conducted to determine the rates at which physical, social, intellectual, and emotional development occur. Probably the most comprehensive of these were the California Studies (17), under the guidance of H. E. Jones. The California Studies conducted during the 1930's and 1940's provided some interesting data on the developmental patterns of physical, intellectual, social, and emotional characteristics, but did not show the extent of the relationships between physical growth and performance and intellectual, social, and emotional development. This kind of analysis was probably not done because the purpose of the study was to see how the status of the subject on a given characteristic changed over a period of time, rather than to determine the contribution of each aspect of development to the total development of the child. Stolz and Stolz (22) also conducted an important longitudinal study but they emphasized physical growth and its relationship to other aspects of development.

Willard Olson's (18) work on the organismic age concept represents one of the first definitive attempts to quantify the contributions of certain physical growth and developmental variables to the total development of the child. Olson proposed that the developmental age of a child, that is, his status on certain variables relative to norms for his age and sex, could be used to predict his school achievement and adjustment at a particular time. Olson posited several kinds of developmental ages which could be used to determine whether a child was developing at a rate that was slower, faster, or the same as the norm. Olson used the following kinds of developmental ages in arriving at an over-all average which he called the organismic age:

Mental Age
Reading Age
Height Age
Weight Age
Dental Age
Grip Age
Organismic Age (average developmental ages)

The organismic age was simply an average of the developmental ages. Olson proposed that it would be possible to obtain a more accurate prediction of school performance using the organismic age concept than using only intelligence or past achievement scores. Klausmier (14, 15) has suggested that organismic age adds little to the prediction of academic achievement. His studies revealed that physical, personality, and sociometric variables have low correlations with reading or arithmetic scores for low, medium, and high intelligence groups. He pointed out that uneven physical development in the various physical measures might have accounted for these low relationships and that the variations in physical development warranted further research. One weakness in the organismic age concept is the idea that the various aspects of development contribute the same amount to total development and thus can be averaged. While the developmental age idea is supposed to take differential rates of growth into consideration, it is still probable that the contribution of each aspect of development to the total development of the individual varies. Nonetheless, Olson made a significant contribution in focusing attention on the fact that physical variables might influence academic achievement and social adjustment.

Several studies (1, 3, 16, 19) have attempted to relate physical growth and performance variables to academic achievement in the elementary school through college. Most of these studies have identified high and low groups on the physical indices and have compared intelligence scores, standardized achievement test scores, and grade point averages of the groups. Generally, the findings show higher academic achievement for the groups that rate high on the physical indices. These studies are far from conclusive because they do not control for factors such as socioeconomic status, nutritional status, and high motivation or aspiration, which might contribute to both physical and intellectual development.

Another group of studies (2, 6, 7, 9, 11, 12, 16) has explored the relationships between physical growth and performance and personal and social adjustment. The usual design of these studies has been to compare participants in athletics with nonparticipants or to compare high physical fitness groups with low fitness groups. The results usually show that the participants in athletics are more popular and more socially acceptable. The data on the personal adjustment is not so clear, but some studies

(20, 21) have suggested that participants in athletics have more desirable personality traits than nonathletes. Again, no other variables have been studied to determine whether there are some selective factors that might predispose certain individuals to choose to participate in athletics. These studies overlook the fact that the differences between participants and nonparticipants may be based on other factors, such as socioeconomic status, sibling order, or the athletic background of the adults in the family. A significant problem in most of these studies is the limited sample size and the limited time period during which observations are made. While these studies are suggestive of relationships between the physical status of an individual and his personal and social adjustment, they do not provide clear-cut evidence that there is a definitive contribution of physical indices to the total adjustment of the individual.

The results of the efforts described above have stimulated some researchers to look into the question of integrated development using more sophisticated research designs. As recently as 1964, a Symposium on Integrated Development was held at Purdue University (23). The purpose of this symposium was to explore some approaches that could be used in studying the contribution of physical growth and performance to intellectual, social, and emotional development. A number of various models were proposed. One model that seemed to have great promise was factor analysis. Despite some of the theoretical weaknesses of factor analysis, the technique seems to be particularly useful in identifying and exploring the various domains of integrated development. If used judiciously, factor analysis can suggest the relative contribution of each aspect of development to total development. One must remember, though, that there is great temptation to put into a factor analysis those variables that will yield the factors that one posits from his theoretical construct. The factor analysis technique quantifies the contribution of each factor to the total variance, thus giving some idea of the contribution of that factor to total development.

Kenyon (13), Ismail (10), and Brown (4) have used factor analysis to explore various aspects of integrated development. The work of Kenyon and Ismail, described in other chapters, deals with the relationship of social and intellectual domains to the physical domain. In general, their results suggest that the relationships between these domains are complex and that much further study is necessary to clarify the relationships.

Recently the writer (5) conducted a four year longitudinal study of physical, intellectual, social, and emotional development using the factor analysis approach to determine their relative contribution to academic achievement. The approach used in the study was to obtain data from a rather large sample on several variables purporting to represent the physical, intellectual, social, and emotional aspects of development; to factor analyze these data in order to identify the factors of development; and finally to compute standard scores (Mean = 5.0, SD = 1.0) for each variable comprising each factor. The standard scores for each variable comprising each factor were averaged and used to compute a score for the factor. These factor scores were then used to predict academic achievement as measured by standardized tests.

Data on the following variables were collected for 193 pupils in the third, fourth, fifth, and sixth grades:

1. Age
2. Height
3. Weight
4. Developmental channel on the Wetzel Grid
5. Right hand grip
6. Left hand grip
7. Standing Broad Jump
8. 50-yard dash
9. Otis Intelligence Score
10. Average reading score on previous Stanford Achievement Test
11. Average arithmetic score on previous Stanford Achievement Test
12. Sociometric choices
13. Social approachability score on SAS Personality Test
14. Stability score on SAS Personality Test
15. Sex

The standard scores for physical growth and physical performance variables were computed separately for boys and girls because it was found that these variables were loaded on sex. The factor scores were then used to compute multiple correlations, with the sixth grade achievement scores in reading and arithmetic and the battery median from the Stanford Achievement Test as the dependent variables.

It was found that the developmental factor structure remained fairly constant over the four year period. The factors that were identified were intellectual development, physical performance, physical growth, emotional development, and physical development. The factor structure and loadings for each factor for the sixth grade are presented in Table 1 as an example of the factor structures. Table 2 lists the factors that were identified in the third, fourth, fifth, and sixth grades. Although there were changes in the loadings on some of the variables on certain factors, there was not enough change to alter the over-all picture. One exception was the differentiation of the physical growth factor into two factors, physical development and physical growth. One conjecture about these findings is that most of the significant developmental changes involving the total organism have taken place prior to the third grade, when the children were already eight years old.

The highest prediction of sixth grade achievement in reading, arithmetic, and the battery median was achieved using the sixth grade developmental score ($R = .73$ to $.81$). The third grade developmental scores based on the pupils' status four years earlier yielded lower multiple correlations ($R = .55$ to $.68$). In all instances the intellectual factor made the greatest contribution to the prediction of achievement. When the intellectual factor was omitted in making the predictions, only the predictions using sixth grade scores yielded significant correlations. These correlations were low, however ($R = .18$ to $.24$), with the physical performance and emotional factors making the largest contributions.

Although it is possible to describe the various factors of development discretely, the findings of the study indicate that the use of scores representing physical performance, physical growth, and emotional developmental factors does not contribute significantly to increasing the efficiency of the prediction of achievement. The intellectual factor makes the major contribution in the prediction of achievement, and the non-

TABLE 1
Factor Loadings on Developmental Factors
(Sixth Grade)

VARIABLE	FACTOR 1 Physical Growth	FACTOR 2 Intellectual Development	FACTOR 3 Physical Performance	FACTOR 4 Emotional Development	FACTOR 5 Physical Development	Communality h^2
Age	—.479	.172	.047	.026	.313	.360
Height	—.825°	.017	.070	.038	.122	.703
Weight	—.695°	.002	.060	.004	—.682°	.952
Wetzel Grid	—.203	.018	—.118	.084	—.826°	.744
Right Grip	—.805°	—.033	—.294	—.100	—.168	.773
Left Grip	—.829°	—.024	—.255	—.096	—.155	.787
Standing Broad Jump	—.225	.041	—.818°	—.109	.050	.735
50-Yard Dash	—.130	—.011	—.779°	—.025	—.034	.625
Agility†	.038	.101	—.452°	—.013	—.069	.221
Battery Median	.014	.957°	—.079	—.090	—.051	.932
Intelligence	—.153	.880°	—.010	.034	.111	.812
Social Approachability	.003	.046	.003	—.828°	.043	.690
Stability	—.043	.175	.044	—.670°	—.131	.501
Sociometric	.101	.078	—.243	—.380	—.209	.263
Reading Average	—.001	.891°	—.076	—.074	—.005	.806
Arithmetic Average	.050	.845°	—.070	—.212	—.054	.769
Sex	—.355	—.025	—.217	—.520	.243	.504
VARIANCE	26.86%	29.38%	15.94%	14.76%	13.06%	

°Variables used in computing the developmental score for each factor.
†New York State Physical Fitness Agility Test was used only in the sixth grade.

TABLE 2

Loadings on Variables Contributing to Each Developmental Factor

INTELLECTUAL FACTOR

3rd grade		4th grade		5th grade		6th grade	
Par. M	.887	Reading Avg.	.883	Reading Avg.	.788	Reading Avg.	.891
Word M	.886	Arith. Avg.	.807	Arith. Avg.	.682	Arith. Avg.	.844
Spell.	.821	Bat. Med.	.955	Otis IQ	.852	Bat. Med.	.957
Lang.	.863	Otis IQ	.635			Otis IQ	.880
Arith. R.	.772						
Arith. C.	.652						
Bat. Med.	.985						
Otis IQ	.577						

PHYSICAL GROWTH FACTOR

3rd grade		4th grade		5th grade		6th grade	
Height	—.438	Height	.654	Height	.927	Height	.825
Weight	—.914	Weight	.991	Weight	.717	Weight	.695
Wetzel Grid	.612	Wetzel	—.630	R. Grip	.447	R. Grip	.805
				L. Grip	.457	L. Grip	.829

PHYSICAL DEVELOPMENT FACTOR

3rd grade	4th grade	5th grade		6th grade	
Not Identified	Not Identified	Weight	—.644	Weight	—.681
		Wetzel	.912	Wetzel	.826

PHYSICAL PERFORMANCE FACTOR

3rd grade		4th grade		5th grade		6th grade	
R. Grip	—.702	R. Grip	.590	R. Grip	—.645	St. Bd. Jump	—.818
L. Grip	—.669	L. Grip	.511	L. Grip	—.578	50-yd. Dash	—.779
St. Bd. Jump	—.548	St. Bd. Jump	.712	St. Bd. Jump	—.658	Agility Run	—.452
50-yd. Dash	.428	50-yd. Dash	.776	50-yd. Dash	.618		

EMOTIONAL FACTOR

3rd grade		4th grade		5th grade		6th grade	
Social App.	—.396	Social App.	—.563	Social App.	—.580	Social App.	—.828
Stability	—.364	Stability	—.574	Stability	—.416	Stability	—.670

intellectual factors do not significantly increase the correlations. These results suggest that there are many factors influencing the prediction of achievement which probably counterbalance the effect of certain organismic changes for the group as a whole.

The study provides a good example of the value of factor analysis in studying integrated development. The factor analysis, computed each year of the study, enabled the investigator to identify the major factors of development and to ascertain when new developmental factors emerged. Examination of the factor loadings on the developmental factors from year to year helped to identify shifts in developmental patterns before different developmental factors are identified. The results of this study show that although the total developmental structure is fairly stable, it is difficult to improve the prediction of academic performance through the use of nonintellectual variables. Perhaps an extension of the factor analysis approach to groups which have very high or very low achievement would provide more on the relationship of nonintellectual factors, particularly those in the physical or psychomotor domain, to academic achievement.

The findings of the factor analysis studies suggest that there are certain aspects of the individual's total development that can be identified and described. These studies, however, give little insight into questions concerning the extent to which physical activity is a principal determinant of or deterrent to other aspects of integrated development. Each developmental factor probably makes a variable contribution to academic performance. Also, the factors that were identified are limited by what variables were included in the original factor analysis. It is probable that the contribution of physical growth and performance to the individual's intellectual, social, and emotional development varies according to the individual and to the type of development (intellectual, social, or emotional) under consideration. Thus, the concept of integrated development is much more complex than is suggested by studies which compare high and low physical groups or performance groups. What is needed are some theoretical models that can be used to postulate the nature of contributions of physical activity to integrated development.

What are some models that can be postulated concerning integrated development? Two of the more prominent possibilities are the genetic model and the environmental model. The genetic model suggests that there is a predetermined rate at which different physical, intellectual, and emotional characteristics develop and that the level of the interaction is determined by the genetic pattern. Closely akin to this model is the maturation model, which suggests that the level of learning or performance is a function of the readiness of the nervous system to respond, such responsivity being genetically determined. The genetic model would be tested best during early infancy and early childhood, up to age three to four, in order to minimize environmental effects. Unfortunately, environmental factors are so prevalent, even in early infancy, that it is practically impossible to test the genetic model of integrated development. The environmental model accounts for many of the environmental factors that affect integrated development, but cannot be considered to be the real determinant of the rate of development or the general quality of development, which is determined genetically.

Possibly a more feasible and more meaningful model is what could be called an "interaction" model. The substance of this model is that there is an interaction between the genetically determined aspects of physical, intellectual, and emotional development, and the environmental influences, such as nutrition, quality of interpersonal and social interaction, and the challenges of the physical environment, that is, temperature or

Figure 1. *Interaction model of integrated development to predict academic achievement.*

Variables	*Genetically Determined*	*Interaction*	*Environmental Modifications*[*]
Physical	1. Growth—Hgt. Wgt.	◄———►	1. Strength—Resistance to Fatigue
	2. Perceptual Motor Patterns	◄———►	2. Rate of acquisition of perceptual motor patterns through experience
	3. Basic Coordination (hand-eye, foot-eye, etc.)	◄———	
	4. Maturation	◄———	
Intellectual	1. Cognitive functions such as memory and association.	◄———►	Reinforcement of cognitive functions
	2. Speed of maturation of ability to perform various intellectual functions.	◄———	
Social	*Not genetically determined.*	———►	1. Interaction of individual with parents, peers, siblings.
		———►	2. Response to social needs of the individual.
		———►	3. Nature of family group
Emotional	1. Level of response to various stimuli (temperature, sound, hunger, etc.)	◄———►	1. Response of parents, siblings, peers, and teachers to individual's needs
	2. Autonomic responses to stress	◄———►	2. Response to environmental challenges

PREDICTED OUTCOME ▼

A Given Level of Academic Achievement
as determined by the Magnitude and
Degree of the Interaction

[*]The magnitude of each vector varies according to the individual and the degree of the interaction.

physical topography. This interaction provides a feedback that can augment or inhibit genetically determined patterns so that certain physical, intellectual, and social behaviors are either augmented or inhibited. As in the case of a computer program some of the feedbacks can be repeated, while in other cases, new feedbacks may occur. The interaction model allows for a limitless number of possibilities and permutations to understand integrated development. Each specific hypothesis about the relationship of physical activity to intellectual, emotional, or social development provides for various types and levels of feedback as a basis for hypothesized outcomes. An example of the use of the feedback model to explain the role of physical growth and performance in the prediction of academic achievement is presented to show an application of the model to one phase of integrated development. (See Fig. 1)

Variations of the model could be used to predict other aspects of integrated development, such as reaction to stress or ability to interact with others.

SUMMARY

The goal of understanding the role of physical growth and performance in the integrated development of man is certainly feasible. In order to achieve this goal, however, it is important that approaches which oversimplify the relationships be avoided. It is unfortunate that some physical educators make exaggerated claims about the contribution of physical activity to man's total well being. Not only are these claims often untrue, but also they have no sound theoretical basis. As has been indicated in this chapter there are many investigators who have been concerned with the interrelationships of physical, intellectual, social, and emotional development, and as a result the level of insight and sophistication in these areas is increasing. More knowledge will be gained about the relationship of physical activity to the integrated development of man if future research designs are based on a variety of models to test hypotheses about integrated development.

REFERENCES

1. Appleton, Lloyd O., "The Relationship Between Physical Ability and Success at the U.S. Military Academy." Doctoral dissertation, New York University, 1949.
2. Biddulph, Lowell G., "Athletic Achievement and Personal and Social Adjustment of High School Boys." *Research Quarterly*, XXV (1954), 1.

3. Brace, David K., "Some Objective Evidence of the Value of Physical Education." *Journal of Health and Physical Education*, IV (1933), 36.

4. Brown, Jr., Roscoe C., "The Role of Physical and Motor Performance in Intellectual Development." *Symposium on Integrated Development* (Lafayette, Ind.: Purdue University, 1964), pp. 11–18.

5. ———, and Henderson, Edward H., "Developmental Index for Describing Child Development," *Instructional Improvement Through Research.* (Albany, N.Y.: New York State Education Dept., 1965), pp. 207–209.

6. Clarke, H. Harrison, and Clarke, David H., "Social Status and Mental Health of Boys as Related to Their Maturity, Structural and Strength Characteristics." *Research Quarterly*, XXXII (1961), 326.

7. ———, and Green, Walter H., "Relationships Between Personal-Social Measures Applied to 10-year-old Boys." *Research Quarterly*, XXXIV (1963), 288.

8. ———, and Jarman, Boyd O., "Scholastic Achievement of Boys 9, 12 and 15 years of Age as Related to Various Strength and Growth Measures." *Research Quarterly*, XXXII (1961), 155–62.

9. Fulton, Ruth E., and Prange, Elizabeth M., "Motor Learning of Highly Chosen and Unchosen Teammates." *Research Quarterly*, XXI (1950), 126.

10. Ismail, A. H., "Motor Aptitude Items and Academic Achievement," *Symposium on Integrated Development.* (Lafayette, Ind.: Purdue University, 1964), pp. 19–31.

11. Jones, Harold E., "Physical Ability as a Factor in Social Adjustment in Adolescence." *Journal of Educational Research*, IV (1946), 287.

12. Jones, Mary C., and Bayley, Nancy, "Physical Maturing Among Boys as Related to Behavior." *Journal of Educational Psychology*, XLI (1950), 129.

13. Kenyon, Gerald S., "The Contribution of Physical Activity to Social Development." *Symposium on Integrated Development.* (Lafayette, Ind.: Purdue University, 1964), pp. 48–54.

14. Klausmeier, H. J., Beeman, A., and Lehmann, I. I., "Comparison of Organismic Age and Regression Equations in Predicting Achievements in Elementary Schools." *Journal of Educational Psychology*, XLIX (1958), 182–86.

15. ———, and Feldhusen, John F., "Organic Development: Relationships Among Physical, Mental Achievement, Personality and Sociometric Measures." *Symposium on Integrated Development*, (Lafayette, Ind.: Purdue University, 1964), pp. 35–45.

16. McGraw, L. W., and Tolbert, J. W., "Sociometric Status and Athletic Ability of Junior High School Boys." *Research Quarterly*, XXIV (1953), 72.

17. National Society for the Study of Education, Forty-third Yearbook, Part I, *Adolescence.* (Chicago: University of Chicago Press, 1944), pp. 100–180.

18. Olson, Willard C., *Child Development* (Boston: D. C. Heath, 1949).

19. Rarick, G. Lawrence, and McKee, Robert, "A Study of Twenty Third Grade Children Exhibiting Extreme Levels of Achievement on Tests of Motor Efficiency." *Research Quarterly*, XX (1949), 142.

20. Salz, Arthur E., "Comparison Study of Personality of Little League Champions, Other Players in Little League and Non-Playing Peers." Unpublished Master's thesis, Pennsylvania State University, 1957.

21. Seymour, Emery A., "A Comparative Study of Certain Behavior Characteristics of Participant and Non-Participant Boys in Little League Baseball." Unpublished Doctoral dissertation, Springfield College, 1955.

22. Stolz, Herbert, and Stolz, Lois, *Somatic Development of Adolescent Boys* (New York: MacMillan Co. 1951).

23. *Symposium of Integrated Development* (Lafayette, Ind.: Purdue University, 1964), p. 61.

24. Van Dalen, Deobald B., Mitchell, Elmer D., and Bennett, Bruce L., *A World History of Physical Education* (Englewood Cliffs, N.J.: Prentice-Hall, Inc., 1953), pp. 54–75.

25. Williams, Jesse F., *Principles of Physical Education* (Philadelphia: W. B. Saunders, 1942), p. 250.

26. Woodworth, Robert S., *Contemporary Schools of Psychology* (New York: Ronald Press, 1948), p. 121.

DAVID R. LAMB*

New Perspectives
on Exercise Physiology

This chapter was written with a threefold purpose in mind. First, it is hoped that it will stimulate those with an interest in the performing body to apply the methods of biochemistry to research in exercise physiology. Second, some of the fascinating problems in this field have been outlined, and speculation has been offered on how basic knowledge of the biochemical responses, when applied to exercise and training, may lead to important applications in the fields of physical education and athletics. Finally, an attempt has been made to support the proposition that every exercise physiologist should have a solid academic background in biochemistry.

THE CHEMICAL NATURE OF MOVEMENT

It is not entirely obvious that chemistry plays any role at all in movement or exercise. What a person sees during a movement such as a one-handed jump shot in basketball is usually a complex series of movements produced by some mechanism involving the shortening and lengthening of muscles.

In reality, such a complex movement begins with electrochemical reactions in the retinas of the eyes and the receptors of the other sense organs. These electrochemical stimuli are transmitted by further reactions

*Department of Physical Education, University of California at Los Angeles.

along sensory nerves to the brain where they are chemically interpreted as a signal calling for a motor response known as "jump shot." Motor stimuli then converge, by way of motor neurons, on the motor endplates of the muscle fibers involved, where the stimuli catalyze the chemical reactions that produce the energy needed for muscle contraction. Muscle contraction itself is probably dependent on chemical bonding for its maintenance.

Even while the chemical reactions producing an actual movement are occurring in the muscles, other important reactions are taking place throughout the body. Fatty acids and glucose are released to the bloodstream from fat depots and liver stores to be extracted and oxidized by the muscles and other tissues. Electrons are transported to molecular oxygen in the mitochondria[1] of the cells as the final step in the oxidative process that underlies the aerobic production of energy. At the same time, cell walls are undergoing changes in permeability so that nutrients can enter and metabolic wastes leave the cells more readily. In short, all movements are a series of integrated chemical reactions designed to keep the body in a condition of homeostasis during and after the movements.

TRADITIONAL EXERCISE PHYSIOLOGY

Historically, exercise physiology has sometimes been the ancillary to the other areas of physiology. It was apparently thought to be a rather unexciting applied field instead of a basic science. Consequently, the basic biochemical mechanisms of physiological response to exercise and physical training were often neglected. Although many studies were reported on changes in heart rate, muscle strength, body temperature, and oxygen consumption during and after exercise, little research was directed at discovering the alterations in body chemistry responsible for those changes.

There were several reasons for the often superficial study of exercise physiology. First, an investigator in this "low-brow" field was often motivated by a desire to improve the performance of athletes and was therefore interested in developing simple physiological methods that could be used on the athletic fields. He may have studied grip strength or heart rate, for example, hoping to use these measures as predictors of success in wrestling or track and field. Although these objectives were perfectly respectable, little basic knowledge of exercise physiology resulted from trying to attain them.

Second, the exercise physiologist was often a physiologist by avocation,

---

[1]The mitochondria, small particles in the cytoplasm of the cells, contain most of the enzyme systems for oxidative energy production.

not by academic training. He may have lacked the background in chemistry and physics necessary to undertake a basic physiological investigation. Fortunately, this situation is rapidly disappearing since the importance of such a background is becoming more widely accepted.

Finally, many of the techniques needed for sophisticated research in exercise physiology have only recently been developed. In the past the stopwatch, the mercury manometer, the electrocardiograph and the Douglas bag were the common tools of the exercise physiologist. Chromatography,[2] electrophoresis,[3] and spectrophotometry[4] are relatively new techniques. Now that these more sophisticated methods are available, more insight should be gained into the nature of the physiological aspects of physical activity.

PROBLEM AREAS FOR A BIOCHEMICAL APPROACH TO EXERCISE PHYSIOLOGY

Metabolic Pathways

A *metabolic pathway* is a series of interrelated chemical reactions by which a given chemical compound is degraded or synthesized within the organism. In Figure 1, a simplified pathway for glycogen degradation in skeletal muscle is shown. This pathway will serve to illustrate all of the succeeding examples of needed research in exercise physiology.

For those unfamiliar with metabolic pathways, it should be pointed out that muscle glycogen, the storage form of carbohydrate in the muscle cells and a polymer of glucose, is the start of the pathway at the top of Figure 1. In reaction number one, a six-carbon molecule of glucose is split from glycogen, and an inorganic phosphate ion is attached to the glucose. This glucose-1-phosphate molecule is broken down by the next nine reactions into two three-carbon molecules of a pyruvic acid salt, pyruvate.

At this point, the pathway can assume two different directions. If the muscles are using oxygen faster than it can be supplied by the blood so that no oxygen is available in the tissues (e.g., during the last 100 yards of a 440 yard dash), the pyruvate is reduced to lactate (reaction 11). When enough oxygen is supplied by the blood to meet muscular demands, a carbon dioxide molecule (CO_2) is cleaved from the three-carbon pyruvate (reaction 12), leaving a two-carbon acetyl molecule bound to a molecule known as Coenzyme A. The acetyl Coenzyme A

[2]Chromatography is a method used to separate chemical constituents of a solution from each other by differentially adsorbing the solutes on various adsorbing substances.

[3]Electrophoresis is a method of separating proteins in solution by determining their migration characteristics in an electrical field.

[4]Spectrophotometry is a method of determining the concentration of a chemical in solution by measuring the transmission of light through the solution.

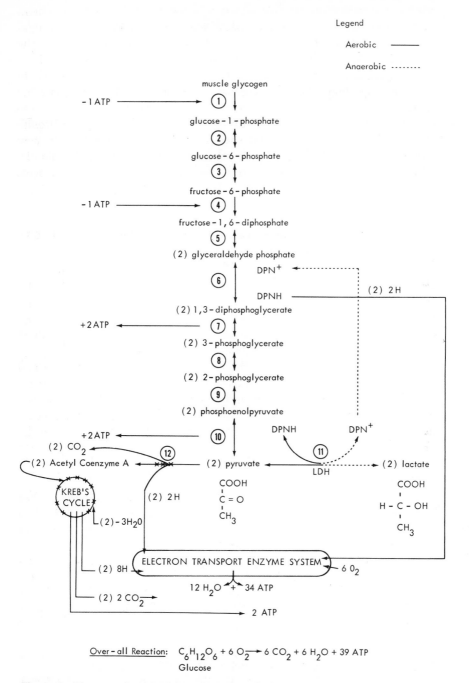

Figure 1. *Glycogen degradation in skeletal muscle.*

molecule then enters the Kreb's Cycle. Here the two-carbon molecule is degraded completely to carbon dioxide and hydrogen atoms. The hydrogen atoms are transferred to molecular oxygen in the mitochondria of the cells by way of a chain of enzymes and coenzymes called the *electron transport system.*

Most of the reactions involved here are reversible. Each of the reactions is speeded up by a protein enzyme molecule. In some cases, as in reactions 6 and 11, the enzyme is ineffective unless a coenzyme is present. In reactions 6 and 11, the coenzymes are DPN^+, the oxidized form of diphosphopyridine nucleotide, and DPNH, the reduced form of the nucleotide.

The kinesiologist is concerned with this particular metabolic pathway because it produces ATP (adenosine triphosphate), which is the high-energy compound thought to be linked directly to muscle contraction. Without ATP, muscle contraction cannot occur. Note that under anaerobic conditions, a net of only three molecules of ATP is produced per glucose-1-phosphate molecule, whereas under aerobic conditions, those same three ATP molecules are added to two ATP molecules produced in the Kreb's Cycle and 34 produced via the electron transport system. One reason that a runner can run so much longer at one-half speed than at full speed is that 13 times as much ATP is produced for each molecule of glucose at half speed than at full speed. This pathway also helps to explain why it is much more efficient for a distance runner to run at a steady rate of speed rather than at alternately fast and slow speeds.

Although glucose and glycogen metabolism were previously thought to be the primary means of producing ATP during exercise, it has now been fairly well established that the oxidation of fatty acids can account for most of the ATP production during some types of exercise (2). The elucidation of important metabolic pathways during different types of exercise and after different regimens of physical training offers unlimited potential for research by the exercise physiologist with a background in biochemistry.

Enzyme Activity

One of the important fields for exercise physiologists to study is that of enzyme activity changes during exercise and training. Since enzyme action is necessary for an effective rate of chemical reaction, it is important to know if some enzymes are activated or inhibited during exercise to increase or decrease the rates of various reactions. For example, if the enzyme that catalyzes reaction four of Figure 1 were inhibited by an increase of some substance in the tissues, ATP production via the glycolytic pathway might be severely restricted. A hypothetical application of such a finding in athletics would be the removal of the dietary source of the inhibiting substance.

Besides activation and inhibition of enzymes already present, the genetic synthesis of certain enzymes needs to be investigated. A genetic deficiency of an enzyme or enzymes could explain some of the individual differences in athletic performance that are often observed. All of us know individuals who look like the "athletic type" but who seem unable to increase their strength or endurance no matter how hard they train. When the gene that produces *phosphorylase* (the enzyme catalyzing the cleavage of muscle glycogen in reaction 1 of Figure 1) is defective, the capacity for muscular work is markedly decreased (5). No matter how diligently one trains, if he has this kind of genetic deficiency, he will not be able to increase his work capacity to any significant extent. Exercise physiologists should study the occurrence of such deficiencies in populations of good and poor performers.

Although each of us has several inborn enzyme deficiencies which may account for some of our poor physical performances, a more common phenomenon in enzyme synthesis is a relative increase or decrease in the *rate* of enzyme synthesis as the result of environmental stress (1, 11). Mechanisms for the adaptive increase or repression of enzyme synthesis have been postulated and confirmed experimentally (8). Since the amount of an enzyme present in an enzyme-substrate[5] system is a vital factor in determining the rate at which end-products are formed, it is important to know if chronic exercise stimulates or retards the synthesis of enzymes with a resultant change in the capacity of the organism to produce and utilize energy at a rapid rate.

For example, under anaerobic conditions it would seem desirable to have a large quantity of the enzyme *lactic dehydrogenase* (LDH) to increase the rate of lactate formation and DPN^+ formation in reaction 11 of Figure 1. The DPN^+ formed would enable reaction 6 to continue, and the ATP production in reactions 7 and 10 could then proceed. Indeed, it has been reported in the Russian literature that rats trained by swimming do have greater LDH activity in skeletal muscle (13). Workers in this country have not confirmed those findings, however (3, 4). Further information on enzyme activity changes after exercise can be found in Kendrick-Jones and Perry (9).

Studies on enzymes should not be restricted to general enzyme activity, because it has been shown that some enzymes (e.g. LDH) are made up of *subunits* which can be combined to form several different *isoenzymes*.[6] Lactic dehydrogenase has been shown to consist of five isoenzymes made up of two different subunits combined in tetrads (12). Under certain

[5]A substrate is a compound that enters into an enzyme-catalyzed reaction.
[6]Isoenzymes are different forms of an enzyme which catalyzes a given reaction.

conditions, one subunit preferentially shifts the equilibrium of reaction 11 to the left and can be called $(+)$ for aerobic, and the other shifts the reaction toward lactic acid and can be called $(-)$ for anaerobic. Figure 2 depicts the different tetrads of $(+)$ and $(-)$ subunits which make up the five isoenzymes of LDH.

Figure 2. *Subunit combinations in the five isoenzymes of LDH.*

(1) $++++$ (2) $+++-$ (3) $++--$ (4) $+---$ (5) $----$

One very interesting study on the LDH isoenzyme activities in the flight muscles of birds showed that birds capable of continued flight for many hours (aerobic work) had isoenzyme 5 of Figure 2 almost exclusively, whereas birds incapable of sustained flight had isoenzyme 1 exclusively (12). Birds of intermediate range flight capacity had isoenzymes 2, 3, and 4. However, the question of whether different types of training may be responsible for stimulating the synthesis of one or another subunit hybrid of LDH in humans remains unanswered. One might be tempted to speculate the interval training for a 440 yard event might cause more of the $(-)$ LDH subunit to be synthesized, whereas training for two miles would stimulate $(+)$ subunit synthesis.

Vitamins, Coenzymes, and Inorganic Cofactors

A *vitamin* is an organic compound that is required for the normal physiological maintenance of an organism. Since the organism cannot synthesize a vitamin, it must be supplied in the diet, in a pill, or in an injection. Although most physical educators know that vitamins are necessary, these compounds are usually thought to be essential for "strong bones," "good eyes," and "good, red blood." Actually, many of the vitamins are important because they form the basic structure of essential coenzymes that act in conjunction with enzymes to catalyze chemical reactions.

In our metabolic pathway for glycogen breakdown (See Figure 1), we have included two coenzymes explicitly, diphosphopyridine nucleotide and Coenzyme A. The vitamin *niacin* contributes to the structure of DPN, and *pantothenic acid* is required as a part of Coenzyme A. Without DPN, reactions 6 and 11 could not occur because DPN serves as a carrier of hydrogen atoms to the electron transport system. Without Coenzyme A, reaction 12 and succeeding reactions in the aerobic production of ATP would not occur. *Riboflavin* is necessary for some of the coenzymes in the Kreb's Cycle and the electron transport system, whereas *thiamine* is a vital factor in the removal of carbon dioxide from pyruvic acid in reaction 12.

Although vitamin supplementation has usually proved of little value in athletics, some studies have shown that vitamins should not be completely overlooked. For example, thiamine deficient rats have much shorter endurance times than normals, and administration of thiamine to such animals restores their work capacity (10). Vitamin supplementation studies for prolonged training periods using humans and animals, however, have not been conducted.

Referring again to reactions 6 and 11 of Figure 1, it should be obvious that the DPN$^+$:DPNH ratio may be a critical factor in determining the direction this metabolic pathway takes. If that ratio is high, then reaction 6 should proceed readily to the diphosphate compound, whereas reaction 11 should proceed to the left. One might speculate on a possible mechanism for adaptation to physical training that would speed up the incorporation of niacin into DPN or one that would change the rate of hydrogen transfer in the electron transport system to alter the DPN$^+$:DPNH ratio.

Several inorganic ions are required as *cofactors*[7] in various metabolic pathways. Magnesium ion, for example, is required as a cofactor in several of the reactions of Figure 1. Copper and iron are important cofactors in the electron transport system. Since such minute quantities of these ions are required, it does not seem probable that mineral supplements would have much effect on athletic performance, but the problem has not been throughly investigated.

Hormones

Hormones, substances produced in specialized cells of the body, have effects on nearly all the cells of the organism. The roles of most hormones in the physiological adaptation to exercise and training are unknown. Although the mechanisms of hormone action are obscure, they are probably intimately associated with enzyme activation and inhibition or with transport of nutrients across cell membranes.

As one of its major functions, *epinephrine*, produced in the adrenal glands, stimulates the production of a cofactor needed for phosphorylase activity. Thus, glycogen degradation in reaction 1 of Figure 1 could not begin without epinephrine since phosphorylase is the enzyme required for the reaction. *Glucagon, from the* α—cells of the pancreas, has a similar action on liver glycogen, whereas *insulin,* from the β—cells of the pancreas, probably increases the transport of glucose from the blood across the cell walls.

Each of the above hormones may affect the metabolic pathway for

[7]Cofactors are compounds which are essential for the activity of certain enzymes.

glycogen degradation and the capacity for exercise. It has been clearly demonstrated, for example, that removal of the adrenal glands markedly reduces an animal's work capacity (6, 7). Other hormones influence mineral and water metabolism, blood pressure, oxidative enzyme activity, digestion, and cell growth. The study of hormones and exercise provides a vast area for basic research in exercise physiology. Techniques for hormone assay are rapidly being improved and simplified. The day may come when an athletic trainer can detect hormone imbalances by a simple urine test and then correct the imbalances or alter training schedules to get the best performance possible from his athletes.

LABORATORY ANIMAL RESEARCH

Most of the research problems we have outlined must be approached at the cellular level and require the use of body tissues. Since most human research in this area is rather impractical, this type of research must begin with laboratory animals.

Kinesiologists are sometimes skeptical of data not obtained from human experimentation. Their reasoning may be based on one or more of the following three assumptions. First, animal research is a waste of time. Any experiment on animals, some say, can be performed equally as well on man. Second, nearly all of the medical research of value to man has resulted from human experimentation. Third, man is a higher being. His makeup is different from that of lower animals, so the results of animal research do not apply to humans.

The first assumption has already been partially refuted by the fact that obtaining tissues from humans is very difficult to do on a large scale. Too many incorrect conclusions have been drawn from clinical studies on one, two, or three human subjects. With animals, one can control diet, temperature, humidity, noise, light, and a multitude of other environmental factors that can have profound effects on experimental results in either man or animals. Animals can be obtained relatively inexpensively so that statistically adequate numbers of subjects can be used. Many laboratory animals reproduce rapidly so that experimental results can be followed for several generations. Experimental agents that may produce fatal toxic reactions or side effects can be used on animals with a resultant saving of many human lives. When a safe experimental procedure is under study, when adequate numbers of subjects are available, and when sound experimental controls can be ensured, humans should be studied if possible. But many valuable experimental techniques cannot be used on humans, and results should first be well established on animals.

The second assumption can be disposed of rapidly by merely listing a few of the major medical discoveries that have occurred as a direct result of laboratory animal research: (a) diphtheria toxins and antitoxins, (b) tuberculin vaccine, (c) hormone production, (d) physiological mechanisms controlling heart rate, blood pressure, and kidney function, (e) effects of atomic radiation, (f) necessity for vitamins and minerals, (g) effects of industrial fumes on internal organs, (h) the cell theory, (i) modern genetics, (j) sulfa drugs, and (k) the value of artificial organs.

Assumption three is somewhat more difficult to refute because there is some truth in it. Indeed, we can never be absolutely certain that a phenomenon observed in animals also occurs in man until it is directly observed in man. But history has proven that many results in animals do apply directly to man, and many of those that do not apply directly require only slight modifications.

There are several reasons why experiments on lower animals have provided us with so much information concerning man. First, the majority of the chemical reactions occurring within living cells in a lower animal are identical with those in man. The material responsible for protein synthesis, whether in a bacterium or a human liver cell, is composed of four basic chemical compounds that determine which enzyme proteins are produced in the cell. Although evolution sometimes alters genetic material so that one or another enzyme is either not produced or is functionally altered, most enzyme systems are identical from cell to cell in all animal species. If identical enzymes are present, then very similar metabolic pathways must result since only enzyme-catalyzed reactions will occur to any significant extent.

By restricting experimentation to mammalian species, even closer agreement between human and animal biochemistry can be expected. Obviously there are some species differences which must be considered, such as relative quantities of hormones produced, diet, basal metabolic rate, spontaneous exercise drive, and vitamin requirements. But when such differences are recognized, and efforts are made to test conclusions drawn from animal experiments on humans, animal research can provide many answers to problems in human exercise physiology.

ACADEMIC PREPARATION FOR EXERCISE PHYSIOLOGISTS

Some people might argue that the exercise physiologist is best educated in departments of physiology or in medical schools. The "pure" physiologist or the medical doctor usually has little or no background in the varied aspects of exercise and athletics. Since the exercise physiologist should have a thorough knowledge of all aspects of human movement, it seems only logical that the exercise physiologist should be trained in departments of kinesiology and physical education.

If the biochemical mechanisms for adaptation to exercise and training are to be elucidated by people with a physical education background, then the university education of these people must include a large amount of work in the biological sciences. Although no course list could possibly cover all cases, the following should provide a working outline of science courses necessary for a reasonable understanding of exercise physiology. This list does not include those normally taught within physical education departments such as exercise physiology, biomechanics, and applied anatomy. In enumerating the number of courses needed, it has been assumed that each course meets five hours per week for ten weeks plus six hours of laboratory per week in the case of courses requiring laboratory work.

Mathematics (through Calculus) (4)	Histology (1)
Physics (2)	Cell Physiology (1)
General Chemistry (3)	General Biochemistry (3)
Organic Quantitative Analysis (1)	Mammalian Physiology (4)
General Zoology (1)	Radiobiology (1)
Gross Anatomy (2)	Statistics (4)
General Physiology (1)	

This sequence of courses will require a rather early decision on the part of the student to concentrate in the area of exercise physiology. Most of these courses should be taken on the undergraduate and early graduate level to leave time for work in advanced topics of physiology and biochemistry, surgical techniques, and laboratory methods.

SUMMARY

The points discussed in this chapter can be summarized as follows:
1. The methods of biochemistry should be applied to studies in exercise physiology because movement is a complex series of chemical reactions which must be understood before movement itself is understood. The basic biochemical mechanisms of exercise must be discovered before sophisticated applications of exercise physiology can be made to athletics and physical education.
2. Research in human movement is the foundation for an academic discipline in physical education or kinesiology. Therefore, exercise physiology, the study of the physiological mechanisms responsible for movement, is a proper concern for physical educators.
3. Physical educators have previously been concerned with gross meas-

urements in exercise physiology because of their immediate applicability to athletic training. If further progress is to be made in the physiology of athletic training, then physical educators must have the science background to study the biochemical aspects of exercise physiology.

4. Our knowledge of exercise biochemistry may soon point the way to improved training techniques.

   a. An understanding of metabolic pathways for energy production and how those pathways are altered can be applied to the coaching of many events.

   b. Progress is being made in the field of enzyme adaptation as one of the effects of training. As yet, however, no specific applications can be made to training.

   c. The genetic absence of certain enzymes may account for the failure of some to respond "normally" to **athletic** training.

   d. Vitamins act in conjunction with **enzymes** to speed up chemical reaction rates and are essential to energy production. However, most Americans receive enough vitamins in their diet, and supplements are not generally needed.

   e. Hormonal imbalances can have powerful effects on the body, and physical educators should be aware of imbalance symptoms in pupils and athletes. The administration of hormones to improve athletic performance cannot be done routinely because of harmful side effects.

5. Many of the biochemical mechanisms involved in human physiology have been and will be elucidated through animal experimentation. Physical educators should not reject the study of animals in their quest to solve human problems.

REFERENCES

1. Beaton, J. R., "Note on Liver Enzyme Activities in Thyroid-Fed and in Cold-Exposed Rats." *Canadian Journal of Biochemistry and Physiology,* XLI (1963), 2041–44.

2. Friedberg, S. J., and Estes, E. H., Jr., "Direct Evidence for the Oxidation of Free Fatty Acids by Peripheral Tissues." *Journal of Clinical Investigation,* XLI (1962), 677–81.

3. Gollnick, P. D., and Hearn, G. R., "Lactic Dehydrogenase Activities of Heart and Skeletal Muscle of Exercised Rats." *American Journal of Physiology,* CCI (1961), 694–96.

4. Gould, M. K., and Rawlinson, W. A., "Biochemical Adaptation as a Response to Exercise; 1. Effect of Swimming on the Levels of Lactic Dehydrogenase, Malic Dehydrogenase and Phosphorylase in Muscles of 8, 11, and 15 Week Old Rats." *Biochemical Journal,* LXXIII (1959), 41–44.

5. Hers, H. G., "Glycogen Storage Disease," in R. Levine and R. Luft (eds.), *Advances in Metabolic Disorders*, Vol. 1 (New York: Academic Press, 1964), pp. 1–44.

6. Ingle, D. J., and Luckens, F. D. W., "Reversal of Fatigue in the Adrenal-ectomized Rat by Glucose and Other Agents." *Endocrinology*, XXIX (1941), 443–52.

7. ———, and Nezamis, J. E., "The Effects of Adrenal Cortex Extract With and Without Epinephrine upon the Work of Adrenally Insufficient Rats." *Endocrinology*, XLIV (1949), 559–64.

8. Jacob, F., and Monod, J., "Genetic Regulatory Mechanisms in the Synthesis of Proteins." *Journal of Molecular Biology*, III (1961), 318–56.

9. Kendrick-Jones, J., and Perry, S. V., "Enzymatic Adaptation to Contractile Activity in Skeletal Muscle." *Nature*, CCVIII (1965), 1068–70.

10. Kniazuk, M., and Molitor, H., "The Influence of Thiamine-Deficiency on Work Performance in Rats." *Journal of Nutrition*, LXXX (1944), 362–72.

11. Vaughan, D. A., Hannon, J. P., and Vaughan, L. N., "Interrelations of Diet and Cold Exposure on Selected Liver Glycolytic Enzymes." *American Journal of Physiology*, CCI (1961), 33–36.

12. Wilson, A. C., Cahn, R. D., and Kaplan, N. O., "Functions of the Two Forms of Lactic Dehydrogenase in the Breast Muscle of Birds." *Nature*, CXCVII (1963), 331–34.

13. Yampolskaya, L. I., "Biochemical Changes in the Muscles of Trained and Untrained Animals Under the Influence of Light Loads." (Russian) *Fiziologicheski Zhurnal SSSR*, XXXIX (1952), 91–99.

JUDITH L. SMITH[*]

Kinesthesis:
A Model for Movement Feedback

Educators have demonstrated repeatedly that learning is impeded unless the learner receives some knowledge about his performance. Such knowledge has been referred to as feedback. Instructors of physical education have used this concept by devising teaching methods and measurement techniques designed to provide the student with feedback about his movement process or the movement product, usually involving a projectile. Information concerning either the movement process or product is provided by auditory, visual, tactile cues or by combinations of such external feedback. The performer also has the potential of being aware of his movement process through kinesthetic feedback, internal feedback which enables him to perceive his own movement without the aid of experoceptive cues.

Central to the development of many instructional methods in physical education is the augmentation of the performer's awareness of his kinesthetic feedback. For example, manual assistance is used while teaching a skill to help the learner "get the feeling" of the proper movement sequence. Similarly, instructors often ask learners to attend to a particular set of external cues with which they can compare or "check" their kinesthetic feedback. Filming the .performance with a videotaper or a movie or graph-sequence camera enables the performer to visualize his

[*]Department of Physical Education—Women, University of Wisconsin. The author is indebted to Professor Maja Schade, Mr. Gordon R. Stephenson, and Miss Anne E. Atwater for comments based upon an earlier draft of this chapter.

movement process. This additional visual information may help him become more aware of the details of his movement (49). Likewise, measurement techniques, such as the Volleyball-Pass Test of Liba and Stauff (29), are designed to give the performer knowledge about certain components of the ball's projection. With such knowledge, specific faults of the movement process can be more readily identified by the performer who soon learns to "feel" the difference between a volleyball pass which has proper vertical and horizontal projections and one which does not.

Although kinesthetic perception has been central to these teaching methods, knowledge about it is meager. Scott's statement in 1955 is pertinent:

> In spite of the fact that physical educators have recognized for years that the sense of kinesthesis must have a relationship to motor performance, we really know very little about how to identify . . . varying degree[s] of . . . acuity. (45: 224)

Attempts to identify the components of kinesthesis, to measure kinesthetic perception, and to investigate its role in learning or general motor ability, have been disappointing. One of the most crucial problems confronting researchers is the lack of a common operational definition. Kinesthesis has been defined as: (a) the ability to maintain a constant pressure against an object, (b) the ability to move the limbs to certain positions, and (c) the ability to maintain balance or achieve a vertical position. Similarly, the receptors for kinesthesis have been identified as: muscle spindles, Golgi tendon organs, free nerve endings in the muscles, tendons, ligaments, and joints; and the vestibular organs. It is evident that such a varied approach to the understanding and measurement of kinesthesis would lead to theoretical chaos and encourage irrelevant research. If physical educators want to understand kinesthesis and its role in motor learning, a concerted effort will have to be made to develop a common operational definition of it and to discover its physiological and psychological mechanisms.

KINESTHESIS—A SENSORY MODALITY

A sensory modality may be defined as a subjectively distinctive response within the central nervous system to the stimulation of a specific group of receptors. The receptors subserving a sensory modality are characterized by their unique anatomical location and by their responsiveness to a particular form of energy. Kinesthesis[1] has been identified

---

[1]The term, a Greek derivative: (*kinesis* = motion and *asthesia* = to perceive) was first proposed by Bell. Medical clinicians still classify kinesthesis under bathesthesia. The sense also has been commonly referred to as the muscle-tendon-joint sense, posture sense, and position-movement sense.

as the sensory modality concerned with movement. The unique stimulus for the kinesthetic receptors is movement, more specifically, movement about a moveable or diarthroidal joint. The receptors are mechanoreceptors; responses are initiated by the deformation of their endings produced by the stretching or compression of the structures in which they are embedded.

To provide the information needed for detailed perception of joint movement, kinesthetic receptors must respond to the following:

1. The onset and duration of the movement
2. The direction of the movement
3. The velocity and acceleration of the movement
4. The range of the movement
5. The static positioning of jointed segments prior to and after movement.

The foregoing description of kinesthesis lacks two aspects which have traditionally been assigned to it: the appreciation of muscular tension, and total body position relative to gravity. It should be noted that both of these can be appreciated without the occurrence of joint movement, as in isometric contractions and a total body tilt (e.g., on a tilt board). According to the description of kinesthesis provided, the common stimulus for activating the kinesthetic receptors is *joint movement*, thus neither the appreciation of muscle tension (a function of pressure receptors within muscle and periosteum tissues), nor the appreciation of total body position relative to gravity (a function of the labyrinthine receptors) can be considered components of kinesthesis. Rather it is suggested here that these are two distinct sensory modalities, each with a unique stimulus and group of sense receptors, whose responses add to the performer's internal feedback.

Of the numerous proprioceptors within the muscular, tendinous, and arthroidal structures, the receptors within the joint capsule and ligaments appear to be the most capable of providing kinesthetic feedback.[2] Although the muscles spindle and Golgi tendon organs have been identified as kinesthetic receptors, recent investigations have demonstrated that these receptors are not suited to provide kinesthetic feedback (32, 44). To detect the position and movement of the limbs, these receptors would have to indicate the absolute length and tension of the muscle and tendon in which they were embedded; neither the Golgi tendon

[2]Sherrington classified all receptors found in muscles, tendons, joints, and the labyrinth as proprioceptors. Merton (32) suggests that the term be abandoned since it fails to denote the functional differences between those receptors which subserve perception and those which do not. Perhaps the two types of proprioception, conscious (kinesthetic, pressure, and vestibular) and unconscious (muscle spindle and Golgi tendon organ) should be reclassified with this point in mind. However, Henry's plea for separation of the two types of "kinesthetic adjustment" (conscious and unconscious) is untenable, for by definition, kinesthesis implies the possibility of conscious recognition.

organ nor the spindle can. The muscle spindle responds to changes in the length of both intrafusal and extrafusal fibers, thus its "measurements" are relative to the length of the intrafusal fibers, which are independently controlled by the fusimotor system (33). The Golgi tendon organ signals muscle tension, but it is stimulated both by stretch and contraction of the muscle; thus impulses from this receptor could not signal the position or movements of the bones (32, 41). Also it might be noted that the nerve fibers from the muscle spindle and the Golgi tendon organs are located in the spinocerebellar tracts and apparently make no direct synaptic connection with the classical sensory areas of the cerebral cortex. To date, attempts to obtain microelectrode recordings of these receptors at the cortex have been successful only outside the classical sensory areas, suggesting that although afferent impulses from the muscle spindle are available at cortical centers, the feedback is most likely used in the integration of motor activity and not in perception (32, 36, 44).

Kinesthetic receptors, located within the joint capsule and ligaments, have been identified by Gardner (11), Boyd (3), Skoglund (46), and Andrew (1). Two types of receptor endings have been described in the joint capsule, spray-type (Ruffini) endings and modified Pacinian corpuscle endings, termed paciniform corpuscles. Only one receptor ending has been identified within the ligament, the free (Golgi-type) ending. On the basis of their particular response, these three receptors have been classified either as movement or position receptors. There is some agreement as to the classification of the three receptors. The spray endings and the free endings have been identified as position receptors, whereas the paciniform corpuscles are reported to be movement receptors.

Utilizing records made from single unit recordings at the peripheral nerves, investigators (11, 35, 46) reported the following to be characteristic of position receptors:

1. Receptors fire at different frequencies for a specific joint angle regardless of the speed or direction from which the position was approached.
2. Receptors adapt slowly and often a single unit has a different adaptation rate for each joint angle.
3. More receptors are responsive to a limited range of the total joint action; i.e., there is a "fractionation of the physiological range of motion." (6)

Thus, the position receptors are slow-adapting receptors whose response is dependent upon joint angle, but independent of movement direction and speed. Conversely, movement receptors are fast adapting receptors whose responses are independent of joint angle (limb position), but dependent upon the velocity, acceleration, and direction of limb movement.[3] Specifically, the following characteristics have been ascribed to movement receptors:

[3]The definitions of movement and position receptors are classical definitions. Re-

1. Receptors adapt rapidly to static positioning of limbs.
2. Many receptors are undirectional; they respond to only one direction of movement.
3. Majority of the receptors are sensitive to the movement velocity; i.e., their overall discharge frequency increases as velocity increases.
4. Units have a rapid onset of firing and low velocity threshold; however, the velocity threshold differs for groups of receptors.

With the feedback available from the position and movement receptors, complex patterns can be established and perhaps "coded" in the sensorimotor cortex.[4] Cohen (6) has suggested a coding system built on the responses from a single receptor and from a multireceptor complex. The structure of the coding is illustrated in Table 1. It is suggested here that information concerning the limb position and the three movement variables can be presented by a combination of single receptor and multireceptor feedback. For example, a single receptor could provide information about the direction of the limb movement by responding to one direction only (undirectional), or by responding differentially to

TABLE 1*
The Coding of Kinesthetic Feedback at Peripheral Centers

Feedback from	MOVEMENT RECEPTORS			Position Receptors
	Direction	Velocity	Acceleration	
Single Receptor	Unidirectional for entire range of motion Differential response for various directions	Frequency of firing dependent on velocity	Change in the firing rate over time	Unique firing rate for each position Different adaptation rate for each position
Multi Receptor	Sequential integration of range fractioning units	Temporal integration a. velocity dependent units b. range fractionating units	Sequential input, dependent on velocity threshold	Range fractionation

*The table was formulated in collaboration with Gordon R. Stephenson, Department of Zoology, University of Wisconsin, Madison.

---

cently Wiersma (52) suggested a third classification, the intermediate receptor, whose response has elements of both movement and position receptors. Wiersma believes that there is a complete gradation of receptors from those responding as pure movement receptors, affected little by velocity or position, to those whose response is affected by both of these variables.

[4] The term "sensorimotor" is used as an eclectic label for the four sensory (somatic) areas of the cerebral cortex, SM I and SM II, which have been outlined and described by Woolsey. (55)

various directions. If several receptors respond only to a specific portion of the movement range (range fractionation), their sequential pattern also would provide information concerning the direction of the movement. Similarly, limb position could be detected by the pattern of single and multireceptor responses (see Table 1). Feedback signalling the velocity and acceleration of movement could be transmitted via the patterning produced by the responses of receptors with differential velocity thresholds.

The coding system which has been suggested is based only on peripheral nerve recordings. Little is known about the central processing or decoding of the complex kinesthetic feedback available at the sensorimotor cortex. It has been demonstrated that large I and II fibers from the receptors from part of the dorsal funiculi (fasciculus cuneatus and gracilis). These neurons synapse in the upper brainstem within the nuclei cuneatus and gracilis with secondary neurons(13). The secondary neurons become part of the medial lemniscal system after synapsing with tertiary neurons in the ventral posterolateral nucleus of the thalamus. The tertiary neurons project to various areas of the sensorimotor cortex. Skoglund (46) and Mountcastle (35) have recorded potentials from kinesthetic receptors at contralateral sensory areas, SM I and SM II, and at ipsilateral sensory areas SM II. Mountcastle and Powell reported:

> All of our observations, obtained upon a large number of cortical neurons sensitive to joint movement, lend themselves to an imaginary reconstruction of the events occuring in the cortex during bodily movement and during steadily maintained attitudes. (35: 197)

Mountcastle, Poggio, and Werner (34) analyzed kinesthetic feedback at the level of the thalamus and reported a high degree of neural integration and convergence. The consequences of such integration at lower levels was noticed by Mountcastle and Powell (35) who reported that the excitatory range of cortical cells was often greater than the receptors to which they were linked. For example, the excitation range of the cortical cells averaged 60 to 90 degrees, while that of the receptor cells averaged only 15 to 20 degrees. These reports tend to suggest that the detailed kinesthetic information emitted by the receptors does not reach the cortical centers which subserve perception; instead only a summary of the integrated information reaches the final centers.

KINESTHETIC PERCEPTION

Kinesthetic perception is more than the reception of afferent impulses from joint receptors at the sensorimotor cortex. Perception includes the complex processes through which the individual receives, extracts, organizes, and interprets sensory information. The extraction of the sensory information may be selective, as Ittleson and Cantril explain: "perceiving is always done by a particular person from his own unique position in space and time and with his own combination of experiences and needs" (23: 2). Perception is also a conscious act, implying that the perceiver will be able to verbalize or communicate in some manner what he has perceived. To date, investigators have approached the study of kinesthetic perception with two methods, the psychophysical and the perceptual motor.

Psychophysical Approach[5]

Early psychologists studied the parameters of kinesthesis with classical psychophysical techniques. Using machines that moved the limbs of passive blindfolded subjects, they attempted to ascertain the minimum angular displacement and minimum velocity of motion which could be detected. Such limens were established for several joints. Goldscheider (14), acting as his own subject, tested nine joints. He reported that the shoulder and hip joints were the most sensitive. Passive movements of 0.22 to 0.42 degrees at a speed of 0.30 degrees per second were detected. Pillsbury (40), and Winter (54), conducted extensive investigations on the elbow joint and reported the limens to vary between 0.20 and 0.85 degrees at speeds ranging from 0.33 to 0.35 degrees per second. Measurements by Laidlaw and Hamilton (27) on sixty subjects yielded results generally in agreement with Goldscheider's. Thresholds at different joints varied between 0.20 and 0.40 degrees; movements were conducted at a constant speed of 0.16 degrees per second. Subjects more accurately assessed movements of the larger proximal joints such as the hip and shoulder, than the smaller distal joints. More recently, Cleghorn and Darcus (5) investigated the perception of passive movements at the elbow joint. The blindfolded subjects were asked to indicate when they first perceived movement and the direction of the movement. The elbow was initially positioned at an angle 30 degrees from full flexion, and movement, either flexion or extension, occurred at controlled speeds (0.05-0.25 degrees per second) through one half, one, or two degrees. The ability of the subjects to detect movement improved as the degree of displacement increased, but decreased as the angular velocity increased. Also, the subjects were able to identify extension with significantly greater accuracy than flexion.

On the basis of these early psychophysical studies, one might conclude that man has a highly developed kinesthetic sense which is both dis-

[5]The investigations of the early psychophysicists on weight discrimination have often been classified under kinesthesis. However, perception of weight or "heaviness" of an object is actually the fusion of the following unitary sense modalities: touch, pressure, muscular tension, and perhaps kinesthesis if joint movement occurs.

criminative and precise. However, because movement limens have been established using passive movement at very slow angular velocities (range 0.16 to 0.33 degrees per second) it is difficult to extend this conclusion to situations involving athletic performance. Movement within the velocity range described rarely occurs during dynamic movement. Angular velocities of joints active during sports skills have been listed by Cooper and Glassow (7). The angular velocities range from 200 to 500 degrees per second for the slower movements of hip and spinal rotation, and from 2,000 to 3,000 degrees per second for the fastest movements of the distal joints such as the wrist. There is neither physiological nor perceptual evidence that detailed kinesthetic information can be received and interpreted during such rapid movement.[6] It is also possible that passive movement produces a different pattern of kinesthetic feedback than active (voluntary) movement, which depends on muscular contraction. It has been suggested that active movement creates greater tension and stretch on the joint capsule than passive movement (46). To date only Lloyd and Caldwell (31) have attempted to test the difference between passive and active positioning of the lower leg at specific angles. A full leg splint was used to immobilize the leg except at the knee joint. Full extension of the lower leg was permitted and approximately 100° of flexion. During passive movement, the subjects had to estimate the joint angle positioned by the investigator; during active movement, the subjects were required to move the lower leg to a specified angle. The results of this study indicated that active movement of the lower leg resulted in a greater accuracy of positioning than passive movement for the middle ranges, but not for the extreme portions of the movement range.

It is evident that more research is needed to determine man's perceptual sensitivity to passive movements at various angular velocities, range of motion, and duration. Also more studies are needed to determine differences between kinesthetic perception of passive and active (volitional) positioning. Unfortunately, those who devise tasks to test kinesthetic perception of volitional movement are plagued with perceptual problems not encountered by those who utilize psychophysical techniques.

Perceptual Motor Approach

Most of the tests devised to indicate sensitivity of kinesthetic perception during volitional movement have utilized what I shall call the perceptual motor approach. Usually the subject is asked to assume certain

---

[6]The physiological data collected to date has been obtained by stimulating the receptors of anesthetic cats and monkeys by passively moving their limbs at slow angular speeds which ranged from 5 to 20 degrees per second.

arm and leg positions which are explained or demonstrated. For example, Scott's battery of tests include such items:

10. Thigh raising—standing, raise leg, knee bent, until thigh is horizontal.
11. Arm raising—standing, abduct arm to horizontal. (45: 325)

Scoring is based on the measurement of the angle formed, the greater the deviation from 90 degrees, the lower the score. Young (56), Phillips (39), Wiebe (51), and Roloff (43), included similar items in their tests of kinesthesis. None of these tests were reported to have high reliabilities (range 0.26=0.68); thus, it has often been concluded that kinesthesis is an inaccurate and unreliable sense. Before such a conclusion is accepted, the following point should be considered. When a subject is asked to assume a certain position, he has to attend not only to his kinesthetic feedback, but to the initial "model of action." No one is born with the ability to assume and recognize 90 degrees of abduction or flexion; just as no one is born knowing that the color red is red. These senses are not absolute; one learns that a certain visual phenomena is called *red*, and one learns that a certain position of the arm will form a 90 degree angle. If an individual has never attempted to abduct the arm to 90 degrees, he will have no past experience from which to make a kinesthetic judgment. Perception requires judgment and interpretation based on the individual's past experience, or kinesthetic memory.

It is not surprising, therefore, that investigators have reported more accurate and reliable results while testing more familiar movements. For example, Phillips and Summers (39) noted that subjects scored significantly higher when they were tested with their preferred arm, as opposed to their nonpreferred arm. These authors also reported: "Whether or not movement is used daily in activity also appears to affect accuracy with which movement can be reproduced through kinesthetic sense" (39: 467). Similarly Lloyd and Caldwell (31) reported that the greatest accuracy of positioning the lower leg coincided with the normal walking arc of the lower leg. They suggest that kinesthetic perception of the limb position appears to be best in the range of motion in which there has been the most previous experience, thus providing support for the assumption that an individual is more capable of evaluating kinesthetic feedback when the movement or positioning is a familiar one.

To avoid the problems that arise when subjects are tested with new movements or positions, a few investigators have tried to familiarize the subjects with the proper kinesthetic "feeling" during the testing period. For example, Phillips and Summers (39) had their subjects experience (via passive manipulation) certain angular positions at the shoulder joint prior to the testing. The subjects were then asked to reproduce the same positions, based on recent kinesthetic cues. Lincoln (30) had subjects learn to turn a hand wheel at 100 rpm. During the learning period one group received verbal comments about their speed deviations ("too slow," "too fast"); the second group received "kinesthetic cues" by having the wheel driven at various speeds, although verbal cues were given to indicate the speed error. The third group was told nothing, but practiced continually with the wheel driven at the desired speed (100 rpm). The groups receiving verbal feedback performed significantly better than those who received none, indicating that kinesthetic perception is enhanced when some standards for judgment are given. Similarly Kerr (25) had his subjects learn to establish and maintain a certain angular velocity while horizontally abducting the arm. Verbal cues such as "too fast," "too slow," and "just right" were given to subjects to provide an absolute standard against which to judge their kinesthetic feedback. Kerr reported that the learning period was relatively unproductive; most subjects could not rely upon their kinesthetic feedback to maintain a highly consistent movement.

The disappointing results of most studies of kinesthetic perception can be attributed to several factors. Investigators have too often tried to test kinesthesis as an absolute sense. Others have isolated it from other sensory modalities which normally provide standards from which kinesthetic judgments are made. However, it is also possible that man cannot rely on his kinesthetic feedback to provide detailed information about his movements. The following could be postulated:

1. Man's kinesthetic sense can provide only a gross representation of his movement. He can get a vague "feeling" of the movement, but he cannot perceive the details.
2. Man is capable of fine kinesthetic perception, but he does not ordinarily attend to the precise feedback, because he is too highly oriented toward external cues.

There is little empirical evidence at this time to substantiate either explanation although there are some suggestive cues. Physiologists have demonstrated convergence of kinesthetic information at thalamic and spinal integration centers (34). Sensory summation of this type could reduce the precision of the feedback. Regardless of the kinesthetic details available for movement perception, it is evident that man does not rely extensively on kinesthetic feedback; he tends to be more visually oriented (42). Only the blind find themselves more dependent on kinesthetic cues. It is well known that the nervous system selectively permits sensory stimulation to enter centers subserving perception, thus it is possible that kinesthetic information is inhibited from reaching higher centers. The reticular formation and the thalamic diffuse projection system (TDPS) are instrumental in this modulation of sensory stimulation. Investigators have demonstrated the effect of such sensory control at all levels of synaptic centers which receive kinesthetic feedback. For example, Harbarth and Fex (15) demonstrated that electrical stimulation of the reticular formation inhibited or increased the firing at the postsynaptic neuron in the dorsal tract. Hernández-Peón (20) demonstrated similar effects at the gracilis cuneatus nuclei, while King et al. (26) demonstrated inhibitory influences on specific somatic thalamic nuclei. Hernández-Peón postulates that sensory filtering prevents an "excessive bombardment of the brain by afferent impulses," suggesting that sensory information not essential at a particular instance is screened out.

If kinesthetic information is selectively prevented from reaching higher centers subserving perception, are there techniques which can be employed to increase the reception or recall of this feedback?[7] A few investigators have attempted to heighten kinesthetic awareness by removing all visual stimuli. Espenschade (8) had blindfolded subjects throw sandbags at a target twelve feet away. The subjects were instructed to "get the feel" of both good and bad tosses. After each toss they were told (via a score) where the sandbag landed. The author noted that the distance scores improve significantly during the 50 trials, although accuracy scores failed to improve. Similarly, Waterland (48) taught bowling emphasizing kinesthetic awareness by having the students bowl with their eyes closed and by mentally practicing before they bowled. Students taught by this method improved significantly faster than those who did not receive this extra emphasis. Investigators such as Watkins (49) have taken a different approach by attempting to maximize the performer's kinesthetic awareness with delayed visual cues. Watkins (49) had varsity baseball players view their batting via motion pictures. The players who viewed their swing reduced their batting errors significantly faster than those who were not filmed. If visual feedback of the movement process is not available, other graphic techniques may be employed to help the student gain a visual augmentation. For example, Howell (22) used force-time graphs of the student's pressure against the starting block. The graphs helped the student visualize the dynamics of his start. Students compared their own force-time graphs with a model graph which had been devised according to kinesiological principles. The students using this graphic aid learned the desired force-time pattern significantly faster than the student who had no graphs.

It is possible that physical educators need to devise more teaching techniques which will help the learner become more aware of his movement process. Films, videotapes, movement graphs, and diagnostic charts

[7]Johnson (24) made an interesting observation a few years ago. He reported that a batter in a "slump" was unable to describe his batting problem. However, under hypnosis the batter was able to describe with great detail the faults of his movement process. Apparently his kinesthetic feedback had been stored for subconscious use only.

can provide the absolute standards from which more detailed judgments and corrections can be made. It is also probable, as Wiktin (53) suggests in his differentiation hypothesis, that certain individuals are more attuned to internal than external cues. Are these individuals capable of learning skills faster; or are they more likely to be more successful in certain activities such as dance, gymnastics, and swimming which provide fewer external cues? These questions and others need to be investigated before the role of kinesthetic perception in motor learning can be determined.

KINESTHETIC ILLUSION

An illusion is a false sensory experience; false because the sensation is imaginary and not based on sensory information transmitted from the receptors to the cortical centers. A kinesthetic illusion would occur when movement is experienced without the actual occurence of movement. For example, an individual with an anesthetized or paralyzed arm may *will* to make a certain movement, and think that he has made it until he looks at the arm and sees that he has failed. Such an "experience" cannot be based on sensory information from the joint receptors because the movement stimulus is absent.

The study of kinesthetic illusions has been minimal. Winter (54) was one of the first to describe a kinesthetic illusion, a phenomena he referred to as perception of the "nil movement." While testing the subjects' ability to detect passive movement, he noted:

> Suggestion plays a strong role. The subject soon gets into the habit of expecting to feel movement, and this causes large errors of anticipation. Often the subject was sure of movement sensations when the board was perfectly still. (54: 376)

Cleghorn and Darcus (5) attempted to study the "nil movement" phenomena by systematically presenting a number of "nil trials" while testing passive movement perception. Of the total "nil trials" presented, 48 per cent were assessed incorrectly, that is, the subjects reported experiencing movements, when no movement occurred. The direction of the movement preceding the "nil trial" had a significant influence on the direction ascribed to the "nil movement." The authors interpreted the "influence" to be some form of sensory carry-over, or afterdischarge of sensory impulses in the cortical cells. The concept of sensory carry-over is not a recent one. Psychologists such as Gibson (13) and Werner and Wapner (50) have studied sensory aftereffects on tactile, visual, and kinesthetic perception extensively. However, the neurological dynamics of these after discharges are not known. Lorento de Nó's discovery of closed chains of neurons in the cerebral cortex led to the assumption that the chains produced "reverberating" responses, responsible for the sensory aftereffects (9). However, at this time there is little evidence to support this assumption.

Recently kinesthetic illusions have been explored by Merton (32). To understand his conclusions, it is necessary to review one of the earliest theories of kinesthesis, the theory of "sensation of innervation." Leading scientists of the late 19th century believed that the impulses from efferent fibers established movement sensations, not the impulses from activated receptors. For example, Müller believed that appreciation of movement: ". . . may in part arise from the consciousness of the amount of nervous energy transmitted from the brain rather than from a sensation in the muscle" (2: 528). Helmholtz referred to the "nervous energy" as a "sense of effort." The theory was abandoned early in the 20th century when Sherrington demonstrated muscle and joint afferents. Since then no literature has been written on the theory, thus it was rather perplexing to find an article by P. A. Merton entitled: "Human Position Sense and the Sense of Effort," dated 1964. Merton writes:

> Sense of effort has been out of the physiologist's vocabulary for half a century, but it now looks as if it should return. To admit its existence implies that we can acquire knowledge of events outside the central nervous system without the use of sense organs. (32: 398)

Merton supports the revival of this concept with the following experimental procedure. A pneumatic tourniquet was placed around the subject's wrist to anesthetize the afferent fibers of the receptors within the muscles, joints, and skin of the thumb. Positionings of the distal joint were then tested while the subjects were blindfolded. The subjects were not able to perceive passive movement of the joint, but they were able to move the phalange volitionally to a specified angle accurately, or as accurately as they had done before the tourniquet was applied. Merton's results concur with the findings of Lee and Ring (28), and Brown, et al. (4). These investigators injected procaine into certain joints, thereby anesthetizing the joint receptors. Although blindfolded subjects were not able to perceive passive movement, they were able to move the limb volitionally to specified positions. Thus these authors urged that a distinction be made between active and passive movement sense, and suggested that the former was mediated by receptors within the muscles and tendons, while the latter was mediated by joint receptors. It has, however, been demonstrated that the receptors within the muscles and tendons are not capable of providing kinesthetic information, therefore the explanation is not acceptable (32, 44). Merton suggests that the accurate volitional positionings which occurred when the joint receptors were anesthetic, were not due to any sensory feedback, but to the "inner consciousness of the act of making the voluntary effort to move," or the sense of effort. To demonstrate this "sense of effort," the author had subjects' thumb movements restrained after they were asked to move them to a specific angle. Since the joint, muscle and tactile receptors of the thumb were anesthetized, the subjects received no sensory information. Nevertheless, the subjects reported that they had moved the thumb to the specified angle, that is they responded to their own sense of effort.

Although Merton fails to offer an adequate explanation for the "sense of effort," a recent model proposed by von Holst (21) to explain certain behavioral and perceptual disorders, offers an attractive hypothesis. An adaptation of the model is illustrated in Figure 1. The model is composed

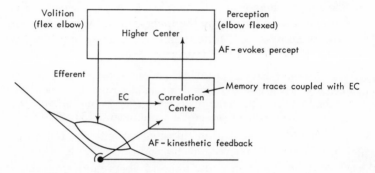

Figure 1. *Schematic representation of von Holst's model of EC and AF correlation and reception for perception.*

of two essential elements. The efferent corollary (EC), an efferent message sent to a correlation center, accompanies the regular efferent impulse during volitional movement. The corollary "informs" the center of the movement about to occur. The afferent feedback (AF) is the sensory feedback which is sent to the center from the receptors. As von Holst implies, this center acts as a comparator, and the EC is compared with the afferent impulses. Held (17) further proposes that the efferent corollary discharges memory traces which previously have been coupled with a specific efferent corollary. Once the memory trace is released, an illusion can be evoked; this illusion would be based on the reception of the memory traces recently coupled with the EC. Thus, as Merton (32) suggests, one could receive sensory information about movement without the aid of sensory receptors. For example, with the initiation of a volitional movement ("flex elbow," Figure 2), an efferent corollary is sent to the correlation center. If elbow flexion is prevented, the efferent corollary has no afferent feedback with which to correlate. The memory trace, instead of acting as a comparator for past experience, evokes a false percept. This movement is not initiated by sensory feedback from kinesthetic receptors, but from the efferent corollary, "the sense of effort." Although the concept of the efferent corollary and the correlation

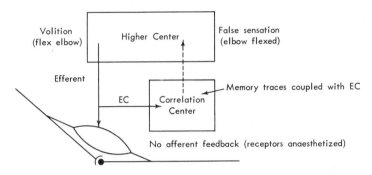

Figure 2. *Schematic representation of a false sensation created by the memory traces evoked by the EC.*

center is purely conjectural at this point, the hypothesis is consistent with the functional structure of the central nervous system. The cerebellum has often been designated as the comparator center, although a higher center has been proposed by Penfield (38) and Paillard (37). Regardless of the structures named or specified, they would have to have access to both efferent and afferent information as well as the memory traces.[8] Held (18) has successfully utilized a similar model to predict certain types of perceptual-motor development and adaptation, while von Holst (21) has accounted for specific visual illusions.

A third type of kinesthetic illusion has been described by Harris and his associates (16,42). In a series of experiments (similar to those designed by Held), they have demonstrated that visual feedback determines the subject's total perception when kinesthetic and tactile feedback conflicts with it. Harris asserts that the kinesthetic information is neither blocked nor ignored by the perceiver, instead there is a "transformation" of the kinesthetic feedback to conform with the "dominant" visual in-

[8]von Holst does not specifically name neurological structures, but refers graphically to higher and lower centers. His refusal to specify structures has resulted in criticism, not unlike that received by Penfield for his hypothesized centrencephalic integrating system. However, von Holst pleads innocent to the charge of scientific heterodoxy by insisting that the behaviorist and the neurophysiologist each be allowed his own models and language until progress is sufficient to warrant a merger.

formation. For example, if a subject were holding a 4 inch stick, but saw the stick as being only 2 inches long (through a reducing lens), eventually the subject would "feel" as though he were holding a 2 inch stick. No explanation is given for the transformation process which produces the kinesthetic illusion. One might argue that Harris (42) and Held (17) have reported similar findings explained by divergent theories which could be merged. It is possible that the coupling of the efferent corollary and the kinesthetic feedback which occurs during the adaptation period results not only in new visual-motor responses (Held), but also in altered interpretations of kinesthetic feedback.

Although the studies reported by Harris and Held have largely dealt with kinesthetic illusions produced under abnormal visuospatial fields, it is possible that kinesthetic illusions occurring under normal conditions are similar. For example, when an individual is learning a motor skill, the task is usually demonstrated for him in some manner. From these demonstrations he forms a "movement model" of the skill with which his kinesthetic feedback can be compared. What happens when the learner claims that he has produced the desired movement, when in fact he has not? Is his kinesthetic illusion produced by a dominant movement model (i.e., the efferent corollary—what he intended to do)? The possibilities for studying kinesthetic illusions are unlimited if the contemporary complex model of kinesthetic perception is used. Certainly, it is not the simple sensory process it was once thought to be.

SUMMARY

To open new perspectives it is often necessary to review the old with new insights afforded by recent information acquired from related disciplines. For this reason, kinesthesis was reviewed as a physiological and perceptual-illusory phenomenon with the purpose of up-dating the conceptual and operational basis from which kinesthesis is studied. The physiological processes which underlie the kinesthetic receptors were described and delineated from other proprioceptive processes once considered to be kinesthetic. Kinesthetic feedback was limited only to that feedback which provided information about segmental positioning and certain parameters of movement: velocity, direction, and duration.

The two methods of testing kinesthetic perception, the psychophysical (passive movement) and the perceptual-motor (volitional movement) were discussed because knowledge about kinesthetic perception has been provided predominantly by those who purport to test it. Special attention was given to the problems encountered by these two methodologies. It was suggested that kinesthesis not be conceived of as an absolute sense or be tested in such a manner that it is isolated from the other sensory modalities which normally provide standards from which kinesthetic judgments are made. Finally the topic of kinesthetic illusion was introduced, for it was felt that perception of movement and position might be veridical as well as illusory. Although kinesthetic illusions have not been studied in detail, it is possible to recognize various types which may be influential in motor learning.

The continued study of kinesthesis in these dimensions should prove valuable to those physical educators who want to learn more about the complex process of motor learning. Skill acquisition involves the continual use of kinesthetic feedback and memory to assist in the production of a consistent movement pattern. Thus a greater understanding of kinesthesis should help physical educators develop teaching techniques which make greater use of the detailed verbal and visual feedback needed to augment kinesthetic feedback and thus to maximize the performer's awareness of his own movement process.

REFERENCES

1. Andrew, B. L., "The Sensory Innervation of the Medial Ligament of the Knee Joint of the Cat." *Journal of Physiology*, CXXIII (1954), 241–50.

2. Boring, E. G., *Sensation and Perception in the History of Experimental Psychology* (New York: Appleton-Century-Crofts, Inc., 1942).

3. Boyd, I. A., "The Histological Structure of the Receptors in the Knee Joint of the Cat Correlated with Their Physiological Responses." *Journal of Physiology*, CXXIV (1954), 469–88.

4. Browne, K., Lee, L., and Ring, P. A., "Sensations of Passive Movement at the Metatarso-phalangeal Joint of the Great Toe in Man." *Journal of Physiology*, CXXVI (1954), 448–58.

5. Cleghorn, T. E., and Darcus, H. D., "The Sensibility to Passive Movement of the Human Elbow Joint." *Quarterly Journal of Experimental Psychology*, IV (1952), 66–79.

6. Cohen, M. J., "The Peripheral Organization of Sensory Systems," in *Neural Theory and Modeling: Proceedings of the 1962 Ojai Symposium*, R. F. Reiss, (ed.), (Stanford, Calif.: Stanford University Press, 1963), pp. 273–91.

7. Cooper, J. M., and Glassow, R. B., *Kinesiology* (St. Louis: The C. V. Mosby Company, 1963).

8. Espenschade, Anna, "Kinesthetic Awareness in Motor Learning." *Perceptual and Motor Skills*, VIII (1958), 142.

9. Fessard, A., "The Role of Neuronal Networks in Sensory Communications with the Brain," in *Sensory Communication*, W. A. Rosenblith (ed.) (Cambridge, Mass.: The M.I.T. Press, 1961), pp. 585–606.

10. Gardner, E., "The Innervation of the Knee Joint." *Anatomical Record*, CI (1948), 109–30.

11. ———, "Physiology of Moveable Joints." *Physiology Review*, XXX (1950), 127–76.

12. ———, "Conduction Rates and Dorsal Root Inflow of Sensory Fibers from the Knee Joint of the Cat." *American Journal of Physiology*, CLII (1952), 436–45.

13. Gibson, J. J., "Adaptation, After-effect, and Contrast in the Perception of Curved Lines." *Journal of Experimental Psychology*, XVI (1933), 1–31.

14. Goldscheider, A., "Unterduchungen über den Muskelsinn." *Archives of Anatomy and Physiology*, (Lpz.), (1889), 392–502.

15. Harbarth, K. E., and Fex J., "Centrifugal Influences on Single Unit Activity in Spinal Sensory Paths." *Journal of Neurophysiology*, XXII (1959), 319–38.

16. Harris, C. S., "Perceptual Adaptation to Inverted, Reversed, and Displaced Vision." Unpublished manuscript.

17. Held, R., "Exposure–History as a Factor in Maintaining Stability of Perception and Coordination." *Journal of Nervous and Mental Disease*, CXXXII (1961), 26–32.

18. ———, and Freidman, S. J., "Plasticity in Sensorimotor Control." *Science*, CXLII (1963), 455–62.

19. Henry, F., "Dynamic Kinesthetic Perception and Adjustment." *Research Quarterly*, XXIV (1953), 176–87.

20. Hernández-Peón, Paul, "Reticular Mechanisms of Sensory Control," in *Sensory Communication*, W. A. Rosenblith (ed.), (Cambridge, Mass.: The M.I.T. Press, 1961), pp. 497–520.

21. von Holst, E., "Relations Between the Central Nervous System and the Peripheral Organs." *British Journal of Animal Behavior*, II (1954), 89–94.

22. Howell, M., "Use of Force-Time Graphs for Performing Analysis in Facilitating Motor Learning." *Research Quarterly*, XXVII (1956), 12–22.

23. Ittelson, W. H., and Cantril, H., *Perception, a Transactional Approach* (New York: Random House, 1954).

24. Johnson, W. R., "Body Awareness in the Non-hypnotic and Hypnotic States." *Research Quarterly*, XXXII (1961), 363–64.

25. Kerr, B. A., "Weight and Velocity Factors in Kinesthetic Learning and Transfer of Training." Unpublished doctoral dissertation, University of Wisconsin, 1967.

26. King, E. E., Naquet, R., and Majoun, H. W., "Alterations in Somatic Afferent Transmission Through Thalamus by Central Mechanism and Barbituates." *Journal of Pharmacology and Experimental Theory*, CXIX (1957), 48–63.

27. Laidlaw, R. W., and Hamilton, M. A., "A Study of Thresholds in Apperception of Passive Movement Among Normal Control Subjects." *Bulletin of the Neurological Institute of New York*, VI (1937), 268–73.

28. Lee, J., and Ring, P.A., "The Effect of Local Anaesthesia on the Appreciation of Passive Movement of the Great Toe in Man," *Journal of Physiology*, CXXIII (1954), 56–57.

29. Liba, M. R., and Stauff, M. R., "A Test for the Volleyball Pass." *Research Quarterly*, XXXIV (1963), 56–63.

30. Lincoln, R., "Learning and Retaining a Rate of Movement with Aid of Kinesthetic and Verbal Cues." *Journal of Experimental Psychology*, LI (1956), 199–204.

31. Lloyd, A. J., and Caldwell, L. S., "Accuracy of Active and Passive Positioning of the Leg on the Basis of Kinesthetic Cues." *Journal of Comparative Physiological Psychology*, LX (1965), 102–6.

32. Merton, P. A., "Human Position Sense and Sense of Effort," in *Symposia of the Society for Experimental Biology*, No. 18, *Homeostasis and Feedback Mechanisms* (Cambridge, Mass.: University Press, 1964).

33. ———, "Speculation on the Servo-Control of Movement," in *The Spinal Cord*, G. E. W. Wolstenhome (ed.) (London: Churchill, 1964), pp. 247–55.

34. Mountcastle, V. B., Poggio, G. F., and Werner, G., "The Relation of Thalamic Cell Response to Peripheral Stimuli Varied Over and Intensive Continuum." *Journal of Neurophysiology*, XXVI (1963), 804–34.

35. ———, and Powell, T. P. S., "Central Nervous Mechanisms Subserving Position Sense and Kinesthesis." *John Hopkins Hospital Bulletin*, CV (1959), 173–200.

36. Oscarsson, O., "The Projection of Group I Muscle Afferents to the Cat Cerebral Cortex," in *Muscular Afferents in Motor Control*, R. Grawit (ed.) (New York: John Wiley and Sons, 1966), pp. 307–16.

37. Paillard, J., "The Patterning of Skilled Movements," in *Handbook of Physiology—Neurophysiology*, Sec. I, Vol. III. (Washington, D.C.: American Physiology Society, 1960), pp. 1679–1708.

38. Penfield, W., "Centrencephalic Integrating System." *Brain*, LXXXI (1958), 231–34.

39. Phillips, M., and Summers, D., "Relation of Kinesthetic Perception to Motor Learning." *Research Quarterly*, XXV (1954), 456–69.

40. Pillsbury, W. B., "Does the Sensation of Movement Originate in the Joint?" *American Journal of Psychology*, XII (1901), 346–53.

41. Ralston, H. J., "Recent Advances in Neuromuscular Physiology." *American Journal of Physical Medicine*, XXXVI (1957), 94–119.

42. Rock, I., and Harris, C. S., "Vision and Touch." *Scientific American*, CCXVI (1967), 96–108.

43. Roloff, L., "Kinesthesis in Relation to the Learning of Selected Motor Skills." *Research Quarterly*, XXIV (1953), 210–17.

44. Rose, G. E., and Mountcastle, V. B., "Touch and Kinesthesis," in *Handbook of Physiology*, Sec. I, Vol. I—*Neurophysiology*. (Washington, D.C.: American Physiological Society, 1959).

45. Scott, M. G., "Measurement of Kinesthesis." *Research Quarterly*, XXVI (1955), 324–41.

46. Skoglund, Sten, "Anatomical and Physiological Studies of Knee Joint Innervation in the Cat." *Acta Physiologica Scandinavica*, Supplementum 124 (1956).

47. Teuber, H. L., "Perception," in *Handbook of Physiology*, Sec. I, Vol. III—*Neurophysiology* (Washington, D.C.: American Physiological Society, 1960).

48. Waterland, J. C., "The Effect of Mental Practice Combined with Kin-

esthetic Perception when the Practice Precedes Each Overt Performance of a Motor Skill." Unpublished master's thesis, University of Wisconsin, Madison, Wisc., 1956.

49. Watkins, D., "Motion Pictures as an Aid in Correcting Baseball Batting Faults." *Research Quarterly*, XXXIV (1963), 228–33.

50. Werner, H., and Wapner, S., "Experiments on Sensory-Tonic Field Theory of Perception, V, Effect of Body Status on the Kinesthetic Perception of Verticality." *Journal of Experimental Psychology*, XLIV (1952), 126–31.

51. Wiebe, V. R., "A Study of Tests of Kinesthesis." *Research Quarterly*, XXV (1954), 222–30.

52. Wiersma, C. A. G., "Movement Receptors in Deapod Crustaea. *Journal of Marine Biological Association* (United Kingdom), XXXVIII (1963), 157–69.

53. Wiktin, H. A., "The Nature and Importance of Individual Difference In Perception." *Journal of Personality*, XVIII (1949–50), 145–70.

54. Winter, J. E., "The Sensation of Movement." *Psychological Review*, XIX (1912), 374–85.

55. Woolsey, C. N., "Organization of Somatic Sensory and Motor Areas of the Cerebral Cortex, in *Biological and Biochemical Bases of Behavior*. Harlow and Woolsey (eds.) (Madison: Wisconsin University Press, 1958), pp. 63–81.

56. Young, Olive, "A Study of Kinesthesis in Relation to Selected Movements." *Research Quarterly*, XVI (1945), 277–87.

HARRIET G. WILLIAMS *

Neurological Concepts
and Perceptual-Motor Behavior

One of our goals as physical educators is to outline the *basic laws* of perceptual-motor functioning in man. To date, little has been written about neurological concepts and their application to physical education. This is not surprising, for our knowledge about the nervous system, although growing rapidly, is still scanty and contradictory.

There is much perceptual-motor behavior that cannot yet be explained neurologically. It is equally true, however, that the study of perceptual-motor behavior involves an indirect assessment of the functioning of the individual's nervous system. We should thus be aware of basic neurological concepts and try to apply them to the problems of perceptual-motor behavior whenever and wherever possible.

The purpose of this chapter is therefore threefold: (a) to set forth some of the basic principles and concepts of neurological functioning; (b) to show, where possible, how they might subserve certain capacities with which we are concerned in teaching and studying perceptual-motor behavior; and (c) to build a general theoretical model of perceptual-motor behavior based on these concepts.

GENERAL NEUROLOGICAL SYSTEMS INVOLVED IN OVERT BEHAVIOR

There appear to be at least six neurological networks that may be involved in what we describe as overt motor behavior. (11, 15, 18, 19) These networks include:

*Department of Physical Education, University of Toledo.

1. *The Classical Ascending Sensory Pathways,* which terminate in the classical cortical receiving areas and which transmit sensory information from specific modalities including vision, audition, olfaction, kinesthesis, and touch.
2. *The Centrifugal Sensory Descending Pathways,* which involve fibers running in the reverse direction but parallel to the classical ascending pathways. These pathways are thought to provide for cortical control over the transmission of sensory data in the classical ascending pathways.
3. *A More General Ascending Sensory System Parallel to the Specific Sensory Pathways,* which passes through the brainstem reticular formation and certain thalamic nuclei and terminates in widespread areas of the cortex. This system is believed to be associated with the general arousal state of the organism. (The level of arousal of the organism has been shown to be an important factor in the selecting, receiving, and processing of sensory information.)
4. *Certain Integrative or Control Systems,* closely associated with the reticular formation and the cerebellum, which are known to have extensive interconnections with vast areas of the CNS and to exert both facilitatory and inhibitory influences upward on cortical activity and downward on sensory and motor activities of the spinal cord as well as on the activity of the peripheral sensory receptors themselves.
5. *The Classical Descending Motor Pathways (Pyramidal System),* which originate in the cortex (primarily in the motor regions although many fibers originate in other cortical areas) to motoneurons located in the spinal cord. The pyramidal system is believed to be the major effector pathway of the CNS.
6. *A Parallel Descending Motor Pathway (Extrapyramidal System),* which is believed to terminate in the motoneurons of the spinal cord by way of the basal ganglia and the brainstem reticular formation. This system is believed to be a primary contributor to the highly refined aspects of skillful, voluntary behavior.

These networks, closely interrelated by specific neural feedback circuits, interact with one another to modulate or control electrical activity culminating in the final motor product. Thus, information entering or leaving the CNS via any one of these channels both modifies and is modified by "contributions" from the other participating networks. It might also be pointed out that four of the six systems are involved in the sensory aspects of the motor behavior, an indication that the appropriate handling of sensory information may be of primary importance in the successful performance of motor behavior.

BASIC NEUROLOGICAL PRINCIPLES:
THE TRANSDUCING OF VISUAL SENSORY INFORMATION

Since the processing of visual information is involved in many of our sports situations, examples of the visual process will best illustrate the basic principles according to which the CNS transduces sensory information into usable neural, form.

Conscious awareness of our visual environment involves the collaboration and integration of the following individual components of light radiation: (a) *intensity*, or the lightness and darkness of visual stimuli; (b) *spatial relationships*, or our perceptions of size, shape, location, and movement of objects in the environment; and (c) *temporal characteristics*, which allow us to see events as occuring simultaneously or successively in time and as lasting for various durations (3). The process of combining and integrating such components into meaningful visual experiences is highly complex and demands an intricate and elaborate mechanism.

Intensive Components (1, 9).

The basic neurological principles of encoding stimulus intensity (the psychological phenomenon of brightness) are fairly well understood. Briefly, the steps leading to the discharge of a nerve impulse for a retinal receptor cell are as follows:

1. The rods and cones of the retina, containing certain photosensitive substances, absorb light energy falling upon the eye.
2. The absorption of light rays by these photosensitive substances initiates a chain of chemical reactions.
3. The result of these chemical processes (involving changes in the resting membrane potential and of the permeability of the cell membrane to sodium and potassium ions) is the discharge of nerve impulses from retinal receptor cells.

The rate of discharge of these nerve impulses is directly related to the intensity of the light rays falling upon the receptor cells. Specifically, the frequency of nerve discharge from a given receptor cell stimulated by a light ray increases with the log of the intensity of that stimulus. In addition, as stimulus intensity increases, increasing numbers of receptors react to the light and begin to fire. Together then, these two phenomena, the frequency of nerve discharge and the number of receptors firing, provide the information from which the various degrees of brightness or darkness of objects in the visual environment are encoded in the nervous system. That is, the absorption by retinal receptor cells of the light energy reflected from an object in the visual environment results in x level of firing in y numbers of optic nerve fibers. This is the neural correlate for stimulus intensity. Other sensory systems are also known to operate upon this same general principle for encoding stimulus intensity.

Spatial and Temporal Components

The great number of visual characteristics that we are able to distinguish (shape, size, spatial location of objects, speed and direction of moving objects, etc.) suggests that encoding the spatial and temporal properties of a visual stimulus requires complex neuroanatomical and functional arrangements.

Receptor Fields (8). The retina itself is complexly organized. For instance, receptor cells of the retina number in the hundreds of millions; a single optic nerve has approximately one million fibers. This suggests that there is a considerable amount of convergence of receptor cells onto ganglion cells. In other words, a single optic nerve fiber may transmit a message gathered originally from as many as a hundred or more individual receptor cells. One might expect such an anatomical arrangement to produce "fuzzy" vision instead of the rather precise visual capacities we possess.

Investigators have observed, however, that retinal cells are organized in what have been called "receptor fields." Receptor fields are groups of receptor cells, located in specific regions of the retina that fire particular optic nerve fibers. Thus we find not simply a convergence of large numbers of receptor cells onto optic nerve fibers but rather the convergence of specific groups of receptor cells onto specific optic nerve fibers. This provides us with another basic principle of neurological functioning—the organization of groups of peripheral receptors into specific, functional units. These receptor fields are believed to be basic functional units subserving much of the precision of our sensory experience, particularly that associated with vision.

Functional Organization (10). The functional organization of the receptor field also plays an important role in the encoding of visual sensory information. Retinal receptor fields are believed to be functionally organized in the form of concentric circles with either an excitatory center, a middle section, and an outer inhibitory circle, or the reverse of these conditions. This functional arrangement results in a very interesting phenomenon. If a group of cells in the excitatory center of a retinal receptor field, T, is stimulated (a light is turned on), the nerve fiber to which these cells are linked, fiber T' responds with increased rates of firing. Conversely, if the light stimulus is then turned off, fiber T' shows a decreased rate of firing (Hartline's On-Fibers). Now, if the outer inhibitory circle of retinal receptor field T is stimulated, fiber T' will be silent, its resting, spontaneous activity inhibited by the onset of the light stimulus. When the light stimulus is withdrawn, there is then observed an *increase* in the activity of this nerve fiber (Hartline's Off-Fibers).

Finally, if the middle circle of this receptor field is stimulated, fiber T' fires rapidly as the light comes on and then slows down, and when the light is turned off, increased rates of firing are again observed in fiber T'. (Hartline's On-Off Fibers).

This functional arrangement indicates that the pattern of response in a single optic nerve fiber is dependent not only on the brightness and darkness of the visual stimulus, but also on the *specific areas* of the receptor fields stimulated. Thus one might hypothesize that the pattern and sequence of firing in a given population of optic nerve fibers might constitute the neural basis for our identification of specific spatial and temporal characteristics of objects in space. When one considers further however, that: (a) as the eye sweeps back and forth across the visual field, countless numbers of these receptor fields are stimulated over time; (b) that retinal receptor fields show a great amount of *overlap* with one another; and (c) that there exists an active antagonism between the various parts of a receptor field (activity in one part can modify or inhibit activity in another), encoding spatial and temporal characteristics of visual stimuli simply in terms of specific patterns and sequences of optic nerve firing become increasingly difficult. Still, the number of possible patterns of nerve impulse discharge inherent within such a functional arrangement are enormous and could allow for great specificity in the peripheral encoding of the most complicated and detailed properties of visual stimuli.

Ratliff's Study. The classic study by Ratliff (16) on the horseshoe crab may serve to illustrate, more specifically, how the foregoing may be accomplished. To be clear, let us look briefly at the anatomy of the eye of the Limulus crab. The eye of this crab is made up of thousands of ommatidia (small grooves) which consist of clusters of receptor cells. Here a single ommatidium may be *roughly* likened to a retinal receptor field. These ommatidia are interconnected by means of axon collaterals which give rise to a kind of "lateral plexus." (This again is *very roughly* analogous to the interneuronal network of the human eye.) Via this lateral plexus, synaptic connections are made among individual ommatidia and consequently interactions among their neural outputs can occur.

Ratliff (16) showed that although individual ommatidia responded with increased rates of firing as stimulus intensity increased, interactions among the output of several ommatidia, stimulated simultaneously, affected the over-all level of neural activity and in this way allowed for a great variety in the patterning of neural output. For example, if ommatidium A were stimulated and firing at a given rate (a function of the intensity of light falling upon it) and ommatidium B were then stimulated, the rate of firing in ommatidium A decreased in relationship to: (a) the physical proximity of the two ommatidia; and (b) the amount of activity occurring in ommatidium B. If a third ommatidium, C, were then also stimulated, the rate of firing in both A and B was affected accordingly. These reciprocal interactions seemed generally to be inhibitory in nature and indicated that activity in one area of the eye could be greatly modified by the nature and amount of activity occurring in closely adjacent areas.

Given these basic facts, we can reconstruct (as Ratliff did) the pattern of neural activity which "accompanies the perception" of the patterned visual stimulus shown in Figure 1. Ratliff (16) observed that when this pattern was projected upon several ommatidia, those ommatidia in the

Figure 1. *Optic nerve response to a patterned visual stimulus.**

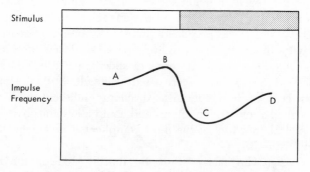

*Adapted from "The Response of Limulus Optic Nerve Fibers to Patterns of Illumination on the Receptor Mosaic" by F. Ratliff and H. K. Hartline, *Journal of General Physiology*, XLII, No. 6, p. 1248, by permission of the Rockefeller Institute Press.

homogeneous "light" sector of the stimulus fired at a fairly *high* and constant rate—the intensity principle (A—Figure 1). Inhibitory interactions among adjacent ommatidia in this "light" area contributed actively to the over-all level of discharge. At the point of greatest stimulus change (the border between the two areas of the visual stimulus), the inhibitory processes about which we have just been talking resulted in an interesting phenomenon. Those ommatidia *near* to the *border* in the "light" sector of the stimulus, being subjected to less inhibition than those farther away in the more homogeneous "light" area, fired at an even higher rate (B—Figure 1). The pattern of activity in the "dark" sector was reversed. Ommatidia in the homogeneous "dark" sector fired at low rates (C—Figure 1). The cells in the "dark" sector close to the border fired at even lower rates as a result of two factors: (a) the over-all decrease in intensity level (brightness) and (b) increased inhibition as a result of the higher rates of firing of cells located adjacent to them in the "light" sector (D–Figure 1).

The indication is then that through active inhibitory processes, there may occur a sharpening of differences inherent in the stimulus itself. The foregoing suggests that the borders of the stimulus are points at which such exaggerated neural activity may occur. Points of great stimulus change may therefore serve as the fundamental elements upon which our perceptions of a given stimulus or stimulus pattern are built (2). For instance, a part of the recognition of the shape of various objects may well be a result of exaggerated neural activity occurring at points where there is a distinct change in the outline or contour of the object.

Just how a particular pattern and sequence of neural activity comes to represent a given stimulus or stimulus situation, regardless of where or how it is seen, is largely unknown, but it undoubtedly requires additional integrator-comparator processes including cortical as well as reticular involvement. For example, the fact that we can move our heads, our eyes, and our bodies away from a stationary object in space without radically changing our perception of that object indicates that higher processes must occur which allow us to maintain our constancy of perception. Although little mention has been made thus far of the cortex in the translating of sensory information into psychological experience, examples of cortical function will be included in the section on kinesthesis.

Summary

Briefly, then, some of the basic neurological principles under-lying the encoding of sensory information are: (a) the intensity principle, which states that the frequency of nerve impulse discharge increases with the log of the intensity of the stimulus; (b) the concept of receptor fields, or the organization of sensory receptors into unique structural and functional units, which allows for greater precision in the encoding of certain characteristics of sensory stimuli; and (c) the processes of reciprocal inhibition, or reciprocal inhibitory interactions between adjacent areas of stimulation. These processes allow for the sharpening up of certain stimulus information (via exaggerated neural activity) and thus also contribute to the precision of sensory experience.

THE NEURAL BASIS OF KINESTHESIS

The importance of kinesthetic memory in the performance of many motor skills is well recognized. It is obvious, for instance, that in order to duplicate or assess a given movement or body position, the organism must have available some source of sensory information upon which to base judgments. This information must permit the individual to discriminate: (a) a change in position of body parts, (b) the extent of the change, (c) the direction of the change, and (d) the speed of the change, as well as the body part or parts involved. The basic neurological principles previously enumerated can now be drawn upon to outline the possible neural schema for kinesthetic functioning (the awareness of position or movement).

Characteristics of Peripheral Joint Receptors

At least four types of sensory endorgans are known to exist in the muscles, tendons, and joints. These include: (a) the muscle spindles, (b) the Golgi tendon organs, (c) the joint receptors (Pacinian corpuscles), and (d) free nerve endings. These receptors as a group, it is believed, are sensitive to, and convey information to the organism about, three states of the muscle: (a) active contraction, (b) passive stretch, and (c) tension. The joint endorgans are believed to be more involved in the recording of joint position and movement than are the muscle spindles or Golgi tendon organs. Our discussion will be limited to the *joint receptors*.

Sensitivity of Peripheral Joint Receptors (5, 14). In general, peripheral joint receptors are responsive to the movement of a joint over an arc of 15-20 degrees. Countless numbers of cells are thought to exist which are sensitive to various portions of the arc of movement for a given joint. When the movement at a joint enters into the "excitatory angle" of its joint receptor, the result is an increase in neural discharge from that receptor cell. This unit continues to fire until the movement goes beyond the excitatory angle to which it is sensitive. Different populations of joint receptors vary as to the angle at which they exhibit their maximal rate of firing. For example, some show maximal rates of firing at complete flexion; others discharge maximally at complete extension while still others fire maximally at angles intermediate to these two extremes. Put on a continuum, the pattern and level of firing in different populations of peripheral receptor neurons could provide information about movement or joint position across the total range of movement for a given joint.

Specific Response Properties of Peripheral Joint Receptors (5). Receptors responsive to movement at a joint can be classified into two fairly distinct groups:

1. *Fast-Adapting Receptors,* or those which fire only when *movement* is occurring at the joint.
2. *Slow-Adapting Receptors,* or those which respond to both *position* and *movement.*

The latter receptors show a transient, high-frequency response to movement. This response is followed by an adaptation to a lower, steady level of discharge which is maintained as long as the joint is held in a given position. The frequency of this steady state discharge is a function of limb position, that is, of the angle at which the joint is maintained. Speed or direction of movement does not, within limits, influence the level of this adapted rate of firing.

To illustrate, let us identify cell A as an elbow joint receptor sensitive to movement within the arc of 75 to 90 degrees of flexion. At a position of 80 degrees flexion, cell A responds at a steady state level of firing, x. If the elbow is then moved to 90 degrees flexion, there is observed a high transient increase in the discharge of nerve impulses from cell A, say $3x$. If the elbow joint is maintained in this new position (90 degrees flexion), the rate of firing of cell A settles down to a new "steady state" level, say $2x$. If the elbow joint is then moved beyond 90 degree flexion, activity in cell A falls to a zero level. In other words, cell A is then no longer active and does not *directly* inform about joint movement or position.

It is interesting to note that both types of receptors respond to movement while position is signalled only by the slow-adapting receptor group. Simply on the basis of *number of receptors* firing, one might then predict that individuals, in general, would be more sensitive to movement at a joint than to specific positioning of that joint. We know of course that this is essentially what psychologists consistently observe. For instance, although a given individual may not always be able to pinpoint precisely the position in which a given limb is held, he rarely fails to perceive even the slightest degree of movement away from that position.

In general, then, movement into an excitatory angle of a peripheral joint receptor results in a transient increased rate of firing from that receptor cell. If the movement stops within this excitatory angle, there is an adaptation over a period of a few seconds to a new and more or less steady rate of discharge. The level of this steady rate of discharge is closely related to the position or angle at which the limb is maintained.

Characteristics of Cortical Joint Receptors

Evidence indicates that afferent fibers from peripheral joint receptors do project to the thalamus and somatosensory areas of the cortex. This indicates that certain cortical cells may be driven by activity occurring in connecting peripheral units. Mountcastle (14) has further identified joint movement as the adequate stimulus for activation of certain cells in the postcentral gyrus. (Such cells, however, are not equally responsive to stretch of the muscle.) These cortical receptor cells appear to be grouped into receptor fields arranged vertically in columns with adjacent columns "fitting" together to form the cortical projection pattern of the body. Somatotopically, units responsive to joint movement seem to dominate Area 2, the most posterior part of the somatosensory cortex, while receptor cells sensitive to stimulation of the skin are predominant in the most anterior portion, Area 3. Area 1 contains cells of both types. The specific linking of peripheral joint receptors with specific cortical neurons in a somatopic representation of the body areas provides a well-defined anatomical nucleus for fine kinesthetic differentation between various movements or positions of specific body parts.

Sensitivity of Cortical Joint Receptors (14). Most cortical joint receptors respond to movement over arcs of 60 to 90 degrees, a considerably wider range of sensitivity than that found in peripheral joint receptors. Some cortical cells are believed to be sensitive to displacement of the joint over as little as 20 degrees of arc but these are few in number. The complexity of the relationship between the peripheral neural event and that recorded centrally is evident when one considers the kinds of integrative processes which must occur in order for a given cortical cell, sensitive to movement over 90 degrees of arc, to fire at increasingly higher "steady state" levels as joint displacement increases from 0 to 90 degrees. Such a phenomenon obviously requires that the cortical neuron be "driven" by input from a number of peripheral receptors whose narrower excitatory angles overlap one another and cover the entire 90 degrees of arc to which the cortical neuron is responsive.

Response Properties of Cortical Joint Receptors (14). Although complete data are not presently available, there appear to be rather precise relationships between the activity of a given cortical receptor cell and the position or movement of the joint to which it is linked. In general, these properties are quite similar to those previously enumerated for the peripheral joint receptors.

Reciprocal Inhibition in Adjacent Cortical Joint Receptors. Mountcastle (14) found that frequently two adjacent cortical neurons responded reciprocally to movement at a given joint. For example, neurons A and B, adjacent to each other in the cortex, might both be sensitive to movement at the wrist joint, neuron A to extension, neuron B to flexion. When extension at the wrist joint occurs, A begins to fire and continues to fire as long as this extension is maintained. Neuron B is simultaneously *inhibited* by the movement of the wrist joint into extension. In other words, B is completely silent whenever the wrist is moved into or remains in an extended position. Conversely, when the wrist is moved into flexion, neuron B begins to fire. If this position of flexion is maintained, B continues to fire and at a rate related to the degree of flexion maintained at the joint. At the same time, activity in neuron A ceases; it is silent and continues to be silent as long as the joint is held in the flexed position.

The effect of this reciprocal inhibitory interaction between active cortical neurons is similar to that discussed in the encoding of visual information. As was true in the former case, these inhibitory processes are believed to result in a "sharpening" of incoming neural kinesthetic information, so that they make a major contribution to the individual's precise differentiation between various movements or positions of the body.

Hypothetical Neural Correlates of Position and Movement

Position. It is not difficult from even this amount of information to visualize what the nature and sequence of the neural events subserving the organism's awareness of position and movement might be. For instance, neural correlates of the position sense (maintained joint position) might be outlined as follows:

1. the specific group(s) of receptor cells actively firing (as well as those that are actively inhibited).
2. the level of steady state firing in this active population of receptor cells.

The specific body part and joint action involved determines which peripheral receptors are active; the topological representation of the body in the cortical receiving area determines the site at which the cortical activity takes place (14). Since peripheral joint receptors are linked both functionally and anatomically to specific cortical receptor cells, the maintenance of a given position results in the active firing of a fairly specific group of cortical cells. The pattern and level of firing in these cells represents the specific angle maintained at the joint. Awareness of body position, therefore, might be described neurologically, as a complex "profile" of the level and pattern of activity in specific populations of cortical neurons and their connecting peripheral units. Specific profiles, then, are associated with various joint positions.

Movement. Movement away from the position described above crosses overlapping excitatory angles of a succession of peripheral joint receptors and is accompanied by transient increases in the rate of firing of these receptor cells. This "complex" of peripheral information is transmitted centrally and undergoes certain modifications as it travels to cortical regions. The specific pattern of afferent input finally received at cortical levels fractionates the total population of cortical units responsive to movement at this joint. Certain cortical cells which were previously uninvolved are now activated, while others (previously active) are now inhibited. Some show transient increases in rate of firing; others decreased rates of firing. Many remain unaffected by the present influx of sensory information. This change in the spatial and temporal characteristics of the pattern of neural activity in both cortical and peripheral receptors signals the organism that movement is or has occurred.

Direction, Speed, and Extent of Movement. Direction of movement from a specified position would then be represented by a "profile of change." That is, the profile of *which* cells show transient increases in rate of discharge and which show decreases in activity, etc., would subserve the perception of the direction of the movement. Speed of movement would be represented by the *rate* or *extent of the transient discharge* to movement. That is, the faster the movement, the greater the transient increases in rate of firing in the active receptor cells. Judgment of the relative speed of two movements would thus involve a comparison of the *level* of *transient* discharge associated with each of the two movements. The degree of difference detectable centrally then would give rise to the individual's difference limen to speed of movement.

Perception of the *extent of movement* under this schema would be accomplished by comparing the present *level* of *steady state* firing with that of the previously held position. The absolute difference between the two would then subserve our judgments of the extent of movement taking place; the greater the difference in levels of steady state firing, the greater the extent of movement.

Where such comparative operations are involved, certain temporal or decay factors may also come into play, so that related psychological judgments should be less precise in these cases than when no such comparative operations are involved. Therefore, performance on tasks of kinesthetic repositioning of the limbs or tasks involving reproduction of specific rates of movement might be expected to be less precise than those involving judgments of the onset or direction of movement.

Summary

In general, movement of a *specific* amount in a *specific* direction at a *specific* joint results in a unique level and sequence of neural activity in a fairly distinct group of receptor cells. One can easily imagine the complexity of events involved when several joint actions in several body parts are integrated into a single, adaptive behavior, such as a tennis serve. Still, simplified as the foregoing discussion may be, it provides a logical framework for understanding the very precise and complex neural events which may underlie our perception of movement and body position.

SENSORY INTEGRATION AND INFORMATION FEEDBACK

The analysis of a perceptual-motor skill from a neurological point of view would suggest that at some point along the way there must be a collaboration of sensory data from the different sensory systems involved in the performace of the behavior. Such interaction or integration of sensory information would appear to be necessary if the total adjustive behavior of the organism is to be effective. Certain neurophysiologists believe that the process of sensory integration is, in fact, the most important task of the central nervous system. Although a discussion of such systems must at this time be cursory, no presentation of neurological concepts would be complete without some mention of sensory integration and information feedback. The primary emphasis here will be on answering briefly: (a) Do mechanisms exist which could subserve functions of sensory integration and feedback, and (b) What are some of the ways in which these mechanisms influence perceptual-motor functioning?

The first question can be answered with minimum effort, for evidence strongly suggests that such mechanisms do, in fact, exist. The second question, however, requires that we look, even if only briefly, at the effect of reticular and cerebellar functioning on perceptual-motor behavior.

The Reticular Formation

Anatomical Characteristics (6, 13, 17). The reticular formation is believed to have reciprocal links with most major structures in the CNS. For instance, there are known to be important and intimate pathways between the reticular formation and the spinal cord. It is believed that certain cells within the spinal cord send axons directly to the reticular formation. Collateral branches from the main axon trunks of the specific sensory pathways are also known to project into the brainstem reticular formation. In addition, many reticular neurons have expansive dendritic extensions which cover wide areas and thus enable the reticular formation to receive sensory information from laterally located nuclei. Other major pathways include reciprocal projections with the cerebellum, the principle nuclei of the thalamus, rhinencephalic structures including the hippocampus and entorhinal areas, the basal ganglia, and vast areas of the cerebral cortex. This vast network of interconnecting pathways provides a basic anatomical framework for sensory integration and feedback processes. Via this network, the reticular formation has access to all basic sensory information reaching the organism, is capable of monitoring or modulating efferent outflow, and can coordinate differences in the two.

Functional Characteristics. GENERAL. (6) Microelectrode studies have shown that individual reticular neurons may respond differentially to a given stimulus and that some are excited by one type of sensory stimulus but not another. For instance, the same stimulus has been found to increase activity in some reticular cells while decreasing activity (inhibition) in others. Further, a particular stimulus is capable of inducing, at different times, either facilitatory or inhibitory responses in the same unit as a consequence of existing conditions of excitability within the reticular formation itself. Such responses appear, however, to be fairly consistent, indicating that specific responses may be characteristic of individual neurons of the RAS. Recent evidence also indicates that the *significance* of the afferent input may determine its ability to evoke a reticular response. All of this suggests, of course, that some kind of organizational or integrational response to complex sensory information may be an important part of reticular functioning.

SENSORY INPUT. The influence of the reticular formation in modifying sensory inputs into the CNS is known to be such that certain sensory signals are transmitted while others are completely rejected or ignored. Granit and Kaada (9) demonstrated the effects of reticular stimulation upon proprioceptive activity. He showed that the small gamma efferents of the anterior horn cell exerted some control over the muscle spindle and that reticular stimulation resulted in the modification of gamma efferent firing and consequently of spindle activity. Both facilitatory and inhibitory effects were noted.

Similar effects of reticular stimulation upon other sensory-perceptual systems have also been established. For instance, the CFF (Critical Flicker Fusion) rate has been shown to increase significantly with stimulation of the recticular formation (12). That is, after reticular stimulation, an individual is able to follow a rapidly flickering light at significantly higher rates of flicker before it appears to fuse into a single, continuous light. Another study (7) has revealed that both accuracy and speed of perceptual responses are enhanced as a result of reticular stimulation.

MOTOR OUTPUT. That reticular stimulation also influences motor activity has been repeatedly demonstrated. For example, experiments on decerebrated or anesthetized cats have shown that movement resulting from stimulation of the motor cortex can be immediately inhibited upon stimulation of certain parts of the reticular formation (medioventral RAS at the bulbar level). In contrast to this, other evidence indicates that facilitatory effects upon spinal motor activity (partly through control over muscle spindle activity) can be produced as a consequence of stimulation of loci higher in the central brainstem reticular formation. These effects are seen in the augmentation of both the stretch and flexor reflexes. In addition to these influences on reflex and cortically-induced movement, excitation as a result of stimulation of the brainstem reticular formation can be made great enough to evoke postural changes, that is, to elicit movement.

The reticular formation, like the pyramidal and reflex systems of movement, appears to exert its influence on movement through inter-neuronal connections rather than by acting directly upon the moto-neurons themselves. Reticular influence upon motor activity is thought to proceed via the recruitment of larger and larger pools of interneurons which in turn exert their effects spatially (and temporally) upon various groups of motoneurons (17).

In summary, then, the foregoing indicates that the reticular system:

1. is capable of enhancing perceptual or sensory discrimination as well as modulating effector output.
2. has the necessary interconnections with the cerebral cortex and other brain structures to monitor or modify activity occurring throughout the CNS.

The Cerebellum (17, 19, 20).

Afferent and Efferent Pathways. The multiplicity of afferent input to the cerebellum suggests that it is a center for the convergence of sensory information from many sources. It was originally believed that the cerebellum received only vestibular proprioceptive afferents, but it is now known that this structure receives afferent inputs from tactual, visual, and even visceral sources as well.

Both physiological and anatomical data define the existence of peripheral afferent pathways which relay in the cerebellar nuclei and ultimately reach the cortex via certain thalamic nuclei. These cerebellocerebral pathways appear to project to both motor and sensory areas of the cortex. In addition, those parts of the cerebellum responding to specific types of peripheral stimuli are reciprocally connected with the cortical receiving areas responding to those same types of stimuli. This suggests a kind of afferent feedback loop with which sensory events in the cortex might be modulated or at least monitored by the cerebellum.

The cerebellocortical pathways are paralleled by similar descending pathways from the cortex to the cerebellum. These pathways arise from widespread areas of the cortex. The entire anterior lobe of the cerebellum, for example, and the motor area of the cerebral cortex have reciprocally connecting pathways. Although no specific functional role has as yet been assigned to these reciprocally connecting pathways, cerebellar influences are thought to be capable of modifying activity in both the sensory and motor cortices.

Contribution to Motor Output. Both facilitatory and inhibitory influences on movement have been observed as a result of stimulation of the cerebellar cortex. Evidence indicates that stimulation of the neocerebellum can increase the excitability of the motor cortex. Some of this effect is believed to be exerted via connections between the two structures rather than through convergence on the reticular substance. In addition, the *same* paleocerebellar stimulation can have completely different effects upon motor responses, the kind of effect being dependent upon the background of activity in the motor cortex. That is, cerebellar influences on cortical motor output may be either excitatory or inhibitory depending upon the *current* activity in the cortical motor areas. Further, combined cerebellar and cortical motor ablations produce greater motor deficits than the summative effects of the two ablations performed separately. This gives some indication of the complexity of the functional relationship between the cerebral motor cortex and the cerebellum.

It is believed that the cerebellum may play an intricate role in the planning and execution of movement in time. Although the cerebral cortex is known to receive widespread sensory information from both proprioceptors and exteroceptors it is generally agreed that coordinated movements cannot be executed by the cortex "single-handed." Impulses cannot be stored in the motor cortex to be discharged after a fixed delay. Therefore, some additional mechanism or connection must be involved in the planned execution of movements over time. Since there are reciprocal connections between the motor cortex and the cerebellum, the motor cortex could discharge in a feedback type of circuit to the cerebellum. In this way, the programming of sequences of movement might be possible. Ruch (17) for instance believes that the role of the cerebellum in behavior is to compare the action initiated at the cortical level with the image of the behavior subsequently performed and ultimately to initiate appropriate responses to resolve any discrepancies or differences between the two. "At any rate the cerebellum has the requisite facilitatory and inhibitory relationship to the motor cortex and to the brainstem mechanisms to aid both systems in starting and stopping movements in the manner necessary for effective, well-directed movement" (17: 297).

Summary

The close and numerous interconnections between the reticular formation, the cerebellum, and other CNS structures represents a basic nerve network by means of which sensory information involved in planned activity could be monitored or modified. Certainly the reciprocal loops between the reticular formation, the cerebellum, and both the sensory and motor areas of the cortex, forming feedback type circuits, have some functional significance. If nothing else, they point to important inherent functional relationships between these structures involving the coordination of sensory input and efferent outflow and thus the production of skillful and refined motor performance.

This suggests, of course, that what we observe behaviorally is not the product of a single, isolated neural event but rather a culmination of highly refined integrated activity involving the participation of many brain structures. As physical educators then, we need to look at overt motor performances not as single, isolated events but as products of complex, continuing, and highly interrelated CNS activity.

THEORETICAL MODEL OF PERCEPTUAL-MOTOR FUNCTIONING

Neurobehavioral Description of a Perceptual-Motor Performance

This now places us at the point of building, step by step, in neurobehavioral terms, a theoretical model of perceptual-motor functioning. To keep such a description within the scope of this writing, I have set the task as the act of picking up a pencil with the following complex, continuing, and highly interrelated CNS activity.

1. The sensory modalities involved in the performance are primarily those of vision and kinesthesis.
2. A spatial interval separates the individual from the pencil.
3. The individual is motivated by the "need" to obtain the pencil.

Although the breaking down of a behavior into discrete steps may in itself distort the picture of what really happens during the performance, these breakdowns also frequently provide insight into the important functional components underlying such behaviors. It is in this light that the following discussion is written.

Step I. Sensory Synthesis. The individual sees the pencil. This implies first a selection of or attention to specific elements in the visual field of the observer (probably reticular involvement). Sensory information from the reflection of the pencil on the retina is then transmitted via the classical afferent pathways to cortical regions. The appropriate ordering of this sensory input, which begins in the eye itself and is subsequently elaborated upon by higher centers, provides the initial information upon which certain characteristics of this object in space are judged. These characteristics include: (a) size, (b) shape, (c) color, which may or may not be pertinent, and (d) spatial location (distance and direction in relationship to the observer). Thus the initial step involved in the performance of a perceptual-motor task is one of receiving and ordering certain specific sensory information, in this case, visual information.

Step II. Sensory Interaction. Simultaneously with the receiving and ordering of sensory information in Step I, the current visual stimulation is compared with that stored from similar stimulus situations encountered by the individual in the past. That is, information concerning the size, shape, and location of the "present pencil in space" is integrated with past information about "pencils in space" in general. Thus, the nature and extent of the individual's prior experience with "pencils in space" will be an important factor in the initial processing of sensory information. The cerebral cortex, the reticular formation, and other subcortical structures may be important sites for such comparative operations.

Step III. Effector Activity I. As a result of the specific sensory processes which have occurred in Steps I and II, a specific effector or motor apparatus is set into action which initiates an appropriate locomotor action. The central order is: "Walk over to the edge of the table!" This movement adjusts the spatial relationship between the observer and the object in space so that the pencil may ultimately be picked up. The fulfillment of this order requires the firing of appropriate groups of motoneurons located in the spinal cord—groups of neurons which have been recruited or readied for firing as a result of the previous sensory activity occurring throughout the CNS.

Step IV. Sensory Feedback and Comparative Operations I. As the individual walks toward the pencil, additional sensory information is fed into the CNS. This sensory feedback consists of:

1. Proprioceptive information transmitted from receptors in the muscles, tendons, and joints of the moving body parts to cortical receiving areas and to other CNS structures as well.
2. Additional visual information which includes:
   a. Information relative to changes in the retinal image of the pencil with the advancing locomotor movement. (The pencil subtends a greater and greater angle on the retina as the individual moves closer to the pencil).
   b. Information from oculomotor activity (processes of accommodation and convergence, etc.) involved in maintaining the pencil in focus on the retina.

These two sources of sensory information are conveyed simultaneously to the CNS and provide a collaborative source of sensory information · upon which direction or modification of the present locomotor act is based. If the pattern of feedback activity coincides with that originally set up by the "central order," the executed locomotor behavior is as "ordered" and this link in the total behavioral chain is complete. If the two patterns of electrical activity do not coincide, further adjustments (additional steps) must be taken until the difference between the two patterns is zero at least minimal. That is, the individual must continue to adjust his position until he can pick up the pencil.

Although we will assume, for the present, that the original "central order" was correct and that by fulfilling this order the individual stops in such a position that he is able to reach out and grasp the pencil, it is obvious that this initial "central order" could be in error. If this were the case, then the position for prehension assumed by the individual would also be in error. If the latter were true, then the subsequent performance of the manipulative cycle of the behavior (reaching for the pencil) might be impossible or at least require further bodily adjustments that were not, so to speak, originally planned for. This of course suggests that the precision of the initial sensory processes upon which the motor acts are based may be vital to the success of the total behavioral act.

Step V and VI. Effector Activity—Sensory Feedback and Comparative Operations II. With the person now in a good position for prehension, the final step in the act of picking up the pencil can be executed. The "central order" is: "Reach out and pick up the pencil." As these final movements are made, sensory information is again fed back into the CNS. This feedback information is from three sources:

1. information derived from movement of the arm and hand in space (proprioception).
2. stimulation from the actual contact between the fingers and the pencil (touch).
3. information from the contracting image of the hand projected on the retina as it coincides with the image of the pencil (visual).

This sensory feedback again passes through certain integrative and comparative operations and is ultimately used, I propose, to assess both the adequacy of the final act in the behavioral chain (the reaching and grasping behavior) as well as the success of the *total* behavior. Again, if the two patterns of electrical activity (that originally set up by the "central order" and that derived from the feedback accompanying the performance of the act) coincide, no adjustments are necessary and the performance is complete. Behaviorally the individual has picked up the pencil and the performance is successful. If there are discrepancies between the two patterns of activity, the pencil has not been picked up, and adjustments or modifications in the behavior must be made until the performance is deemed satisfactory. The achievement of some degree of coincidence between these two patterns of electrical activity may, in fact, be what is involved in the process of "learning" a particular skill.

To define a point at which the processing of sensory information, the basis for the reaching and grasping behavior, was begun, we must go back in time. The sensory processes underlying the "central order" for locomotion are certainly not isolated or distinct from those which give rise to the "ordering" of the manipulative behavior. It is indeed highly probable that both orders are inherently linked to the initial sensory activity of Steps I and II. This suggests that although the order for the manipulative behavior may be transmitted simultaneously with that for the locomotor behavior, it is programmed, via intricate feedback circuits, to occur at a point later in the total behavioral cycle. When this point in the cycle is reached, the order is carried out, and the individual reaches out to pick up the pencil. This delayed programming could be achieved by means of the numerous feedback loops (mentioned previously) which exist between cortical areas and the reticular formation, cerebellum, or other subcortical structures.

Basically, then, four steps are involved in the performance of a perceptual-motor behavior. These may be described as: (a) *sensory synthesis*, or the processing of present stimulus information; (b) *sensory integration*, or the integration of present with past sensory information; (c) *effector activity*, the movement; and (d) *sensory feedback* and *comparative operations*. Although our illustration and discussion has focused upon a task somewhat removed from ordinary gross motor performances, this general formulation can be extended to include situations analogous to many of our sports situations by simply adding an external moving object. The general outline of events remains the same. For example, successful movement performance in a sports situation obviously requires the processing of sensory information (synthesis, integration, comparison). Here the initial sensory processes become more complex because adequate sensory synthesis and integration must include the handling of such information as speed and direction of the moving object. There is more emphasis on the precision of these initial sensory processes since in most sports situations there is little if any time available for making large unplanned-for adjustments in either positional or manipulative behaviors. That is, there is no time to "rejudge" the stimulus situation.

General Discussion and Implications

The foregoing formulation suggests then:

1. that perceptual-motor performance may be conceived of as a complicated, overlapping series of sequences of sensory-motor-feedback events.
2. that there may be, grossly, *two* such highly interrelated programs of events common to most gross motor performances: those leading to the positioning of the body in space, or *positional events*, and those leading to proper manipulation of smaller body parts or implements, *manipulative events*.
3. that the success of the total motor performance is dependent upon the integrity of each step in the cycle but more particularly upon the integrity of the sensory processes involved in Steps I and II.

Therefore if behavior B is some function of the two programs of events,

$$B = f\ (P + M)$$

where P = the positional cycle, and
M = the manipulative cycle.

Inadequacies in B may then arise from discrepancies in either P or M, i.e., position or manipulation. If the cycles P and M are, as proposed, highly interrelated and based upon the sensory processes involved in Steps I and II (the processing of *present* sensory information and the integrating of this data with *past* sensory information), then inadequacies in the over-all behavior should result primarily when these sensory functions are faulty or in error. If the use of sensory feedback from the presently performed behavior is added to this list of sensory functions, we have then three major points at which breakdowns (as well as modifications and corrections) in perceptual-motor performances might occur. All of this then places emphasis upon the sensory-perceptual facets of motor performance. In other words, if there is no damage to the central or peripheral motor apparatus, then factors limiting the learning and performance of a given movement skill may be primarily sensory-perceptual in nature. Such factors could include:

1. the kinds of sensory-perceptual demands involved in the movement skill itself.
2. the individual's capacity for handling such sensory-perceptual requirements.

What do we actually know about the role of such sensory functions in perceptual-motor performance? I should like to assert that presently we know little if anything about the kinds of perceptual demands involved in the learning or performance of motor activities commonly taught in physical education programs. There is also little substantial fact relevant to individual capacity for processing the sensory information involved in gross motor performances. Although we might logically assume that the ability or inability of the individual to process specific kinds of sensory information is due to certain inherited capacities, age-maturity factors, or certain psychoemotional characteristics of the individual, we have little experimental evidence available to indicate what role, if any, these factors may play in the learning or performance of a motor skill. Take the age-maturity factor for example. Birch (4) has shown that the average child may not be able to effectively coordinate visual and kinesthetic information into a single, adaptive behavior until between the ages of six and eight. If coordination of information from these two sensory systems is vital to the performance of a given perceptual-motor skill, the child prior to this age may not be able to effectively execute this behavior simply because he is not capable of refined visual-kinesthetic functioning. Evidence such as this is indeed scarce, but it suggests the need for research to help narrow the gap between fact and fancy with regard to sensory processes in perceptual-motor functioning.

What then about information feedback? If one of the points at which breakdowns or modifications and corrections in a performance can occur is that point where the performance just completed is compared with the central order for that performance, then *specific* and *immediate* feedback information concerning the success or failure of a given movement performance would seem to be important in the development of that behavior. This does not mean the simple verbal feedback that is commonly used, but rather information feedback specific to points at which the behavior has broken down or requires further refinement. Here again we need to create and use instruments and situations which will provide specific feedback to the individual concerning his performance and to investigate systematically the effectiveness of this information feedback on the learning and performance of the motor skill.

The implications are clear; the possibilities for research are limitless. Still we cannot just say: "Do creative research." "Be creative teachers." To be creative, whether in teaching or research, requires insight into the problem at hand. (And more often than not, the problems confronting us in physical education are not easy ones.) Insight or creativity does not just happen; it is more a product of thorough academic preparation, competent guidance, and sound criticism than of specific inherited capacities. Our responsibility as educators is to lead the way to creativity and insight in future physical educators by providing them first with a sound academic foundation. This includes preparation in such related disciplines as psychology, physiology, neurology, and mathematics. Secondly, we must make available opportunities for students to develop and use new teaching and research techniques. This means providing space, time, and leadership for stimulating laboratory and teaching experiences. In other words, we must create an atmosphere in which both graduates and undergraduates may intelligently seek answers to problems which have puzzled us for years. If we are to do this with the dedication, competence, and enthusiasm required for such a task, we too must continue to grow in our command of special areas of knowledge as well as in our application of them.

REFERENCES

1. Adrian, E. D., "The Impulses Produced by Sensory Nerve-Endings, Part I." *Journal of Physiology*, LXI (1926), 49–72.
2. Attneave, Fred, "Search for Perceptual Elements." Lecture given in the Department of Psychology, University of California, Los Angeles, Spring, 1966.

3. Bartley, S. H., "Central Mechanisms of Vision," in *Handbook of Physiology*, Vol. I (Washington, D.C.: American Physiological Society, 1959), pp. 713–40.

4. Birch, Herbert, and Lefford, Arthur, "Intersensory Development in Children," *Monographs of the Society for Research in Child Development* XXVIII (1963), 2–47.

5. Boyd, I. A., and Roberts, T. D. M., "Proprioceptive Discharges from Stretch Receptors in the Knee-Joint of the Cat." *Journal of Physiology* CXXII (1953), 38.

6. French, J. D., "The Reticular Formation," in *Handbook of Physiology*, Vol. II (Baltimore, Md.: Waverly Press, Inc., 1960), 1281–1306.

7. Fuster, J. M., "Effects of Stimulation of Brainstem on Tachistoscopic Perception." *Science* CXXVII (1958), 150.

8. Granit, Ragnar, *Receptors and Sensory Perception* (New Haven and London: Yale University Press, 1962).

9. ———, and Kaada, B. R., "Influence of Stimulation of Central Nervous Structures on Muscle Spindles in Cat." *Acta Physiologica Scandinavica* XXVII (1952), 130–60.

10. Hartline, H. K., "The Response of Single Optic Nerve Fibers of the Vertebrate Eye to Illumination of the Retina." *American Journal of Physiology*, CXXI (1938), 400–415.

11. Jung, Richard, and Hassler, Rolf, "The Extrapyramidal Motor System," in *Handbook of Physiology, Vol. II* (Baltimore, Md.: Waverly Press, 1960), pp. 863–928.

12. Lindsley, D. B., "The Reticular Formation and Perceptual Discrimination," in *Reticular Formation of the Brain*, Jasper, H. H. (ed.) (Boston: Little Brown & Co., 1958).

13. Magoun, H. W., *The Waking Brain* (Springfield, Ill.: Charles C Thomas, 1965).

14. Mountcastle, Vernon B., and Powell, Thomas P. S., "Central Nervous Mechanisms Subserving Position Sense and Kinesthesis." *Johns Hopkins Hospital Bulletin* CV (1959), 173–200.

15. Patton, Harry D., and Amassian, Vahe E., "The Pyramidal Tract: Its Excitation and Functions," in *Handbook of Physiology*, Vol. II (Baltimore, Md.: Waverly Press, 1960), pp. 837–62.

16. Ratliff, F., and Hartline, H. K., "The Responses of Limulus Optic Nerve Fibers to Patterns of Illumination on the Receptor Mosaic." *Journal of Genetic Psychology 42*: 1241–1255, 1959.

17. Ruch, T. C., Patton, H. D., Woodbury, J. W., and Towe, A. L., *Neurophysiology* (Philadelphia: W. B. Saunders Co., 1963).

18. Sokolov, Eugene Nikolaievich, "Neuronal Models and the Orienting Reflex," in *The Central Nervous System and Behavior*, Mary A. B. Brazier (ed.) (Washington, D.C.: Josiah Macy, Jr. Foundation; The National Science Foundation, 1960).

19. Terzuolo, C. A., and Adey, W. R., "Sensorimotor Cortical Activities," in *Handbook of Physiology, Vol. II* (Baltimore, Md.: Waverly Press, 1960), pp. 797–836.

20. Brookhart, John M., "The Cerebellum," in *Handbook of Physiology*, Vol. II (Baltimore, Md.: Waverly Press, 1960), pp. 1245–80.

BRYANT J. CRATTY*

Imprinting and Human Action

An extensive body of scientific and semiscientific literature produced in the 1920's, 1930's and early 1940's explored the relative contribution of inherited versus learned traits to the total human personality. Twin studies, in which one twin was taught while the other ignored, exemplify this trend. Other investigators measured the correlations of IQ between siblings, twins, and children who were not related in order to assess the contributions of nature versus nurture to intelligence. By World War II, the more sophisticated students of human behavior had resolved the argument by concluding that human behavior depends on *both* inherent and learned experiences.

Recent experimental and clinical literature on child development, however, suggests that there may be a third kind of behavior that is influential of human action. Several scholars, in order to explain emotionality, gender identification, and the formation of various social attributes in children, have looked at a phenomenon previously the concern of animal behaviorists.

Zoologists for the past fifty years have been intrigued by a "wired-in" mechanism called imprinting.

Imprinting may be defined as an automatic behavioral tendency triggered by occurrences early in the life of animals, which leads them to engage in persistent perceptual-motor activities. Studies of imprinting

*Department of Physical Education, University of California at Los Angeles.

have ranged over a wide variety of species. Both motor and perceptual events have been studied as tendency-evoking events, and emotion, sexual response, perception, and motor activity have been studied as behaviors upon which imprinting has had an effect.

The belief that learning in infancy influences adult behavior antedates Freud. Imprinted behavior, however, seems different from learned behavior. We will first examine the zoologists' findings: the conditions under which imprinting occurs and the nature of imprinted behaviors. We will then describe several attributes of human children which, it has been suggested, are influenced by imprinting. The literature suggests that there are relationships between certain perceptual events and some human actions, which may be partially accounted for by imprinting. Admittedly, the statements about human imprinting are, at the present time, heavily permeated with inferences unsubstantiated by solid evidence. This speculation, however, should lead to important experimental efforts.

Perhaps most fanciful of all are the ideas presented in the conclusion of the chapter. It is felt, however, that this mild form of intellectual dishonesty will be tempered somewhat by this early admission of the speculative nature of these ideas.

ANIMAL IMPRINTING

The literature on imprinting in animals dates from the turn of the century. Craig, experimenting with wild pigeons, found that in order to crossbreed two species it was first necessary to raise the young of one species with the adults of the other (4). Upon reaching adulthood the birds reared in this manner tended to mate with birds of the same species as their foster parents. Other interspecies sexual fixations were reported in birds and fishes at this time. Heiroth and his wife, hand-rearing the young of several species of European birds, reported in 1910 that many of the social responses of these birds were directed toward their human companions (11).

Lorenz was the first to call this phenomenon *imprinting* and to point out that it appeared to occur at a critical period early in the life of an animal. Lorenz suggested that imprinting was related not only to sexual behavior but also that it influenced selective evolution.

Systematic studies of imprinting in animals are comparatively recent. Although the most popular animal for study has been the chick, imprinting has also been observed in insects, fish, dogs, and other mammals, including sheep, deer, and buffalo. These and later studies can be placed within several classification systems. Some investigators have explored the critical time periods during which imprinting seems to occur, while others have been interested in the types of perceptual events which seem to trigger imprinting. At times these problems have been studied under the natural conditions of the animal's life environment, but recently scholars have used the laboratory in order to gain better control over the many variables. Some researchers have been concerned with the animals' movements, while others have concentrated on their perceptual processes.

A typical experimental arrangement for the study of imprinting in animals includes a circular walk-way in which a chick a few hours old is placed. In the center of this walk, attached to an overhead pulley, an object is placed, the speed of which can be controlled by the experimenter.

A great many variables have been inserted into such experimental arrangements including changes in the stimulus conditions as well as changes to the organism (for example the administration of drugs or hormones). The animal is said to be imprinted when it follows the moving stimulus. Care is taken not to expose the chick to any other moving stimuli and to control other variables, such as ambient noises.

One of the first findings of these studies was the discovery that there was a critical time period during which a chick was most likely to be imprinted after birth. Charts plotting the imprinting period in chicks, for example, usually indicate that the best time for imprinting occurs between the 9th and 20th hour after emergence from the egg (12). It has also been discovered that imprinting seems to occur immediately after birth during the period in which the animal becomes mobile, but before fear or avoidance of moving objects is shown (12). In other words, the animals seem to need adequate locomotor ability, but the fear of external moving objects diminishes susceptibility.

Various experimental conditions can prolong the critical period. In one study, for example, it was found that the imprinting period could be lengthened if the animal was placed with others who had been previously imprinted. There seemed to be a kind of social facilitation that stretched the imprinting period. As chicks observed others of their kind following moving stimuli, they showed distinct evidence of being imprinted, even though they had reached an age in which imprinting would not usually have occurred.

It has also been shown that the sensitive period of imprinting can be positively influenced by hastening the maturation of perceptual ability. Experiments in which the animals' performance on various discrimination tasks was evaluated suggest that for optimum imprinting conditions the development of perceptual awareness should also be considered.

Elucidating this finding are studies which demonstrate that the more "striking" in appearance the stimuli are (e.g., striped), the more marked the behavior is. A rotating disc is usually found to be a more powerful imprinting stimulus than a stationary one.

The influence of novelty on the visual perception of young chicks (and humans) has been studied by Frantz. He found that form and pattern perception are influenced by maturation and visual experience at critical ages. His findings are derived primarily from investigations which clocked the time chicks and humans visually fixate on stimuli of various degrees of complexity (5) (6). Some authorities suggest that perceptual processes override the importance of motor development in the imprinting of chicks.

Further substantiating the importance of perception, are studies which indicate that chicks can be imprinted to motionless objects. Movement either of the imprinted animal or of the stimulus is not always necessary to attract the former to the latter.

Auditory stimulation also influences imprinting behavior of animals. Ducklings, for example, have been imprinted to the parents' "voices" without the presence of a visually inspected object similar to their parents in form. Other studies have demonstrated that imprinting can occur when various laboratory-produced noises are presented during the critical periods.

The importance of motor activity in imprinting is supported by the finding that cold delays the occurrence of a following response apparently because of its physiological effects on movement, and by the finding that increasing the animal's effort by making him walk up inclined planes or cross over hurdles, facilitates imprinting. Thompson and Dubanoski, for example, found that chicks imprinted best when they followed moving objects—better than when they had been confined in moving boxes behind moving surrogates, behind screens while observing a moving stimuli, or when both the chick and surrogate were fixed (14).

In summary, the research suggests that there is a critical period in the lives of most animals during which imprinting is best accomplished and that both unique perceptual events and motor activity facilitate imprinting (12). Beach and others have suggested that the importance of early experiences on imprinting is related to the establishment of what Hebb has termed "phase sequences" within the cortex of the animals; various perceptual events key and trigger more complex sequences of cells supportive of perceptual-motor behavior (1). Others have hypothesized that these apparently innate preferential choice behaviors are triggered neurally by retinal ganglion cells.

The most controversial questions about the cause of animal imprinting revolve around the importance of effort versus perceptual-display. Close examination of the literature, however, suggests that the relative importance of motoric versus perceptual activity is a function of the experimental arrangements and of the animal species under study.

A number of conditions have been found to block or retard imprinting. The most reliable reducer of imprintability in animals is the introduction of conditions which produce fear. For example, immobility rather than imprinting was induced in chicks after they had been held head down for fifteen seconds. In another investigation rats exposed to water traumatization in infancy became "emotional" and made more errors in water escape mazes than adults. The animals in this study did not seem to generalize their fear to all stressful situations, however. Puppies from 3–4 weeks old were also emotionally disturbed by flashing lights and similar techniques. It is found on the other hand that puppies and rats who are handled and fondled imprint better than animals who are not accustomed to such handling. Their "fear period" seems postponed by human contact of this nature.

Early sensory deprivation also seems to postpone the age at which imprinting can occur. In one study, it was found that depriving ducklings of the opportunity to observe patterned lights early in their lives impeded the acquisition of imprinted responses.

There also seems to be an optimum level of arousal necessary for effective imprinting. For example, sedatives introduced into the animals' bloodstream generally impede imprinting.

The findings from a number of studies carried out with stricter controls than were used in the early studies suggest that sexual attachment is basic to imprinted behavior. In many experiments the animals first followed and then attempted to copulate with stimuli to which they had been imprinted. This kind of sexual fixation toward humans is sometimes seen in animals who have been hand-reared. Imprinting in animals has been shown to lead to sexual displays by birds and to typical aggressive behavior as the sexual partner is sought.

In addition to the conditions which induce or retard imprinting, a more basic question is whether imprinting is similar to, or distinctly different from, conditioned learning. Those who think the two are similar have produced findings that imprinted behavior can be extinguished like a learned response by the imposition of negative motivating conditions. In addition, objects to which chicks have been imprinted have been shown to act as reinforcers in the learning of a typical T maze.

More evidence is available, however, which argues that imprinting is distinct and different from conditioned learning. The following differences are usually cited.

1. In imprinting, *primacy* of experience leads to greater retention than does *recency* of experience as is often the case in learning.
2. Heightened activity levels usually facilitate imprinting, whereas in

other investigations extraneous motor activity has been shown to interfere with classical conditioning.

3. Imprinting behavior is relatively difficult to extinguish whereas much learned behavior is not.

4. Imprinting may only occur during critical early periods in the organism's life; learning is a continuous lifetime process.

5. Massed practice seems to facilitate imprinting, but spaced practice usually facilitates learning.

Thus imprinting seems to be the emergence of certain behavioral tendencies triggered by exposure to identifiable perceptual events at critical periods in their life span. Most of the evidence suggests that behavioral patterns of this nature cannot usually be explained within classic learning theory, nor by reference to standard maturational concepts.

HUMAN IMPRINTING

An examination of the literature in sociology, anthropology, child development, psychiatry, and psychology leads to the speculation that perhaps some types of human behavior depend on specific kinds of perceptual experiences introduced early into the child's life at propitious times. Among the more substantial documents attesting to the possibility of human imprinting are those describing the later personality development of infants who are subjected to varying degrees of maternal deprivation.

Studying the later behavior and perceptual capabilities of children who were exposed to early institutional care during the first six months of life, Goldfarb concluded that problem behavior was evidenced by most of the children who were deprived of proper early maternal stimulation. On the other hand he found that children who were placed in foster homes *prior* to the age of six months, did not suffer similar personality defects in adolescence (8).

Furthermore, Goldfarb found that the children who were deprived of normal stimulation because of residence in foundling homes were inferior in verbal and non-verbal IQ measures, and in their ability to reproduce various visual designs. In addition these children were extremely passive in later life. Goldfarb theorized that this passivity resulted from their early routinized existence.

Brodbeck and Irwin studying the emergence of speech behavior in infants six months of age similarly discovered that the development of speech in 94 children without families was markedly deficient when compared to that of a similar group of children who suffered no familial deprivation. The International Phonetic Alphabet was used as an evaluative tool, and in all cases the means for the orphans were below those of the infants in families both as to type and to frequency of speech sounds elicited (3).

Several investigators have studied the development of emotional behavior, both its general and specific components, within recent years.

For example, it has usually been found that affection is seen in infants by about four months of age, as shown by an outgoing striving approach to others. Certain specific affectionate behaviors are seen during this period. Spitz and Wolf, studying the emergence of smiling, for example, state that this response is triggered initially at about the second month and is extended by the child to others in a meaningful way between the third and sixth months of age (16). In a controlled investigation of the kinds of perceptual events which seem to trigger smiling, Spitz found that movements of the mouth and face were the critical stimuli. Other researchers using two-dimensional models of the human face to study the emergence of smiling in infants, also found that vocalizing contributed positively to this behavior. Similar to the findings previously presented regarding the effects of fear on imprinting, Spitz found that the smiling response was inhibited when various emotional disturbances were elicited in the child.

The observations by Bridges supply further indications which seem to restrict the optimum time during which human imprinting may occur (2). Observing 62 infants in a foundling home, Bridges concluded that children begin to smile at about three months, anger develops between three to four months, and by six months of age children show fear when a stranger approaches.

The evidence cited above led Gray to theorize that the critical imprinting period in humans probably lies between six weeks and six months of age. He further suggests that it begins with the onset of learning ability, continues during the development of the smiling response, and terminates with the fear of strangers (9). Since we are going to speculate on human imprinting, we might postulate that various kinds of imprinting in humans may occur within several different periods in the child's life. Specific kinds of experience may trigger different facets of behavior as certain critical periods are reached.

Evidence for the importance of early perceptual experiences in the life of the human infant may be obtained from the writings of clinicians who work with children blind from birth. It has been noted that children who become blind at about six months of age from retinal blastoma or similar conditions are intellectually superior in later life to most children who are truly blind from birth. Even though the children who lose their sight within the first year have no conscious recollections of the visual world, they seem to retain helpful kinds of imprinted perceptions which may make them intellectually superior to the child truly blind from birth.

Others have hypothesized that other kinds of behavior in humans may be influenced by processes closely resembling imprinting in animals. Drs. Green and Money, studying effeminacy in boys, have speculated that behavior inappropriate to a child's biological sex may be the result of faulty imprinting (10). Their hypothesis extended further thus suggests that appropriate masculine and feminine patterns of movement and gestures may be the result of imprinting. Clinical evidence supporting these psychiatrists' assumptions arise from case studies of effeminate boys who exhibited inappropriate behavioral patterns from early infancy. One boy, for example, was seen to behave like a girl prior to walking, while another grasped a purse when making his initial efforts at locomotion.

Effeminate behavior in boys is manifested in complex ways. They are usually not aggressive when aggressiveness is obviously called for. They "talk" with their eyes. Their throwing and walking movements are restricted. Their voices are "too high," and at times they prefer to play games with members of the opposite sex. Although it is usually assumed that the male child makes a shift from non-specific sexual behavior to specific masculine behavior patterns at about the age of 3½ to 4½ perhaps some *perceptual* "triggering" has occurred prior to this age if we are to believe Gray's hypothesis concerning the critical period for imprinting in humans.

Previously cited evidence pointed to the probability that nonhuman animals, particularly when hand-reared, imprint to humans. Animals at times make overt sexual responses to their human companions when their contact with their own species has been limited or has been prevented altogether during infancy. Conversely, a series of narrative accounts points to the possibility that at times humans may have imprinted to animals. With early exposure to an animal society, human infants could thus be expected to adopt behavioral characteristics which mark them indelibly after returning to society.

Animal experimenters have found that they may imprint chicks to clicks, to the sound of their parents' "voices," and to other auditory cues. Recently it has been speculated that human infants may in some way be imprinted to their mothers' heartbeat. The preferred tempo of childrens' rhythmic behaviors, some suggest, may be triggered by the heart rate of their mothers. The rocking "blindisms" shown by sightless children may be another example of motor behavior elicited by the auditory cue heard in their pre-birth environment.

The bulk of the narratives concerning children reared among wolves, bears, and similar animals have sprung from the folklore of various regions throughout the world. Early references to such happenings are found in the classic Roman story of Romulus and Remus. Other versions have been reported from Estonia, Germany, Greece, Turkey, Persia, and from various American Indian tribes. India has been the most frequent source of such stories during the past 150 years. Many stories of infants reared by beasts are told as straightforward mythological accounts of fabled heroes. Some, however, may represent true occurrences. Gesell in 1941 reported a documented account of two children who spent their infancy under the maternal care of wolves and who later were rescued by a Rev. Singh in the Mindapore region of India.

In general such children are reported to be unable to master speech, and can manage to walk upright only with training. Their general demeanor is described as more animal than human when they first return to civilization. They usually are reported to prefer raw meat, and frequently are said never to have acquired the ability to smile. Although Tylor in 1863 (15), and Mandelbaum in 1943 (13) present hypothetical evidence that *all* such stories are fables rather than fact, these narratives nonetheless point to the widespread belief of the importance of early childhood experiences. At the same time they raise the haunting specter that perhaps some human infants raised in a den of wolves may have become irrevocably wolf-like for the remainder of their lives.

A number of questions underly the supposition that humans can be imprinted. A basic question is how "animal-like" one considers humans to be. Some feel that we should consider human beings separate and apart from members of the animal kingdom. The foregoing material is based on the premise that while humans can carry out remarkable tasks utilizing verbal symbols, can store their thinking for future generations to profit from, and in other obvious ways have modified their environment to their own advantage, they are, in the final analysis, an extremely capable animal. Thus it is reasonable to expect that imprinting can occur in humans, perhaps with the modifications suggested by the following questions.

1. If imprinting occurs in humans, does it occur at a *single* period in their life span, or at *several* critical periods, depending upon the occurrence of specific kinds of perceptual events?

2. Can imprinting occur perceptually in infancy and be stored to be revealed later in specific kinds of motoric behavior?

3. What is the influence of various social conditions, such as maternal deprivation or the presence of siblings, on human imprinting?

4. What are the relationships between the development of fearful responses in humans and imprinting? Does fear truly impede imprinting, or does it merely signal the close of one early imprinting period?

5. What is the influence of various hormones on imprintability? Is it possible that the presence of sex hormones in humans at critical times will elicit certain kinds of triggered behavioral patterns, as does the presence of these same kinds of hormones in animals?

6. Are certain kinds of humans more susceptible to behavior elicited by imprinting? How may such humans be identified; are they more prevalent in a primitive or a modern society?
7. What are the interrelationships between imprinted behavior and learned behavior? What kinds of learned motor activities are impeded or facilitated by various kinds of "wire-in" behavior?
8. How specific is imprinted behavior? As specific as smiling, throwing, etc., or as general as a masculine component in movement?
9. What kinds of motor activities may be influenced by imprinting? Do these include walking, throwing, climbing, or what?
10. Is there a tendency for imprinted behaviors in humans to be subordinated to learned behavior? If this occurs, at what ages might it occur?
11. How might educators and physical educators exploit the process of imprinting in operational ways to enhance classroom learning and perceptual-motor capabilities?
12. What kinds of research designs might be employed to explore some of the questions posed on these pages?

In the paragraphs that follow no attempt has been made to treat all of the questions posed above comprehensively. Instead, certain problems have been selected and tentative answers advanced which only brush the surface of some of the complexities outlined on the previous pages. It is hoped that this information will stimulate the reader to formulate his own postulates, and at the same time to examine and to observe more critically the behaviors elicited by children. If educators hope to change behavior, they will be more effective if they can discover which behaviors are relatively fixed, which are easily changed, and which are modifiable only over an extended time period. It is suggested that educators will be more effective if they make only reasonable demands on those in their charge, trying to change only those behaviors that are truly pliable and accepting the fixed nature of others.

Since the focus of the text is on man in action we will examine some instances in which imprinted behavior might influence the motoric activities of infants, children, and adolescents. A number of behavioral patterns are discussed which imply that certain *emotional* characteristics are due to imprinting. For example, intense "puppy love" on the part of an adolescent could be explained by reference to the literature relating hormonal injections to sexual imprint in animals. One might hypothesize that the human animal is susceptible to sexual imprinting of a similar nature during early adolescence when greater amounts of sex hormones are present in his biochemical make-up.

Other emotional characteristics more closely related to motor activity might also be imprinted. Reference to the previous literature outlining the effects of experimentally induced "water trauma" upon the later imprintability of rats might be related to a marked fear some children develop when confronted with aquatic activities. In areas of our country where the climate encourages the widespread use of swimming pools, children at extremely young ages are subjected to various types of swimming "instruction." Although the acclimatizing of a young infant to water might be explained by reference to various built-in reflexes which control breath-holding and a cross-extension patterning of the limbs, the success some babies seem to achieve in early aquatic training might also be explained by reference to the concept of imprinting. There may be an opportune time during which a child might best be exposed to aquatic activity. By the same token failure to expose the child to water during this period may produce the commonly experienced water trauma which sometimes persists into adulthood. Many of the readers have perhaps worked with children in whom this undesirable emotional state has been established.

Thus it is suggested that there is an optimal time in the life of the human infant during which he should be introduced to swimming, a time immediately following the development of perceptual-motor characteristics which permit him to regard the situation and to move his limbs in a general cross-extension pattern. This period of optimal imprintability may terminate with the onset of fear of external objects and situations.

In recent clinical work the writer has been confronted with boys whose movement characteristics elicit social punishment from their peers because of marked feminine qualities. These boys, from nine to eleven years of age, move in a restricted manner, throw with their elbows held in toward their sides, and walk with a narrow gait pattern. A total complex of more subtle characteristics augment these modifications of the boys' gross action patterns. They generally "talk" with their eyes, and their voices are too high. They prefer to play games that are traditionally consigned to girls. Appropriate masculine aggression is usually absent in situations obviously calling for hostility (i.e., they smile "too much").

One explanation of the marked persistence of this behavior, and of its usually early appearance is that it is imprinted. This statement, of course, raises more questions than answers, if one subscribes to Gray's hypothesis that imprinting in humans occurs before the age of six months. How is this complex pattern wired in at such an early age? Do children select a gender with which to identify before they are able to behave, perhaps through some kind of perceptual process in the early months of infancy?

And, more important, just how might gender imprinting occur in humans? Does it depend on early tactile experiences with the like or unlike parent, on feeding schedule, or on rewards emitted by a parent for various kinds of behavior later in life than Gray suggests?

It is usually held that before the age of four the child is relatively "sexless" and after that age tends to identify with one or the other parent. Thus it might be suggested that early perceptual experiences with a parent before this time represents preparatory mechanisms which result in the child later molding his behavior after one of the parents.

The occurrence of this atypical behavior in boys has several implications for their performance of motor skills. In addition to the inappropriate amount of space they habitually use when throwing and engaging in similar activities, they also seem unable to marshall force when performing, and are apparently incapable of directing their aggression in tasks when it might be helpful to do so.

Inability to be forceful may also be indicative of early maternal deprivation and the subsequent production of an apathetic approach to life's activities. This early disinclination to be forceful later compounds itself. After repeated failures to engage in forceful acts they fail to develop the *capacity* to exert tension. On the other hand the frequent exercise of the perceptual-motor apparatus in forceful acts engenders a greater capacity to strike a blow or otherwise engage in vigorous activities. Thus the characteristic level of arousal of the human may also be the result of imprinted behavioral patterns, as may the quality of specific movement patterns.

There are some indications that movement behaviors may be both the result of early imprinting plus learned modifications. Walking and throwing, for example, may be examples of action patterns that are initially triggered by a specific kind of perceptual event (e.g., the abrupt result of releasing some object from the hand), which are later modified by specific learning experiences.

There are further indications that the human organism may be susceptible to various kinds of imprinted behaviors triggered by perceptual events occuring at *several critical times* during his life span. Reference to the animal research suggests ways in which this kind of segmented imprinting may take place. Gray, for example, suggests that there are four periods in the life of an infant which are related to imprintability: (a) prelearning, during which the nervous system matures and various perceptual-motor capacities are developed, (b) a period during which the child imprints to a parent, (c) the period denoting the development of fear in the infant, and (d) in-group learning influenced by individuals other than the child's parents (9).

The animal research previously cited suggests that if an animal does not imprint to his parents, he may imprint to his siblings. At times conditions may favor the imprinting to siblings rather than to parent. By the same token the human infant may, under certain, not fully understood conditions, not imprint to parental stimuli but to *his* siblings.

Evidence that femininity in boys is more prevalent in families in which the male is younger than one or more sisters supports the validity of this assumption.

A molecular examination of the processes underlying imprinting in animals presents additional evidence that in humans the period during which imprinting might occur may be more extended or occur in series, rather than during a single time span as in the case of animals. Some researchers now feel that this wired-in programming may be triggered by the chemical substances DNA and RNA (deoxyribonucleic acid and ribonucleic acid). It has been suggested that these substances are not only responsible for innate responses exhibited during imprinting, but may also be related to the internal monitoring and programming of the imprinting process. Thus animals, perhaps because of their simpler genetic make-up, may be controlled by a simpler biochemical program than humans. Humans may be governed by a more elaborate triggering mechanism at the cellular level.

Further speculations might be presented concerning the inheritance of imprintability in humans, and the nature of the human who might be expected to be more susceptible to this kind of behavioral programming. For example, the retarded or emotionally unstable may be more likely to exhibit imprinted behavior, as in the animal studies where it is usually found that the more domesticated animals are more difficult to imprint.

Workers in a number of associated disciplines might suggest other instances which either confirm or deny some of the assumptions made on the previous pages. It is hoped that scholars interested in various components of the human action system will indeed question this admittedly speculative material. Such questioning, it is hoped, may lead to further inquiry into this and associated problems, and may also perhaps promote greater sensitivity on the part of individuals trying to improve the perceptual-motor attributes of children and youth.

REFERENCES

1. Beach, F. A., and Jaynes, J., "Effects of Early Experience Upon the Behavior of Animals," *Psychological Bulletin*, LI (1954), 239–326.
2. Bridges, K. M. B., "Emotional Development in Early Infancy," *Child Development*, III (1932), 324.
3. Brodbeck, A. J., and Irwin, O. C., "The Speech Behavior of Infants Without Families," *Child Development*, XVII (1946), 145–56.
4. Craig, W., "The Voices of Pigeons Regarded as a Means of Social Control," *American Journal of Sociology*, XIV (1908), 86.
5. Frantz, R. L., "The Origin of Form Perception," *Scientific American*, CCIV (1961), 459–75.

6. ———, "Form Preferences in Newly Hatched Chicks," *Journal of Comparative Physiological Psychology*, L (1957), 422, 430.

7. Gesell, A., *Wolf Child and Human Child* (New York: Harper & Row, Publishers, 1941), p. 107.

8. Goldfarb, W., "The Effects of Early Institutional Care on Adolescent Personality," *Journal of Experimental Education*, XII (1943), 106–29.

9. Gray, Philip H., "Theory and Evidence of Imprinting in Human Infants," *Journal of Psychology*, XLVI (1958), 155–66.

10. Green, Richard, and Money, John, "Effeminacy in Prepubertal Boys, Summary of Eleven Cases and Recommendations for Case Management," *Pediatrics*, XXVII (1961), 2.

11. Heinroth, O., *Proceedings of the Fifth International Ornithological Congress* (1910), 589–702.

12. Hess, Eckhard H., "Two Conditions Limiting Critical Age for Imprinting," *Journal of Comparative Physiological Psychology*, LII (1959), 515, 518.

13. Mandelbaum, David G., "Wolf-Child Histories from India," *Journal of Social Psychology*, XVII (1943), 25–44.

14. Thompson, W. R., and Dubanosky, R. A., "Imprinting and the Law of Effort," *Animal Behavior*, XII (1964), 2–3, 213–18.

15. Tylor, E. E., "Beast Children," *Anthropological Review*, I (1863), 21–32.

16. Spitz, R. A., and Wolf, K. M., "The Smiling Response: A Contribution to the Ontogenesis of Social Relations," *Journal of Genetic Psychology*, Monograph No. 34, (1946), 57–156.

E. DEAN RYAN°

Perceptual Characteristics of Vigorous People

In a schoolyard a group of boys are playing baseball. A fast pitch is lined to left center field for what appears to be a sure hit. The center fielder, however, somehow anticipating where the ball is headed makes a rather routine catch for the out. In the library of the same school two girls sit quietly studying a history text. Suddenly one of the girls looks up and remarks, "Doesn't that just drive you wild?" The other girl, with a look of surprise inquires, "Doesn't what drive me wild?" "That clock. The ticking is so loud that I can't concentrate." The second girl comments that she was completely unaware of any noise made by the clock. In another corner of the library two boys are discussing their impending visit to the dentist. One is quite upset over the prospects because the experience has always been so painful; the second boy is unconcerned because the drilling never bothered him.

These three isolated incidents have two very obvious, but frequently overlooked, points in common. First, perception is involved in practically everything we do. It is difficult to think of any act that doesn't involve perception of some kind. The simplest acts, such as bending over to pick up a ball, or placing a glass on a table, are really quite complex. There must be an obvious coordination between what one perceives and what one does. In the example of the boys playing ball the batter had to see the ball to hit it. The outfielder probably saw the pitcher, knew where the

°Department of Physical Education, University of California at Davis.

ball was pitched, watched as the hitter stepped into the pitch, heard the ball being hit, and finally saw the ball in flight. In the example of the girls in the library it was the sound that was being perceived; in the example of the boys going to the dentist, the perception of pain was remembered.

The second point the three incidents have in common is that although we all may receive the same objective stimulus complex we don't all perceive it the same way. The outfielder, for a variety of reasons, was able to perceive where the ball was going and get to it quicker than most other players. One girl in the library was bothered by the loud ticking of the clock, the other girl was completely oblivious to the noise. To her it simply wasn't loud. The boys visiting the dentist both had the same drill used on their teeth. To one it was a very painful experience, to the other it wasn't.

In all probability each of us is living in a world that is unique to us alone. Although we may all receive the same physical stimuli, each of us perceives it in a different way. For the physical educator the crucial question is whether these differences in perception influence our choice of activities or our performance in them, and if so, how?

One approach to this general area was made by Ryan and Kovacic (9). They felt that the ability to tolerate pain might be related to the type of activity (or lack of it) that a person engaged in. In many sports, such as football or boxing, the ability to withstand pain would appear to be essential to successful performance, while in sports such as tennis or golf, the ability to withstand pain is probably less important. An individual with a high pain threshold might be oblivious to the bumps and bruises received in a football game; the individual with a low pain threshold might avoid such contact.

To test this hypothesis three groups of male students were selected. One group who participated in contact sports (football, boxing, or wrestling) during college, a second group had participated in non-contact sports only, such as tennis or golf, and a third group had not participated in varsity athletics of any kind.

Three methods were used to deliver controlled pain. Radiant heat was used to measure the pain threshold, that is, when pain was first noticed, and two other methods were used to measure how much pain the subject was willing to endure. The first, gross pressure, was assumed to be representative of the bumps and bruises received in body contact, and the second, muscle ischemia, was assumed to be representative of the pain associated with severe muscle fatigue.

There were no differences between the groups in pain threshold. They all perceived the sensation of pain at approximately the same point. There were, however, significant differences in how much pain the three groups were willing to tolerate. For both measures of pain endurance the group composed of contact athletes tolerated the most pain, the non-athletes tolerated least, and the noncontact athletes fell between. After each subject had received the first pain trial the experimenter commented that the subject's score was quite a bit lower than the average of the group tested, and the subject was asked to take the test a second time. This was done regardless of the subject's actual score. The contact athletes made marked improvement on the second attempt, the noncontact athletes improved some, but the nonathletes actually tolerated less pain than on the first attempt. These results clearly indicate that there is a relationship between differences in perception and the type of activity in which a boy chooses to participate.

The question of cause and effect—whether a boy learns to tolerate pain because he engages in contact sports, whether he engages in contact sports because he can more easily tolerate pain (either for physiological or psychological reasons), or whether the two covary with a third but unexplored source—is, of course, unanswered by these data. It has been suggested that pain threshold is associated with physiological components. If this is true, then the results of this experiment suggest that differences between activity groups are psychological in nature and probably the result of cultural or environmental influences. There are, however, a number of possible explanations for these results, some with a psychological slant, others more physiological in nature, but all capable of at least partially explaining the differences found in this study.

Zborowski (11) has suggested that two culturally determined attitudes, pain expectancy and pain acceptance, are important to differences in pain response. Pain expectancy is the anticipation that pain is unavoidable in a given situation. Pain acceptance is characterized by a willingness to experience pain. As an example, labor pain is generally expected as part of childbirth in all cultures. In some cultures, the pain is not accepted and various means are used to alleviate it, but in others pain is accepted, and little or nothing is done to relieve it. It may be that the differences found in the study of athletic participation are due to differences in pain acceptance. The contact athletes, and to a lesser extent the noncontact athletes, have frequently been in situations where pain is unavoidable. Through parental or peer pressure it is possible that the ability to tolerate pain has been associated with "manliness" by the athlete and as such is socially valued. The nonathletes, on the other hand, have much less often been in situations where pain is unavoidable and thus have not associated the ability to tolerate pain with socially desirable traits or characteristics.

Another possibility may be that because of repeated experiences with pain, the contact athlete will be more realistic in his evaluation of the significance of pain and thus will fear pain less than the nonathlete. It has been pointed out that the significance of the pain experience is important in determining how "painful" the experience appears to be. An ache beneath the sternum, since it suggests the possibility of sudden death from heart failure can be a wholly upsetting experience, but the same intensity and duration of ache in a finger is a trivial annoyance and is easily disregarded (1). It is possible that contact athletes, having had previous experience with the two types of pain used in the test, were fully aware that the pain experienced was not of a harmful nature. The nonathletes, because of little experience with this type of pain, had no way of knowing whether or not the cleat used in the experiment might break a bone or puncture the skin. The differences on the second trial can be explained the same way. The contact athlete, having experienced the initial pain, would have some reference point from previous experience and be aware that the stimulus was not going to do physical damage. The nonathlete, on the other hand, having had limited experience with painful stimulation, would be less apt to know how serious the pain actually was, and thus, due to apprehension, tolerate less on the second trial.

The most intriguing explanation, however, is that the relationship between pain and type of athletic activity might have been due to differences in a general perceptual characteristic of "augmenting" or "reducing" sensory inputs. It has been demonstrated that certain individuals appear to consistently reduce the intensity of their perceptions while others tend to consistently augment the intensity of perception (4). Pain and suffering are related to these contrasted perceptual types. Those who reduce the intensity of perception tolerate pain well, those who augment tolerate pain poorly. Those individuals who tend to consistently reduce have been shown to be more extroverted than those who augment, less tolerant of sensory deprivation, more mesomorphic, and to judge time as passing more slowly than augmenters. Significantly more reducers were found in a delinquent group and significantly fewer augmenters than would be expected by chance.

All of the characteristics of the reducer, tolerance of pain, intolerance of sensory deprivation, mesomorphy, extroversion, and to an extent the characteristics of the delinquent, have frequently been associated with athletic groups. If indeed, the reducers suffer from lack of stimulation as suggested by Petrie, then they would need change, movement, speed, and possibly body contact, rather than more sedentary pursuits.

To test this hypothesis a second experiment was conducted (8). It was hypothesized that groups participating in contact sports would possess the perceptual pattern of the reducer and thus reduce most in their estimation of kinesthetically perceived size, have faster reaction times, faster movement times, judge time as passing more slowly, and would tolerate most pain. Groups not interested in athletics would possess the perceptual characteristics of the augmenter, and thus reduce less in their estimation of kinesthetically perceived size, have slower reaction times, slower movement times, judge time as passing faster, and tolerate less pain. Groups participating in noncontact sports would tend to fall between the other two groups on all tests.

A questionnaire was administered to a group of high school students. They were asked their likes, dislikes, hobbies, and recreational pursuits. On the basis of their answers three groups of subjects were selected. Group I was composed of boys who expressed a liking for contact athletics and were at the same time actually participating in contact sports (football or wrestling). Group II was composed of boys who expressed an interest in noncontact sports and were also participating only in noncontact sports (golf, tennis, track), and Group III was composed of boys who had expressed a dislike for athletics and were inactive as far as sports were concerned. The subjects assumed they had been randomly selected and were unaware that athletic participation was a factor.

The subjects were tested on simple reaction time, movement time, pain tolerance, time estimation, and augmentation and reduction as measured by the change in kinesthetically perceived size. The results are summarized in Table 1. There were significant differences between groups on all tests except reaction time and movement time, with the group composed of contact athletes tolerating most pain, underestimating time, and reducing subjective estimation of kinesthetically perceived size. The group of nonathletes tolerated least pain, overestimated time, and had a tendency to enlarge subjective judgment of width on the kinesthetic test. The noncontact athletes fell between the other two groups on all tests.

The study clearly supports Petrie's theory of a generalized tendency for certain individuals to consistently reduce or diminish their perception of stimulation and for others to consistently augment or enlarge perception. Further, the study indicates that the type of activity an in-

TABLE 1
Mean Scores for Athletic Subgroups

Task	Contact Athlete	Noncontact Athlete	Nonathlete
Reaction Time	.201 sec.	.208 sec.	.213 sec.
Movement Time	.117 sec.	.123 sec.	.117 sec.
Time EST (120 sec.)	103.6 sec.	119.1 sec.	122.3 sec.
Time EST (20 sec.)	18.3 sec.	20.7 sec.	21.5 sec.
Pain Tolerance	285.75 mm/Hg	231.00 mm/Hg	207.50 mm/Hg
Change/Kinesthetic Size	−.258 in.	−.212 in.	−.095 in.

dividual chooses to participate in is related to his perceptual type. The contact athlete displayed the characteristics of the reducer, making the greatest subjective reduction of kinesthetically perceived size after stimulation, tolerating most pain, and consistently judging time as passing more slowly than did groups composed of noncontact athletes or nonathletes.

Differences in pain tolerance could be explained by simply assuming that contact athletes were more motivated to withstand pain, although it would be difficult to explain why motivation of the two athletic groups would differ. Further, time estimation and estimation of kinesthetically perceived size are less amenable to changes in motivation. No amount of conscious effort should induce a naive subject to vary time or kinesthetic sensitivity in one direction or another.

We have mentioned augmentation and reduction and the work of Petrie as it related to the study of athletic participation, but now let us examine the work of Petrie and her associates more closely. What is it that is being investigated, and what are the major findings? Finally, does the theory provide a basis for further work in areas related to physical education and athletics, and to education in general?

Petrie's original interest was in the control of pain and suffering. She observed that when patients suffering from severe pain had a prefrontal lobotomy to relieve the pain certain personality characteristics were changed. Surgery to the prefrontal areas of the brain so increased the tolerance for pain that the patient could sleep without pain and wake without moaning. The source of pain had not been dealt with, nor had the threshold for pain been altered, instead the person experiencing the pain had been altered. The patient appeared more extroverted, more tolerant of pain, and less tolerant of sensory deprivation.

Her work in this area indicates that a normal person—one without prefrontal lobotomy—who is exceptionally tolerant of pain has the personality and perceptual style of the individual after prefrontal lobotomy, whereas one who cannot tolerate pain resembles in personality a patient before prefrontal lobotomy.

On the basis of her work Petrie has identified three perceptual types. First, the reducer, who is tolerant of suffering and who tends subjectively to decrease what he perceives. Second, the augmenter who is just the opposite of the reducer. The augmenter tends to be intolerant of pain and to subjectively increase what he perceives. Finally the moderate who alters only slightly what he perceives.

Augmentation and reduction have been estimated by measuring the change in kinesthetically perceived size after stimulation. Subjects are blindfolded and feel with the thumb and forefinger of the right hand a standard wooden bar. At the same time, with the thumb and forefinger of the opposite hand they feel a long tapered wooden bar and attempt to locate an area that seems as wide as the test bar. A larger (or smaller) test block is then rubbed. Thereafter, the original test bar is again equated with the tapered bar, and the difference between the two subjective estimations is computed. At the end of the period of rubbing, the test bar is usually perceived by the extreme reducer as being about halved in size, by the extreme augmenter as about doubled. The augmenter enlarges the estimated size of the block after stimulation with both a larger and a smaller test block. The reverse is true for the reducer, who decreases in both cases.

There would seem to be accumulating evidence that what is being measured kinesthetically is one aspect of the generalized tendency for the reducer to diminish the perception of all stimulation and for the augmenter to enlarge it—two contrasting processes manifesting themselves in persons with different personality characteristics.

As mentioned, the reducers tolerate pain well, the augmenters poorly, and the moderates fall between these two extremes. This has been shown to be true of the experimental pain of heat, muscle ischemia, and pressure, as well as the pain of surgery and the pain of childbirth (4).

If the reducers' tolerance for pain is partially due to their tendency to diminish the intensity of stimulation they receive from the environment, then that tendency should become a handicap in a situation where there is a sparsity of stimulation. To test this hypothesis a number of subjects were placed in tank-type respirators where stimulation was at a minimum. The augmenters, as measured by kinesthetic sensitivity, tolerated starvation of sensation better than did the reducers, as measured by their willingness to remain in the tank significantly longer than the reducers (5). This difference is exactly the reverse of the behavior of these two types under stress of pain.

In studying a group of young delinquents (7) it was found that there were significantly more reducers among the delinquents than would be expected by chance, and significantly fewer augmenters. In addition reducers have been shown to be more mesomorphic (10), to judge time as passing more slowly than the augmenters (4), and to be more extroverted (4). Further, there is some indication of a sex difference with the males leaning more toward the reducing end of the scale and the females more toward the augmenting end (5).

Recently a list of 150 adjectives were given to a small group of high school students. They were asked to check those adjectives that they felt most closely described themselves. Thereafter, those adjectives checked by reducers in the group were compared to the adjectives checked by the augmenters. The reducers described themselves as: alert, cautious, clear-thinking, conscientious, dependable, determined, dreamy, efficient, enthusiastic, impatient, individualistic, industrious, intelligent, leisurely, modest, obliging, organized, practical, precise, quick, relaxed, self-confident, and tactful. The augmenters described themselves as: bossy, careless, imaginative, logical, loud, sensitive, and serious. The total number of adjectives checked appeared to differ between the two groups, with the reducers checking approximately 20 per cent more adjectives than the augmenters. An individual checking a great number of adjectives has been described as emotional, adventurous, wholesome, conservative, enthusiastic, frank, and helpful. He is active, apparently means well, but tends to blunder. The individual checking few adjectives tends more often to be quiet and reserved, more tentative and cautious in his approach to problems and perhaps at times unduly taciturn and aloof. He is more apt to think originally and inventively, but is perhaps less effective in getting things done (3). These results should be viewed with some skepticism since the sample size was quite small. Nevertheless, the results are interesting, since the augmenters and reducers describe themselves in much the same way as would be predicted from studies cited earlier.

Although Petrie's work encompasses over 10 years of research the theory is still in the formative stages. Much of what has been covered in this discussion has been oversimplified for the purpose of explanation and clarification. Much more basic research must be done before we have a complete picture of the typical reducer and augmenter.

How is this theory related to athletics, physical education, and education in general? In spite of the fact that the concept of perceptual augmentation and reduction is incomplete, there are many fascinating avenues for the physical educator. We have already seen that the contact athlete tends to be a reducer and the nonathlete an augmenter. Where do we go from here?

Again for clarification let us oversimplify the picture. At the elementary or junior high school level the reducer would tend to be male, extroverted, loud (whether he sees himself this way or not), unable to sit in one place too long, always going to get a drink or go to the toilet, often poking the person in front or back of him, and unable to concentrate or pay attention for extended periods of time. The augmenter, on the other hand, is more apt to be female, introverted, quiet, able to concentrate and pay attention. All of us have seen these types in our work with children. These descriptions lead to a number of predictions. First, in the typical classroom the young reducer would appear to be at a decided disadvantage. Here is a person who reduces all stimulation. He is placed in a setting where stimulation is typically at a minimum. Further reduction of the already minimal stimulation would be expected to be uncomfortable. Remember, the reducer could stand less confinement than the augmenter. Thus we would predict that the reducer would need to seek additional stimulation of one kind or another. For this reason we would expect the reducer to be more of a behavior problem, at least in the younger years, and we would expect his academic achievement to be less than it should be in relation to his ability. In other words we would expect the reducer to be an underachiever. Whether this is actually so is open to question. There have been no studies in this area. We do know, however, that among both delinquents and athletes there are more reducers than you would expect by chance. Perhaps the reducers, lacking stimulation, have turned toward either athletics or delinquency for additional stimulation. The education of both the reducer and augmenter should take into consideration both their vulnerabilities and strengths. It is quite possible that the test of kinesthetic sensitivity might be an excellent screening device in the counseling and understanding of children.

This same reasoning brings us to a second point—the similarity between the delinquent and the athlete. Perhaps both groups have the same basic need. Perhaps through more varied programs of physical education activities we can head off the potential delinquent, enabling him to get the needed stimulation in a desirable way. Petrie, in discussing the delinquent, states,

> We suggest that the education of such delinquents and predelinquents needs to make allowance for their vulnerabilities and strengths. They need change, movement, and speed, actual rather than "symbolic" instruction, bright colors, music, and company. The fact that many of these "delinquent" youngsters come from deprived homes means that their needs are even greater than the needs of a similar perceptual type, youngsters who are fortunate enough to have swimming, rowing, traveling, club activity and the like as part of their birthright. (7)

There is still another possible implication for physical education. Can the pattern of the reducer be temporarily changed through physical activity? It has been suggested that stimulation in one sense modality can influence performance in other sense modalities. What would the effect of physical stimulation be on the reducer and the augmenter? Would activity temporarily relieve the reducer's need for stimulation or would it make him more of a reducer? What about the augmenter? Again there is no research on this subject. There is, however, a study that may give us a clue. An experiment was conducted to determine the effect of audioanalgesia on kinesthetic augmentation and reduction (6). Audioanalgesia is a recently developed method of trying to increase tolerance for pain by exposing the patient at the time of his pain to stimulation with sound. Audioanalgesia had a marked influence on the augmenter, making him more like a reducer. There appeared to be a slight change in the reducer toward the augmentation end of the scale. The change, however, was not significant.

Another basic question that may have implications for physical education centers around the problem of exactly what is reduced. Let us look at several examples for clarification. It has been written that occasionally musicians, particularly drummers, will take narcotics because the musician says that he feels as if he were floating in air. Everything, including the individual, seems to be moving very slowly. Because everything seems to be moving so slowly apparently the person is able to react more rapidly than would be possible without the drug. Suppose the same thing happened in athletics. If a ball appeared to be coming toward home plate very slowly, would we be better able to hit it? As the ball was hit, if it appeared to move very slowly would we, as outfielders, be able to get to it faster? Could it be that some individuals actually see motion as being slower than the average person? Could this be one of the reasons why some athletes seem to consistently get the jump on the opponents? Could it be that the reducer actually reduces the speed of objects around him? If so, we would expect him to be able to react faster than the moderate or the augmenter. Still another question can be asked. Can we, through stimulation, temporarily change our perception of speed? Common sense says we can. If we look at a pitch thrown from 50 feet away for a few times, what will happen when the pitcher moves back to his regular distance? We would expect the ball to appear to move slower than it did, thus giving the hitter a better chance to hit. Will the results be the same for both augmenters and reducers?

There are a number of points that complicate our discussion of speed. Our perception of how fast an object is moving depends on the background, or the "field" that surrounds the objects. Imagine yourself standing on top of the Empire State Building. As you look down you see tiny cars moving very slowly along the street. In this example you have a very small object against a very large background or field. If you are standing on the street corner, however, the cars would seem to zip by at a very rapid rate. Here the object is very large in relation to the field or background.

At this time we don't know what the augmenter is augmenting. The same is true of the reducers. Does the reducer diminish the size of the field in relation to the object being judged? If so, reduction would seem to be a disadvantage. On the other hand, if everything is reduced, both the moving object and the background, then reduction would seem to be an advantage. If the object being judged is reduced and the background is not influenced, then again reduction would be advantageous.

Some people have commented that when Petrie describes the augmenter and the reducer she is simply describing the introvert and the extrovert. To an extent this is true. Petrie's contribution, however, is in suggesting *why* people behave as they do. The reason the individual tolerates pain or is intolerant of sensory deprivation is, Petrie suggests, because of his perceptual characteristics. He is either increasing or decreasing the intensity of stimulation. With this knowledge we are in a position to better understand and predict behavior.

Much of the discussion, including the reasons for and possible consequences of augmenting and reducing stimulation, is pure speculation based on little more than wild guesses. There has been, as yet, too little basic research in the area to allow us to say with reasonable certainty just what we can actually expect. With the little evidence that is available, however, the concept of augmentation and reduction as a general perceptual characteristic does appear to have implications for physical education and athletics.

While the emphasis in this chapter has been on perceptual augmentation and reduction it should be understood that this is only one small aspect of perception. There are unlimited opportunities for research in the area.

Recently Ryan and Lakie, in an unpublished study, investigated the reaction times and movement times of baseball players as contrasted to people who had not played baseball. The statement had been made that the reason some ball players "get the jump" on a ball hit in their direction was because they had faster reactions. For a number of reasons this didn't appear to be the answer to the investigators. Two groups of subjects were selected, one group composed of subjects who had played baseball in high school or college, the second group composed of subjects who reported that they did not play baseball. Their reaction times and movement times were tested under three different conditions. A timer was constructed that could be activated by either light or sound. In the first testing situation, when a red light, located on the left of a display panel, was lighted, the subject would strike a red button located on the left of a switch panel. When a green light, located in the middle of the display panel, was lighted, the subject would strike a green button located in the middle of the switch panel, and when a yellow light, located on the right of the display panel, was lighted, the subjects would strike a yellow button on the right of the switch panel. When the lights came on two clocks were activated. One would measure how long it took the subject to start after the light signal (reaction time) and the second clock would measure how long it took the subject to move to the switch once he had reacted (movement time). In this condition, sometimes called a test of disjunctive reaction time, there was no difference between the two groups of subjects in reaction time or movement.

In the second condition a gun was constructed to fire a plastic missile. When the missile was fired to the subject's left he would strike the red button on the left of the switch panel. When the missile was fired directly at the subject he would strike the green button in the middle of the switch panel, and when the missile was fired to his right he would strike the yellow button on the right of the panel. The noise of the missile being fired activated the timers, and as before, the clocks were stopped when the appropriate button was touched. In this second condition again there was no difference between the two groups on reaction time or movement time.

In the third condition a rubber batting tee was placed in the middle of a large gym. A batter would hit a tennis ball off the tee to the left of the subject, to his right, or directly at him. As before the subject would respond by striking the appropriate button. The sound of the bat activated the clocks which were stopped as the subject hit the appropriate switch. The batter was instructed to stand flat footed (not to step into the ball) and do all he could to prevent subjects from guessing where the ball would be hit. There was a significant difference between the two groups in reaction time, with the baseball players reacting faster than the non-baseball-player. In fact some of the baseball players were reacting in 70 to 80 milliseconds. For simple reaction time to sound, that is, reaction time when no choice of movement has to be made, the average time for an adult to react is approximately 140 milliseconds. For a choice situation we would expect that time to increase considerably. Thus, the reaction time of 70 to 80 milliseconds indicates that subjects were actually starting to react before the ball was hit. When questioned after the experiment none of the subjects were aware of clues that would permit them to react before the ball was hit. They reported that they were unable to guess where the ball was going before it was hit. In spite of the fact that they could report no clues, it is obvious from their reaction times that they were picking up information. Unfortunately, the study sheds no light on the question of what the baseball players were seeing that the nonbaseballers weren't. It seems clear, however, that it is a perceptual process of some kind that accounts for the increased speed rather than the baseball players simply being inherently faster.

Would it be possible to train people to "see" faster? During World War II tachistoscopic training was used to improve observers' ability to identify aircraft. Pictures of airplanes or ships were flashed on a screen at .01 second. Frequently, the people were unable to see anything on the first exposure. After training, however, observers could tell how many aircraft were in a flight, and what type of plane was pictured. After the war this same technique was used to improve reading skill. Words or groups of words were flashed on the screen, and the reader was forced to read larger and larger blocks of material. Could tachistoscope training be used to increase the perceptual ability of a hitter, or a fielder, or a tennis player at the net? An experiment to determine the value of such a process would be very easy to design and conduct, and if the results were positive the technique would prove most valuable in a practical sense.

Tachistoscopic training has already been used in an effort to improve the perceptual ability of football players (2). Although the results of the study were inconclusive because there was no control group, it would appear that the ability to recognize fundamental football defenses quickly is improved through the tachistoscopic training. The same technique might be used to train passers to spot receivers downfield.

Another question seems appropriate. Is peripheral vision related to perception of speed? In our earlier discussion of speed we stated that it seems reasonable to assume that perceived speed depends on the relationship between the moving object and the background that it is moving across. If the background is large in relation to the size of the moving object, speed would seem relatively slow, while the reverse would be true if the moving object were large in relation to the background. The individual with a wide field of vision would be expected to perceive speed differently from an individual with "tunnel vision." Are individual differences in peripheral vision related to perception of speed? If so, are these differences great enough to be of practical value in athletics? If so, can we increase peripheral vision?

Many of the suggestions in this chapter are rather superficial. Even if we knew the answers performances might not be influenced a great deal. Some of the suggestions and questions raised, however, are important from both a theoretical and a practical standpoint. Of one thing we can be certain. Perception plays an extremely important part in behavior, and an understanding of its influence on man in action is essential.

REFERENCES

1. Beecher, H. K., *Measurement of Subjective Responses; Quantitative Effects of Drugs* (New York: Oxford University Press, 1959).
2. Damron, C. Frazier, "Two and Three Dimensional Slide Images Used with Tachistoscopic Training Techniques in Instructing High School Football Players in Defenses." *Research Quarterly*, XXVI (1955), 36–43.
3. Gough, H. G., and Heilbrun, A. B., *The Adjective Check List Manual* (Palo Alto, Calif.: Consulting Psychologist Press, 1965).
4. Petrie, A., "Some Psychological Aspects of Pain and the Relief of Suffering." *Annals of the New York Academy of Science*, LXXXVI (1960), 13–27.

5. ———, Collins, W., and Soloman, P., "The Tolerance for Pain and for Sensory Deprivation." *American Journal of Psychology*, LXXIII (1960), 80–90.

6. ———, Holland, L., and Wolk, I., "Sensory Stimulation Causing Subdued Experience: Audio-Analgesia and Perceptual Augmentation and Reduction." *Journal of Nervous and Mental Disease*, CXXXVII (1963), 312–21.

7. ———, McCulloch, R., and Kazdin, P., "The Perceptual Characteristics of Juvenile Delinquents." *Journal of Nervous and Mental Disease*, CXXXIV (1962), 415–21.

8. Ryan, E. D., and Foster, R., "Athletic Participation and Perceptual Augmentation and Reduction." Unpublished manuscript, University of California, Davis.

9. ———, and Kovacic, C. R., "Pain Tolerance and Athletic Participation." *Perceptual Motor Skills*, XXII (1966), 383–90.

10. Wertheimer, M., "Figural Aftereffects as a Measure of Metabolic Efficiency. *Journal of Personality*, XXIV (1955), 56–73.

11. Zborowski, M., "Cultural Components in Response to Pain." *Journal of Social Issues*, VIII (1952), 16–30.

HELEN M. ECKERT°

Perceptual-Motor Characteristics of Young Children

From the first gasp and cry at birth, nearly all overt responses of the human organism to sensory stimuli are muscular. The early motor responses of the child are extremely limited compared with those of the adult, and it is obvious that the attainment of adult levels of motor response involves a long process of development and learning.

In infancy and early childhood, physical and mental activities are closely related (1). Honzik and others (12) have shown that the Bayley motor scale is capable of differentiating between normal infants and those with suspected neurological disorders. At older age levels, the motor performance items of the Lincoln Adaptation of the Oseretsky Tests of Motor Proficiency, particularly those involving simultaneous movement, produced statistically reliable differences between feeble-minded and normal children (20).

Many neurologists and psychologists feel that motor activities play a major role in intellectual development. Sherrington (19) states that the motor act, mechanically integrating the individual, seems to start the mind on its road to recognizability. Furthermore, he claims that as motor integration proceeds, the mind proceeds with it. Piaget (17), Hebb (10), and Kephart (13) have stressed the importance of muscular activities in the development of basic concepts, while Held (11) maintains that the continued use of motor activities is essential to the maintenance of established perceptual judgments.

°Department of Physical Education, University of California at Berkeley.

Stimulation of the sensory endorgans produces activity in the sensory projection areas of the cerebral cortex, which is regarded as input. All the sensory inputs operating in the organism at a given moment are then integrated so that a single response can be generated on the basis of all the inputs. The integrative process also incorporates past experience into a general pattern of cortical activity, which includes the contribution of all the senses and the association areas. It is believed that a scanning mechanism then translates this pattern of cortical activity into an output, or motor, pattern (13). The effectiveness and validity of the integrative process, however, is not established until feedback information concerning the output pattern has been received. The perceptual process can therefore be classified as a servomechanism, or a closed system of control. The effectiveness of the feedback mechanism in the learning of motor skills by children is illustrated by observations that failure in catching or in striking results in changed motor patterns on subsequent trials but that success produces a repetition of the same motor patterns (8, 22). Because input and output functions form a closed system of control, Kephart (13) believes that we cannot separate perceptual activities from motor activities but must think of the entire process as perceptual-motor.

Because of space limitations this chapter will focus on eye-hand coordination, which, phylogenetically, reaches its highest development in man. Although the lower primates are known to throw branches or stones at an opponent, they rarely hit their target (6). The human being, on the other hand, has evolved the capacity to hit stationary and moving objects at some distance. This difference between the species in the ability to coordinate the sensorimotor functions of the eye and hand has been closely associated with differences in the neurological apparatus that mediates these functions (18, 19).

SURVEY OF THE LITERATURE

The hand and arm, particularly the hand, contain the endorgans of at least seven distinct senses—muscular, articular, tendinous, pressure, pain, warmth, and cold. The anatomical structure and placement of the limb is also such that bending the elbow places the hand, with its many endorgans, very close to the endorgans associated with the eye, nose, mouth, and ears. It is not surprising, therefore, that the hand is one of the most important instruments with which the infant secures his impressions of the world around him.

Other than eye movements, the first motor explorations of the infant are made with the hand. Of course information also reaches the infant through vision, hearing, and touch, but these are externally induced and do not require the active participation of the infant. Learning involves an active seeking of stimuli or, as Sherrington (19) puts it, "an 'urge' seeking satisfaction." Therefore, the eye and hand, as the first body members over which the infant gains control, become his first volitional means of contact between himself and his environment.

Observational studies by Gesell (4) and Piaget (17) have indicated that physical movements involving eye-hand coordination dominate the observable activities of the infant and young child. In general, the infant gains control of his oculomotor muscles by the 16th week, reaches out for things from the 16th to 28th weeks, and then increases his ability to grasp, manipulate, and transfer objects as his hands become free from support and locomotory activities. Halverson (7) made a comprehensive analysis of the cinematographic records of prehension in infants. He found that from 16 to 28 weeks the amount of time an infant spent in gazing at a cube placed in front of him increased. After 28 weeks there was a gradual decline in the duration of gaze. The duration of gaze was related to the infant's efforts to reach the cube. Even though the cube was placed within arm's reach, his attempts to reach it failed approximately 90 to 95 per cent of the time at 16 weeks. By 24 weeks, half of the infants were able to touch the cube on the first try, and the other half were actually able to grasp it. After 28 weeks all the infants could grasp the cube when they wanted to. Coralling the cube with both hands gave way to reaching out with one hand directed toward the object so that only the index and medius fingers passed over it. Twenty-eight weeks may, therefore, be considered the critical period in infant prehension. This is also the age at which the duration of gaze is longest.

Aside from Halverson, most of the investigators have been concerned with eye-hand coordination as a factor in general motor ability. They have investigated its relationship to mental age, readiness for first grade, reading readiness, mental retardation, and later school achievement. Few have been concerned with the development of eye-hand coordination per se. Meyers and Dingman (15) performed a factor analysis on the eye-hand tests of track-tracing, rotary pursuit, circle-dotting, hole-punching, tweezer tasks, cube-stacking, nut-stacking, dot-tapping, and finger-tapping in preschool children. At three years of age, static precision, dynamic precision, reaction time, and dexterity emerged as identifiable psychomotor factors, and speed emerged at four years. However, studies of children 4.5 to 6 years old, using eye-hand coordination items such as putting marbles in a slot, tapping a bell, card sorting, and punching holes suggest that motor speed is highly specialized. In this instance, correlations were barely appreciable when the type of activity, the body segments, and laterality were all different (3).

A number of studies indicate that biological maturation and practice, when experimentally induced and when they occur in the course of everyday activities, are important factors in the learning of eye-hand coordination tasks. Biological maturation is important in the transition from a palmar to a pincher grasp and in the effectiveness of practice at various age levels. Different amounts of practice have produced varying results for eye-hand coordination items at different age levels. In general, practice is more effective in older children in whom practice on simple eye-hand tasks improves performance on more complicated tasks of the same nature.

Carlisle (2) studied the effects of six practice sessions, spaced twice a week over a three week period, in two types of tasks, one with stationary and one with moving objects. Practice in the tasks with stationary objects did not result in continued improvement. The best score generally occurred within the first three sessions for peg-shifting, marble-sorting, disk-sorting, and bead-stringing. For these tasks, the performance curves tended to have an inverted U shape, indicating rather rapid improvement followed by a deterioration in performance. Of the two tasks with moving objects, the best performance in the rotary dot pursuit task occurred during the fifth practice session, but the rotary circle tracking task showed consistent improvement. Improvement from first trial to best trial was significant in all stationary object tasks and circle-tracking. Improvement from first to last trial was significant only in bead-stringing and circle-tracking. As in the static precision and dynamic precision factors (15), low to moderate correlations were found between tasks with stationary objects and tasks with moving objects.

Logically, eye-hand coordination tasks with stationary objects should be simpler than those with moving objects. The results of Carlisle's study, however, indicate a deterioration of performance for tasks with stationary objects following an initial improvement, and a consistent improvement for tasks with moving objects. One possible explanation is that the tasks with stationary objects were too simple and that the children became bored. Conversely, the tasks with moving objects may have been more challenging since they are "emerging" skills at this age. In another study of practice effects, in which an epicyclic rotary task was used, a four-year-old experimental group improved significantly in performance after eight practice sessions whereas no significant improvement occurred in three-year-olds with the same amount of practice (14). Clearly, we know very little about the placement of various types of eye-hand coordination tasks in relation to the maturational development of the child.

Kephart (13) believes that functional eye-hand coordination is essential to the development of the concepts of laterality and directionality and in temporal-spatial translation. His work with slow learners in the elementary grades led him to the conclusion that they were discouraged, as infants or young children, from exploring and manipulating a variety of objects and as a result were lacking in basic perceptual-motor skills. He proposed a developmental program for what he considered to be the basic perceptual-motor skills and included among them a large number of eye-hand coordination tasks. These tasks are designed to help the child develop adequate concepts of laterality, directionality, time, space and figure-ground relationship.

Haring and Stables (9) used Kephart's basic developmental program but adapted it to meet the individual needs of the thirteen retarded children in their study who received training over a seven month period. This experimental group was compared to a control group of children using as criteria eight tests considered to measure a variety of visual perception and eye-hand motor coordination skills. The tests were matching, coloring, puzzles, cube and parquetry patterns, cutting, pegboard patterns, drawing, and visual recall. Significant improvement was found in the fine perceptual-motor coordination of the experimental children in comparison with the control group and, in a follow-up test administered four months later, differences still favored the trained children.

The foregoing study definitely indicates a transfer among similar eye-hand coordination tasks but does not necessarily indicate the development of specific concepts. To test such development, the experimental design would have to incorporate different media; for example, the commonly used comparison of pencil-and-paper tasks with "purely" motor tasks. A comparison of the Frostig subtests of eye-motor coordination, form constancy, and spatial relationships with performance on an epicyclic rotary task by 26 three-year-olds and 36 four-year-olds showed no significant relationships between the pencil-and-paper visual developmental subtests and performance on the eye-hand motor task. However, the four-year-olds did perform significantly better than the three-year-olds on both the visual developmental subtests and on the epicyclic rotary task (14).

A more comprehensive study by Trussell (21) of the motor skills and the perceptual and conceptual attributes involved in reading readiness revealed a similar lack of relationship. In this study, 75 first and second grade children were given the Lincoln-Oseretsky Motor Development Scale, a balance test (stabilometer), and a rotary pursuit task to test their motor skills. The perceptual tests were the Marianne Frostig Developmental Test of Visual Perception and the Metropolitan Achievement Test (reading achievement and word discrimination). Eye dominance was determined by two sighting tests and handedness by the preferred hand used during the tests. The latter items were included because a great deal of discussion and research has centered around the influence of unilateral and mixed dominance in eye-hand coordination tasks and perceptual development.

A factor analysis of the various items indicated that reading skills, perceptual skills, and motor skills formed patterns of association among themselves and were inclined to exhibit independence, rather than inter-dependence, with each other. One factor, identified as "reading maturity," had substantial loadings on the two reading tests and age, and lesser loadings on the Frostig subtests of eye-motor coordination, form constancy, and position in space. "Perceptual maturity," the second factor, loaded substantially on the Frostig subtests of figure-ground perception and spatial relationships and to a lesser degree on age and eye-motor coordination. The third factor, "motor coordination," was heavily loaded on the items of the Lincoln-Oseretsky Motor Development Scale, and a fourth factor was substantially loaded on the stabilom-eter and pursuit motor tasks and to a lesser degree on the Frostig subtest of form constancy. Were it not for this latter loading, the fourth factor might be called "motor experience." There were significant positive relationships between age, motor, visual, and reading functions which were considered to be a probable reflection of a general developmental mechanism. Furthermore, when mixed versus unilateral eye-hand dominance groups were compared, none of the tests indicated a significant difference in mean scores.

FURTHER STUDY

The foregoing survey of experimental studies indicates that there is very little factual knowledge about eye-hand perceptual-motor development. There are, however, a number of theories of perceptual-motor development that stress the importance of physical movement in infancy and childhood for the development of various percepts and concepts. Detailed observational studies of children from birth to maturity have led both Piaget (17) and Gesell (4) to the conclusion that sensorimotor activities are essential to the subsequent development of generalizations and concepts. The need for repetition of sensorimotor activities for neuronal fixation of movement patterns is also stressed by Hebb (10) and Grey Walter (5).

Since the kinesthetic sense is activated by all movement, as well as by no movement, it is not surprising that it figures prominently in theories of perceptual-motor development. Kephart (13) believes that the kinesthetic sensations of arm and hand movement, in eye-hand activities, integrate with the visual sensations coming from the eye at the time of activity to form a visual-kinesthetic configuration. This would appear to be a relatively simple interneuron relationship. Such an assumption of simplicity, however, is not valid since one must also account for the many abortive arm and hand movements before hand-object contact is achieved (7). Obviously some sort of feedback mechanism is essential to signal "success" or "no success." If unsuccessful, the integrated visual-kinesthetic pattern must be erased or perhaps stored in a "not-to-be-repeated" category. Previously mentioned studies indicated a tendency not to repeat unsuccessful patterns in catching and striking (8, 22). If the action is successful, the integrated visual-kinesthetic pattern must be repeated a number of times until fixed (5, 10) and this process is undoubtedly complicated by numerous unsuccessful trials interspersed among the successful trials.

The first arm and hand movements of infants are bilateral. Later, either hand is used indiscriminately until the child begins to establish more fixed hand-use preferences around five years of age (4). Kephart believes that the early bilateral and indiscriminate periods are essential to the development of the concept of laterality. Through the integrated visual-kinesthetic patterns resulting from such hand activity, the child gradually learns to distinguish between his right and his left side and to control both sides of his body separately and simultaneously. Laterality, therefore, has as its reference point the child's own body, and Kephart claims that some children have difficulty in crossing the center division line between right and left for any one hand (13).

Kephart also believes that laterality leads to directionality. Again, the infant's first information about the coordinates of space is considered to come from the kinesthetic awareness of differences in the movements involved in various activities. Chief among these directional differences is right-left differentiation. It should be pointed out, however, that space is three-dimensional and to assign a primacy to right-left orientation is to place an undue emphasis on one of the coordinates of space that has been found to be associated with reading readiness. Any movement in space must be defined in terms of all three coordinates even though a particular movement may be predominantly in only one or two coordinates. Therefore, any attempt to reach and grasp a cube must involve right-left orientation, or directionality; the placement of the cube above or below the level of the eyes; and the distance of the cube from the body. All these factors are included in the kinesthetic sensations that are integrated with the visual sensory input during any particular eye-hand task. It is possible that the transition from a circuitous route in the grasping of a cube to a more direct approach with minimal lifting of the arm and the passing of the index and medious fingers directly over the cube may reflect the progressive development of a perceptual concept of space.

The child's concept of space must also involve judgment of objects beyond arm's reach. It is theorized that this development involves the movement of the eyes along the outline of the stimulus and a matching of the resulting visual sensations with previously fixed integrated visual-kinesthetic patterns from movements within arm's reach. A projection is then made upon which a judgment of direction, distance, and, for moving objects, speed of movement, is based (10). Spatial directions and spatial relationships have been noted by Piaget (17) and Gesell (4) to develop first in relation to the child himself. Relations between objects are developed at a later period. Thus, in his early development, the child locates and relates two objects to himself independently. Later he is able to conceive of one object in relation to the other, either to right or left, without the intervening step of locating each object in relation to himself.

Temporal aspects are also a feature of space. Not only does the child have to reach further for a more distant object, it also takes longer for the hand to reach the object. With moving objects, especially those moving toward the child, time is also an important factor since the child must wait until the object comes within arm's reach. Temporospatial integration would therefore appear to be a feature of the development of the concepts of time and space. However, some separation of these concepts must also occur and it is possible that such eye-hand tasks as shifting pegs, in which there is not much change in spatial patterning but there is a difference in elapsed time depending on the number of pegs, may be useful in developing the independence of these concepts.

It is quite obvious that experimental research has not kept pace with theories based on observational studies. Beyond the period of infancy, little relationship has been found, for normal children, between various eye-hand perceptual-motor tasks and the tests we currently employ to measure various concepts. That such a relationship may exist is suggested by experimental studies of neurologically handicapped and retarded children. It is possible that the "urge seeking satisfaction" and the pliability of the normal child are such that he learns the basic concepts of laterality, directionality, space, and time perhaps in spite of what we teach him. Certainly, in order to make an intelligent assessment of how to help a child, we need to know what we may expect in terms of normal development in various aspects of eye-hand perceptual-motor tasks.

If the theorists are correct and conceptualizations develop from perceptual-motor tasks, perhaps an analysis of the movements in the various tasks that can be successfully performed by children at various age levels will shed some light on the perceptual concepts which are being developed at that time. Eye-hand tasks may be generally divided into those with stationary objects and those with moving objects. Stationary objects must, of necessity, be within arm's reach. Moving objects may be of three categories: (a) those within arm's reach at all times, (b) those moving from out of arm's reach to within arm's reach, and (c) those projected from within arm's reach toward some target at a distance. Our current information about the interrelationships of these types of eye-hand, perceptual-motor tasks is very scanty but does indicate a clustering of slightly higher correlations within each general category than between the categories (2, 15).

The types of movements possible with stationary objects may be categorized according to the three planes of space. In relation to the child, these are movements (a) towards the body, (b) away from the body, (c) parallel to the body, either right or left, (d) upwards, and (e) downwards. Early reaching and grasping involves movements both away from the body and toward the body. The natural cohesion of this type of action makes it very difficult to separate the two components for more minute examination. Eye-hand tasks such as disk-sorting or peg-shifting, however, could be arranged so that the object is moved either toward or away from the body. A comprehensive examination of the directional movements used in manipulating stationary objects, similar to Halverson's study of prehension (7) could contribute to our knowledge of normal development in this area. This information might then facilitate our understanding of the relationship of these perceptual-motor skills to the development of perceptual concepts.

The movements used in eye-hand tasks with moving objects could be analyzed similarly. Here, however, the path of the moving object presents additional factors to consider. For example, whether the object were moving in a straight line, either toward or away from the body, in a circular, square, or triangular pattern, or in an irregular pattern would have to be considered. Whether the object were moving at a steady speed or with a change in speed would also have to be considered.

The recognition of form or pattern is also an important feature of the more complex eye-hand tasks with stationary objects in which the object must be transferred in more than one direction. Kephart theorized that this type of recognition is vital to the development of an adequate figure-ground relationship. For example, if a child is tracing a square pattern, he must be able to perceive and identify the form of the pattern as a whole and yet deal with the lines and angles separately at the same time. The parts of any pattern must be perceived separately, in relationship to each other, and as a whole simultaneously (13). In this kind of perception, the movements of the eye become more important as the pattern becomes more complex (1). Although eye movements increase in complexity with increasing complexity of pattern, eye-hand coordinations are confined to adjustments in specific areas of the pattern. A comprehensive study of eye movements, in addition to hand movements, would therefore be valuable in charting the progressive development of figure-ground relationships.

These suggested investigations would require a great deal of minute and exacting work, but would result in an immense quantity of data. They could very well be further complicated by recent discoveries that the chemical composition of the brain is associated with brain function and personality. Grey Walter (5) has also concluded, from an analysis of EEG records normal individuals can be characterized into three basic personality types on the basis of their alpha rhythms. Such additional knowledge, however, should not deter the investigation of eye-hand perceptual-motor learning but should assist in the understanding of the results of such investigations. In the past, we have looked at eye-hand tasks in general and drawn conclusions about the specificity of each task. Perhaps if we examined the many specifics of movement within a large number of tasks, we would reach some general conclusions about the development of eye-hand perceptual-motor tasks and perceptual concepts.

ACTION FOR NOW

The foregoing review of the literature and suggestions for further research point where we have information and where we lack it. Halverson's exacting study of the development of prehension gives us a very good picture of what to expect in the way of reaching and grasping from 16 to 52 weeks (7). Observational studies are the main source of information about eye-hand tasks from one to three years of age. There are more observational and experimental studies on children over three years old. By age three, however, most children are fairly proficient in handling stationary objects and also show reasonable proficiency in tasks where the object is moving in a simple pattern within arm's reach. Since the best age for reaching and grasping was found to be 28 weeks, it would seem that the period between 28 weeks and three years is one in which great gains are made in the manipulation of objects. As such, this may also be the age period at which the child is establishing many of the perceptual concepts which some theorists consider to have their origin in eye-hand, perceptual-motor tasks.

Other perceptual-motor tasks, especially those associated with locomotion, also take increasing amounts of the young child's effort and time. These cannot be neglected if the child is to develop in a normal, well-rounded manner. Aside from concern for the child's health, probably the most important contribution a parent can make to the child's development is to provide the opportunities and instruments for safe experimentation in as wide a variety of perceptual-motor tasks as possible. The parent should also be aware of the child's tendency to spend more time with a new, or emerging, perceptual-motor task. Such unequal distribution of a child's time should not cause concern unless it becomes obvious that some other developmental area is being neglected to the extent that the child's progress is below the normal range. In this event, every effort should be made to encourage the child toward more active participation in the neglected perceptual-motor area.

The discussion has dealt mainly with eye-hand tasks; therefore, an examination of what we currently know about eye-hand development and of possible objectives should provide some guidelines for encouraging development in this area. The need for repetition in order to eliminate unsuccessful responses and fixate successful responses has been stressed. This indicates that the child should have the opportunity to experiment with any task as much as he wishes. As long as he feels he has not mastered the task he will continue his experimentation, provided, of course, that it is not too difficult, in which case he will either not undertake the task on his own or will discontinue it very quickly. When a child has mastered a specific task to his own satisfaction, he usually becomes bored and stops.

Child development theorists have suggested that the concepts of laterality, directionality, space, and form are developed through visual-kinesthetic integration of various eye-hand, perceptual-motor tasks. We have few facts at present to support these theories, nor do we know exactly which eye-hand tasks are more likely to produce specific types of concepts. This does not mean, however, that we can reject the theories entirely, nor that we should despair at the immense number of eye-hand tasks that could be used. Instead, we should assume that the more varied the perceptual-motor opportunities for the child, the better the chances are that he will develop normal orientations with respect to himself and his environment. Since it is impossible to present the entire gamut of eye-hand tasks to the growing youngster, we must make sure that his repertory will include at least those perceptual-motor tasks that are logically related to the various facets of laterality, direction, space, and form.

A number of investigators have also found a clustering for tasks with stationary objects and for tasks with moving objects. This indicates that the child will need ample opportunity to experiment with both static and dynamic objects. The finding is also disturbing in that it gives little indication of transfer between these categories. Perhaps when we find out more about the specific components of these tasks, we may also get some leads that will show us how to teach for generalization and transfer.

Our knowledge of the perceptual-motor characteristics of young children is based mainly on observational studies, some longitudinal but the majority cross-sectional. Theories have been developed, on the basis of such studies, of the role of perceptual-motor activities in the development of various concepts. However, investigations that have explored the relationship between various eye-hand, perceptual-motor tasks and tests purporting to measure various concepts have reported little relationship for normal children. It is possible, however, that a more detailed examination of the various specifics of eye-hand tasks may result in a better understanding of various perceptual concepts. In the meantime, it is the responsibility of those who work with young children to see that they have the opportunity to explore and experiment with as wide a variety of perceptual-motor tasks as possible.

REFERENCES

1. Bayley, Nancy, "The Development of Motor Abilities During the First Three Years." *Monographs of the Society for Child Development*, No. 1 (1935).
2. Carlisle, N. S., "Eye-Hand Coordination of Four Year Olds in Tasks with Stable and Moving Objects." Unpublished Master's thesis, University of California at Berkeley, 1966.
3. Gates, A. I., and Scott, A. W., "Characteristics and Relations of Motor Speed and Dexterity Among Young Children." *Journal of Genetic Psychology*, XXXIX (1931), 423–53.
4. Gesell, A., *The First Five Years of Life* (New York: Harper & Row, Publishers, 1940).
5. Grey, Walter, W., *The Living Brain* (Harmondsworth, Eng.: Penguin Books, 1961).
6. Goodall, J., "Tool Using and Aiming in a Community of Free-Living Chimpanzees." *Nature*, CCI (1964), 1264–66.
7. Halverson, H. M., "An Experimental Study of Prehension in Infants by Means of Systematic Cinema Records." *Genetic Psychology Monographs*, X (1931), 107–286.
8. ———, and Robertson, M. A., "A Study of Motor Pattern Development in Young Children." Report at the National Convention of the American Association for Health, Physical Education and Recreation, March 20, 1966.
9. Haring, N. G., and Stables, J. M., "The Effect of Gross Motor Development on Visual Perception and Eye-Hand Coordination." *Journal of the American Physical Therapy Association*, XLVI (1966), 129–35.
10. Hebb, D. O., *The Organization of Behavior* (New York: John Wiley & Sons, 1949).
11. Held, R., "Plasticity in Sensory-Motor Systems." *Scientific American*, CCXIII (1965), 84–94.
12. Honzik, M. P., Hutchings, J. J., and Burnip, S. R., "Birth Record Assess-

ments and Test Performance at Eight Months." *American Journal of Disabled Children,* CIX (1965), 416–26.

13. Kephart, N. C., *The Slow Learner in the Classroom* (Columbus, Ohio: Charles E. Merrill, 1960).
14. Lowe, R. J., "The Relationship Between a Visual-Developmental Test and Performance on a Visual-Motor Task in Three and Four Year Olds." Unpublished Master's thesis, University of California at Berkeley, 1965.
15. Meyers, C. E., and Dingman, H. F., "The Structure of Abilities at the Preschool Ages: Hypothesized Domains." *Psychological Bulletin,* LVII (1960), 514–32.
16. Munn, N. L., "Learning in Children," in L. Carmichael (ed.), *Manual of Child Psychology* (New York: John Wiley & Sons, 1954).
17. Piaget, J., *Play, Dreams and Imitation in Childhood* (New York: W. W. Norton & Co., 1962).
18. Revesz, G., *The Human Hand* (London: Routledge and Kegan Paul, Ltd., 1958).
19. Sherrington, C., *Man on His Nature* (Cambridge, Eng.: Cambridge University Press, 1951).
20. Sloan, W., "Motor Proficiency and Intelligence." *American Journal of Mental Deficiency,* LV (1951), 394–406.
21. Trussell, Ella, "The Relation of Performance of Selected Physical Skills to Perceptual Aspects of Reading Readiness in Elementary School Children." Unpublished Doctoral dissertation, University of California at Berkeley, 1966.
22. Victors, E. E., "A Cinematographical Analysis of Catching Behavior of a Selected Group of Seven and Nine Year Old Boys." *Dissertation Abstracts,* XXII (1961), 1903–4.

A. H. ISMAIL[*]

The Relationship Between
Motor and Intellectual Development

Body and mind are never independent. Such a subdivision is entirely arbitrary and unfounded. Although much remains to be learned about the brain and central nervous system, neurologists in general agree that the idea of two lives, somatic and psychic, has outlived its usefulness. Thus, the psychosomatic concept of medicine recognizes this fact of biological integration and acknowledges its significance.

THEORIES IN PERSPECTIVE

A survey of some related theories is of prime importance. One is the organismic age theory by Olson (56), which proposes that the performance of a child is associated with certain factors closely related to his total motor, emotional, social, and intellectual development. Along this line Gestalt psychology has considered the individual as a "whole" within the framework of his environment. Hence educators, as well as psychologists, should recognize that development is the result of a complex interaction between heredity, maturation, and environment. Educators who try to separate these elements are overlooking a fundamental principle of developmental psychology. Woodworth and Sheehan (71) say:

> Untangling the influences of nature and nurture is a delicate operation that is never completely successful, and on the question of their relative con-

[*]Department of Physical Education for Men, Purdue University.

tributions to perceptual development, research findings can be offered in support of either position.

Doman and Delacato (18, 19, 20) emphasize the need for neurological organization, which, in normal children, is the result of uninterrupted ontogenetic development. Therefore, they advocate the neural patterns omitted during the neurological development of the child be introduced in order to compensate for these missing links.

The perceptual-motor concept of Kephart (46, 47) stresses the complete perceptual-motor development and explains learning difficulties as a result of a "breakdown" in the child's perceptual-motor development.

Neurologists agree that in order for the organism to perceive a complex motor task correctly, all structures in the central nervous system must be fully developed and physiologically "ready" to integrate stimulus and response patterns. All theories are consequently built on the basic assumption that perceptual-motor training, which takes advantage of the relationship between sensory processes and motor responses, acts through the cortex and lower brain centers to improve perceptual and motor functions.

Motor performance stimulates the central nervous system to such an extent that the underdeveloped, dead, or dying cells will either be rehabilitated or their function assumed by other or newly generated cells. Joseph Altman (67) is among those who support the possibility of neurons undergoing mitosis when he states:

> . . . new neurons might nevertheless arise from undifferentiated precursors, embryonic cells that might differentiate, becoming neurons, after multiplication.

Doman lets the child rebreathe much of the air he exhales because he claimed that "this method of increasing carbon dioxide content at the cortical level is a well known chemophysiological aid to the cortex's making better use of the oxygen which is supplied" (20).

Steinhaus (65) calls our attention to the fact that the most important sense organ in the body is muscle tissue, since some 40 per cent of the axons in the motor nerve to a muscle are actually sensory fibers that carry impulses to the brain.

THE NATURE OF THE MOTOR OR
PHYSICAL ATTRIBUTES STUDIED IN THE RESEARCH

Before presenting the literature dealing with the relationship under consideration, it is of importance to discuss the status of motor or physical attributes researchers generally employ.

Items that measure motor or physical fitness are frequently used. On the other hand, measurements of gross and fine perceptual-motor performance are also employed. Regardless of the usefulness of these measures, there have been conflicting results when these measures were correlated with intellectual variables. Apparently, we need to analyze and define motor measures precisely before relating them to intellectual tasks. Furthermore an adequate description should be given of the administration of these items in the testing situation. In addition, a full description of the subjects involved should yield important information both for interpreting the results and for making proper generalizations. The problem of motor performance measures is further discussed by Keogh (44). Studies that either define or clarify motor attributes are nothing but a humble effort in the right direction. In 1927, Farmer (22) found that the term *motor* was too wide and suggested that a narrower view be taken and that tests be divided according to the particular type of motor performance they seemed to test. Similarly, Seashore (61) investigated the relationship between fine and gross motor abilities. No over-all positive relationship was found between them.

In order to define the term *motor aptitude* Ismail and Cowell (34) conducted a study to identify the factors that could explain 25 selected items authorities claim measure such motor aptitude. Five independent factors were extracted and named. These factors were: speed, growth and maturity, kinesthetic memory of the arms, body balance on objects, and body balance on the floor.

Bass (2) made an analysis of balance items to determine the different factors affecting balance. She extracted nine factors of which five were given names. These factors are: general eye-motor factor, general kinesthetic response, general ambulatory sensitivity, function of two vertical semicircular canals, and tension-giving reinforcement. Also studying balance, Travis (69) reported the following findings: (a) the dynamic component of equilibration was quite unrelated to the static component: (b) no relationship was found between balancing skill on the stabilometer and the ability to maintain manually the orientation of the rotation chair; (c) low correlations were found between perceptual and motor components of body orientation on the rotation chair; (d) weight is more important than height in dynamic stabilometer performance; (e) weight and height have no importance on sway scores, rotation scores, steadiness, or manual pursuit; and (f) visual cues are of help in both dynamic and static equilibrium.

Using the multiple-group method of factoring, Cumbee, Meyer, and Peterson (17) investigated motor coordination items. They extracted nine factors and named four. These factors were: balancing objects, speed of change of direction of arms and hands, total body quick change of direction, and body balance. As a result it was concluded that a different definition of motor coordination for different age levels should be considered.

Cratty's theory (12), dealing with constructs at two levels which mold perceptual-motor functioning, was revised. The two levels are those specific to the task and a general one, such as ability to analyze an activity. Recently, he proposed the inversion of "Vernon's Pyramid" assuming that factors at three levels influence final performance and learning output (13). "General behavioral supports" which influence a variety of human behaviors, including intellectual as well as perceptual-motor abilities, are located at the base of the pyramid. At the second level are the various perceptual-motor factors isolated by factor analytic studies. At the apex of the pyramid are the specific factors. Thus, the conflict between specificity and generality of perceptual-motor behavior could be explained by such constructs.

The work of Frank (25) supports the concept that generality is related to the influence of level of aspiration on performance. Further, Ryan (60) explains that the feelings of an individual about his performance potential and strivings may influence his performance and learning in a diversity of tasks. Other investigators who support the existence and importance of generality of behavior are Duffy (21), Magoun (52), Fleishman (23), and Cratty (14, 15). Evidence that skilled output is also governed by factors specific to the tasks and the situation is also abundant. Examples of studies supporting specificity are being conducted by Strong (66), Henry (31), and Namikas (54).

In conclusion, additional research is needed to clarify the generality and specificity concepts in perceptual-motor skills, level of aspiration, and other factors that might influence motor performance.

A SELECTION OF RELATED LITERATURE

According to Gates et al. (27) the development of behavior is influenced by two factors, growth and learning, and these are often so closely interrelated that it is impossible to separate them. If we are to educate a child, however, it is necessary to have a clear understanding of him as a whole, and this entails a clear knowledge of how each aspect of growth depends on, and interacts with, every other aspect of growth. The interrelatedness of growth is well described by Breckenridge and Vincent (8) when they say of a child:

> His intellect is related to his physical well being; his physical health is sharply affected by his emotions; his emotions are influenced by his school success or failure, by his physical health, and by his mental adequacy. His growth, physical, intellectual, and social, is a product of his

family history, his personal history, his current satisfactions and strains. His daily schedule affects all phases of his growth, and, in turn the pattern and speed of his growth affect his reaction to his daily schedule. What he accomplishes in school, in play, or in any other part of his living is deeply affected by his physical health, by his mental adequacy, by his interest in his work or play, and by his emotional freedom to attend to it.

STUDIES OF RETARDED CHILDREN

Comparing the motor proficiency of feebleminded children with normals, Sloan (63) used the Lincoln Adaptation of Oseretsky Tests. He found that the retarded children were significantly poorer than the normal children on all the proficiency tests. The abilities tested were: general static coordination, general dynamic coordination, dynamic manual coordination, speed, and simultaneous voluntary movement. These findings were confirmed by Malpass (53).

Reynolds and Chalmers (59) compared the learning ability of subnormal and normal children using the motor task of mirror drawing. They found the normal children superior to the subnormal. This finding was supported by Rarick and McKee (57) when they used two extreme groups of third-grade children. The two groups were selected with a battery of physical performance tests. When the two groups were compared they found that the superior group in physical performance was also superior in scholastic ability. In another study, Francis and Rarick (24) used 284 mentally retarded boys and girls whose ages ranged from 7.5 to 14.5 years and whose IQ's were between 50 and 90. The retardates were compared with normal children of the same age using a battery of eleven motor performance tests designed to measure strength, power, balance, and agility. The following findings were reported: (a) the trend in strength for each sex followed approximately the same pattern as in the normal children, although at a lower level at every age; (b) the means of both boys and girls on most measures were two to four years behind the published norms of normal children, and the discrepancy increased with age; and (c) intelligence was positively correlated with most of the motor performance tests. Similar results were reported by Blatt (6).

Thurstone (68) compared mentally retarded and normal children for gross motor achievement on eight items. He found significant differences between the two groups in favor of the normal children on the ball throw for distance, ball punt for distance, ball throw for accuracy, standing broad jump, side slipping, forty-yard run, right grip strength, and left grip strength.

Using 170 mentally retarded boys, Heath (30) found a correlation coefficient of .66 between mental age and beam-walking scores of endogenous (hereditary) mentally retarded children. He found no relationship between motor and mental scores for the exogenous (nonhereditary) retardates. Thus, he suggested the possibility of etiological classification through test performance.

Relatively high correlations between IQ and motor ability were found by Howe (32) and Oliver (55). Guyette et al. (29) reported that positive medium correlation coefficients are generally obtained between IQ and motor ability scores of retarded children. Further, they indicated that balance items tend to discriminate highly between normal and retarded children. Similarly, Cratty (16) reported a correlation coefficient of .63 between IQ and a test battery of gross motor attributes for retarded children. The battery consisted of the following subtests: body perception, gross agility, balance, locomotion agility, throwing, and tackling. Furthermore, he indicated that the magnitude of this coefficient reflects the extent to which "movement accuracy and cognition are inseparable in the retarded."

Keogh and Keogh (45) compared a group of educationally subnormal (ESN) boys ages nine and ten with a group of normal school boys ages six through nine on the ability to copy four simple line patterns by drawing and by walking. The ESN boys were similar to the normal six-year-olds on both tasks and significantly worse than all other normal groups. No differences were found between walking and drawing patterns for the normal boys. The ESN, however, were significantly poorer in the ability to walk than to draw patterns. Both objective scores and the subjective evaluation of performance suggest that the ESN boys had extreme difficulty in organizing their gross movements to re-execute patterns in a larger spatial field. Thus, the gross movement patterns performed by the ESN are apparently related to age, intelligence, and varying conditions of disturbance or delay in development. Similar results, using paper and pencil tests have been reported by Bender (4), Frostig et al. (26), and Koppitz (51).

In summary, it could be concluded that there is a positive correlation between mental and motor abilities which is higher in more retarded populations.

STUDIES OF NORMAL POPULATIONS

Several studies have been done comparing athletes with nonathletes in terms of intellectual performance, for example, Snoddy and Shannon (62) and Reals and Rees (58). No significant differences in intelligence were found between the two groups. In addition, neither Keeler (43) nor Johnson (41) were able to find a significant relationship between physical performance as measured by the Johnson Test and intelligence scores. However, reviewing 17 investigations dealing with the relationship between athletic participation and academic scholarship in high schools, Jacobson (39) concluded that athletes are higher than nonathletes in terms of academic achievement as measured by school marks. Furthermore, their academic achievement does not suffer during participation. It was pointed out by Jenny (40) that McCloy's Motor Quotient is closely correlated with intelligence. Jenny maintained that one reason athletes sometimes make poor grades is that too much attention is given to sports and not enough to classroom work.

The relationship between physical fitness and intellectual performance has been investigated by many researchers. Weber (70) found a significant correlation of .41 between physical fitness scores and grade-point averages using college freshmen. Using 207 boys and 202 girls in the first grade, Kagerer (42) found significant relationships between the Metropolitan Readiness Test scores and the two items of the Kraus-Weber Test. The two items purport to measure strength of the upper and lower back muscles. Barry (1) examined the related patterns in academic achievement, motivation, and cardiovascular and motor fitness in freshmen students. Twelve factors were isolated and named. Two of the factors were labelled self-inflicted-discomfort and assertion-by-power. In the self-inflicted-discomfort factor, grade-point average had a high factor loading with other motor and cardiovascular fitness items. In the assertion-by-power factor, grade-point average had a high factor loading along with assertion, self-sentiment, pre- and post-exercise systolic blood pressure, mile run, and standing broad jump.

Several studies, however, have reported nonsignificant relationships between physical fitness and intellectual performance. In general, studies along this line seem to indicate that the relationship between physical fitness and intellectual performance is far from firmly established.

The relationship between physical growth and intellectual performance has been investigated by several researchers. Bayley (3) studied 61 babies in terms of growth and intelligence and found no relationship between the scores in the first few months of life and scores earned at the end of the first year. Consequently, later intelligence could not be predicted from the scores on tests made in infancy. Bloomers, Knief, and Strand (7) studied 120 preadolescent children using the Organismic Age Concept. They found that measures of growth items were not related to academic achievement. Furthermore, they concluded that growth tends to proceed at the rate at which it starts out. Sontag, Baker, and Nelson (64), in a longitudinal study, found no relationship between physical growth rate and mental growth rate during late preschool and early school years, from about four to eight years of age. Klausmeier, Beeman, and Lehmann (49) found that height, weight, grip strength, dental age, and carpal age contributed little to predicting arithmetic and language scores. Also, Klausmeier and Check (50) reported that a low level of physical growth within the child did not accompany low achievement in arithmetic and reading. Furthermore, uneven physical growth did not accompany low achievement in arithmetic and reading. In addition, the children of low intelligence did not differ significantly from average and highly intelligent children in terms of phyiscal growth measures. Gleason and Klausmeier (28) found consistent negative correlations between uneven physical growth and achievement in reading, arithmetic, and language in preadolescent children.

The insignificant relationships that are consistently found between physical growth and intellectual performance, indicate that physical growth items are poor predictors of intellectual items.

Numerous studies have been conducted on the relationships among physical growth, physical and/or motor attributes, intellectual performance, and sometimes emotional traits. Again the purpose of these studies was to determine the best nonintellectual items for predicting intellectual performance. Brown and his associates (9, 10, 11) embarked on a longitudinal study that started during 1960. They found that physical performance and emotional development make the largest nonintellectual contribution to predicting intellectual performance (arithmetic achievement and Battery Median). Based on his experience along this line of research Brown (9) concluded that the relationship between intellectual development and physical and motor performance has been greatly oversimplified. This has resulted largely from the use of the correlation technique in which the correlation coefficients are usually inflated by contaminating factors. Furthermore, he believes that physical performance is a discrete developmental characteristic and that there is some factor related to the growth and maturation of the nervous system that affects both physical and intellectual performance. In addition, he maintains that longitudinal studies should be conducted involving populations of different kinds of children, many other physical and motor items, and social and emotional variables in order to understand the individual as a whole and the contribution of physical activity to the concept of integrated development.

Bengston (5) studied the interrelationships among perceptual motor development, motor performance, school achievement, and intelligence of nine-year-old boys. She found significant relationships between school achievement subitems, word knowledge and reading, and a perceptual motor survey. The relationships between school achievement subitems and motor performance tasks were low except for the throw for accuracy and shuttle run items. She concluded that the observed interrelationships among the motor tasks supported the theories dealing with specificity of complex movements.

From this review of the literature dealing with normal populations, one might infer that the relationship between intellectual and motor performance is not as conclusive as that between physical growth and intellectual performance. These results motivated the writer to study this relationship systematically. Since the motor domain includes different motor items of various functions, it was thought necessary to define this domain operationally. Undertaking this definition, the writer (10) employed the factor analysis technique to identify the factors which different authorities claim to measure motor aptitude. As a result, Ismail and Cowell (34) were able to define motor aptitude by the factors isolated. Five factors were extracted and named: (a) speed and strength, (b) growth and maturity, (c) kinesthetic memory of the arms, (d) body balance on objects, and (e) body balance on the floor. However, one definite shortcoming in this study was the absence of motor coordination items. Hence, in the follow-up studies, the writer included motor coordination items which were identified as an independent factor. Finally, it was possible to define motor aptitude by the five independent factors extracted in addition to the motor coordination factor.

After defining motor aptitude by the factor analytic technique, Ismail, Kephart, and Cowell (38) studied the relationship between motor aptitude and intellectual achievement. The investigators isolated a factor called "development." In this factor only the Otis IQ test, the Stanford Academic Achievement test, coordination items, and some balance items had high factor loadings. It was concluded that these items have much in common, as witnessed by the factor loadings, and they present evidence supporting the theory of the individual as a "whole" only in terms of the motor and intellectual domains. In addition, the authors were able to predict intellectual performance from motor aptitude test items. However, the degrees of freedom associated with the predictions were limited, which affected the reliability.

Recently, Ismail and Gruber (37) tried to identify the factors present in a wide variety of motor aptitude and intellectual achievement items in preadolescent children. Again, using the factor analytic technique, the investigators were able to extract more or less similar factors as before. The factors were: (a) academic factor, in this factor the Otis IQ scores, Stanford Academic Achievement scores, coordination scores, and some balance scores had high factor loadings, (b) general balance factor, (c) physical growth and maturity, (d) coordination of lower limbs, (e) kinesthetic memory of the arms, and (f) dynamic balance on objects. Moreover, no difference was found in the pattern of the factor structure in terms of sex and total group. Thus, the findings obtained from this study validate those previously found by Ismail, Kephart, and Cowell (38).

After ascertaining that motor aptitude and intellectual developments are related, Ismail and Gruber (36, 37) investigated the possibility of estimating certain intellectual parameters using motor aptitude items. As a result, several regression equations were developed to estimate intellectual scores for total group, boys, girls, high achievers, medium achievers, and low achievers. In addition, regression equations were developed for estimating the Otis IQ score, paragraph meaning, word meaning, arithmetic reasoning, and arithmetic computation, and the total Stanford Academic Achievement scores. The amount of variance (R^2) associated with the several regressions were sufficient for either selection or prediction.

Ismail and Gruber (35, 37) investigated the relative contribution of several kinds of motor aptitude items in estimating intellectual performance. They concluded that the best predictors for estimating intellectual performance are coordination, balance, and growth items, in that order. Speed, power, and strength items have low and nonsignificant predictive power in estimating intellectual achievement.

All the supportive findings pertaining to motor and intellectual development are based on correlation techniques only. Such findings should not be interpreted in terms of cause and effect. Therefore, in an attempt to investigate the validity of the findings achieved by correlation, Ismail (33, 37) conducted an experiment to investigate the relative effectiveness of an organized physical education program on IQ and intellectual achievement scores. Two matched groups consisting of 71 pre-adolescent children were selected according to six criteria which included IQ and intellectual achievement scores. A nested factorial design involving four factors was employed. The four factors were: sex, levels of achievement, paired subjects, and groups (experimental and control). In this design, the paired subjects, comprising the experimental and control groups, were nested under levels of achievement and sex. It was concluded that an organized physical education program had no effect on IQ scores. However, it had a favorable effect on intellectual achievement scores.

The statistically significant increase in intellectual achievement associated with the experimental group came as a slight surprise since the physical education program was conducted for only one year. It is the writer's opinion that the effects of a quality physical education program on intellectual achievement should be much greater over a longer period of time. Speculating that the trend of improvement would have continued over a period of four years or more, a greater difference would have been observed in favor of the experimental group. This would be due to the fact that the experimental group would be exposed constantly to a better physical education program and would thus develop better neurological bases for learning through two approaches, the classroom and the gymnasium programs. Or, since the child can express himself through play activities, the psychological satisfaction of achievement through play might provide the child with additional confidence and feelings of adequacy which should assist in classroom work. Certainly, the experimental approach should be adopted with children of all ages and grade levels. It is not clear what constitutes the best amount of exposure to an organized physical education program or what effect such exposure has on a child's intellectual development.

In conclusion, although some scattered light has been shed on the relationship between motor and intellectual performance, this relationship has not yet been solidly confirmed. Some of the difficulties encountered have resulted from failure to: (a) define various motor items precisely, (b) define populations from which samples are drawn, (c) consider quality of measurements as well as quantity, (d) describe the testing setup, which affects performance, (e) consider the previous experience of the child with items involved, (f) standardize the directions in the administration of the items, (g) select a proper and relevant design, and (h) observe the sources of bias which stem from the experimenter, the research assistants collecting data, and early data returns.

Assuming that researchers correct for these difficulties and others they might encounter, the relationship between motor and intellectual performance is likely to be less controversial.

REFERENCES

1. Barry, Alan J., "A Factorial Study of Motivation, Physical Fitness, and Academic Achievement in College Freshmen," Unpublished manuscript, University of Illinois, 1961.

2. Bass, Ruth I., "An Analysis of the Components of Tests of Semicircular Canal Function and Static and Dynamic Balance," *Research Quarterly*, X (1939), 33–52.

3. Bayley, N., "Individual Patterns of Development," *Child Development*, XXVII (1956), 45–75.

4. Bender, Lauretta, "A Visual Motor Gestalt Test and Its Clinical Use," *American Orthopsychiatric Association Research Monograph No. 3*, (1938).

5. Bengston, Gwenn M., "The Relationship between Perceptual–Motor Development and Motor Performance of Nine-year-old Boys," Unpublished Master's thesis, University of Colorado, 1966.

6. Blatt, B., "The Physical, Personality and Academic Status of Children Who Are Mentally Retarded Attending Special Classes as Compared with Children Who Are Mentally Retarded Attending Regular Classes," *American Journal of Mental Deficiency*, LXII (1958), 810–18.

7. Bloomers, P. L., Knief, M., and Strand, J. B., "The Organismic Age Concept," *Journal of Educational Psychology*, XLVI, (1955), 142–50.

8. Breckenridge, M. E., and Vincent, E. L., *Child Development*, 3rd Ed. (Philadelphia: W. B. Saunders Co., 1955).

9. Brown, R., "The Role of Physical and Motor Performance in Intellectual Development," *A Report-Symposium on Integrated Development*, Purdue University, June, 1964.

10. ———, Henderson, E., et al., "Measuring Physical, Intellectual, and Social-Emotional Development," Paper presented at American Educational Research Association, Feb., 1962.

11. ———"The Use of a Developmental Index to Predict Pupil Achievement," Unpublished manuscript, New York University, 1963.

12. Cratty, Bryant J., *Movement Behavior and Motor Learning*, (Philadelphia: Lea & Febiger, 1964).

13. ———, "A Three Level Theory of Perceptual-Motor Behavior," *Quest*, V (1966), 3–10.

14. ———, "The Influence of Small-Pattern Practice Upon Large Pattern Learning," *Research Quarterly*, XXXIII (1962), 523–35.

15. ———, "A Comparison of the Learning of Fine Motor Skill to Learning a Similar Gross Motor Task, Based Upon Kinesthetic Cues," *Research Quarterly*, XXXIII (1962).

16. ———, "The Perceptual Attributes of Mentally Retarded Children and Youth," Department of Physical Education, University of California at Los Angeles, 1966.

17. Cumbee, Frances Z., Meyer, M., and Peterson, G., "Factorial Analysis of Motor Co-ordination Variables for Third and Fourth Grade Girls," *Research Quarterly*, XXVIII (1957), 100–108.

18. Delacato, Carl H., *The Diagnosis and Treatment of Speech and Reading Problems* (Springfield, Ill.: Charles C Thomas, (1963).

19. ———, *The Treatment and Prevention of Pending Problems* (Springfield, Ill.: Charles C Thomas, 1959).

20. Doman, Glenn, Lecture given at the Institute for the Achievement of Human Potential on January 10, 1966.

21. Duffy, Elizabeth, *Activation and Behavior* (New York: John Wiley & Sons, 1962).

22. Farmer, J., "A Group Factor in Sensory Motor Tests," *British Journal of Psychology*, XVII (1927), 327–34.

23. Fleishman, E. A., and Hempel, W. E., Jr., "Changes in Factor Structure of a Complex Psychomotor Test as a Function of Practice," *Psychometrika*, XIX (1954).

24. Francis, R. J., and Rarick, G. L., "Motor Characteristics of the Mentally Retarded," *American Journal of Mental Deficiency*, LXIII (1959), 792–811.

25. Frank, J. D., "Recent Studies of the Level of Aspiration," *Psychological Bulletin*, XXXVIII (1941).

26. Frostig, M., Levever, D. W., and Whittlesey, J., "A Developmental Test of Visual Perception for Evaluating Normal and Neurologically Handicapped Children," *Perceptual Motor Skills*, XII (1961), 383–94.

27. Gates, A. I., Jersild, A. T., McConnell, T. R., and Challman, R. C., *Educational Psychology*, 3rd Ed. (The Macmillan Co., 1949).

28. Gleason, G. T., and Klausmeier, H. J., "The Relationship Between Variability in Physical Growth and Academic Achievement Among Third and Fifth-Grade Children," *Journal of Educational Research*, LI (1958), 521–27.

29. Guyette, Anna, Seymour, W., Henry, W., and John, D., "Some Aspects of Space Perception in Mental Retardation," *American Journal of Mental Deficiency*, LXIX (1964), 90–100.

30. Heath, Roy S., "Railwalking Performance as Related to Mental Age and Etiological Type Among the Mentally Retarded," *American Journal of Psychology*, LI (1942), 240–47.

31. Henry, Franklin, "Increased Response Latency for Complicated Movements and a (Memory Drum) Theory of Neuromotor Reaction," *Research Quarterly*, XXXI (1960), 24–33.

32. Howe, C., "A Comparison of Motor Skills of Mentally Retarded and Normal Children," *Experimental Children*, XXXV (1959), 352–54.

33. Ismail, A. H., "The Effect of an Organized Physical Education Program on Intellectual Performance," paper presented at the meeting of the Association Internationale Des Écoles Supérieures D'Éducation Physique, Paris, Sept. 5–10, 1966.

34. ———, and Cowell, C. C., "Factor Analysis of Motor Aptitude of Preadolescent Boys," *Research Quarterly*, XXXII (1961), 507–13.

35. Ismail, A. H., and Gruber, J. J., "Predictive Power of Coordination and Balance Items in Estimating Intellectual Achievement," *Proceedings of 1st International Congress of Psychology of Sport*, Rome, April, 1965.

36. ———, "Utilization of Motor Aptitude Tests in Predicting Academic Achievement," *Proceedings of 1st International Congress on Psychology of Sport*, Rome, April, 1965.

37. ———, *Motor Aptitude and Intellectual Performance* (Columbus, Ohio: Charles E. Merrill Books, Inc., in press).

38. Ismail, A. H., N. Kephart, and Cowell, C. C., *Utilization of Motor Aptitude Test Batteries in Predicting Academic Achievement, Technical Report No. 1*, (Lafayette, Ind.: Purdue University Research Foundation, 1963).

39. Jacobson, J. M., "Athletes and Scholarship in High School," *School Revue*, XXXIX (1931), 280–87.

40. Jenny, John H., "The M. Q. is as Important as I. Q.," *Journal of HPER*, XXX, (1959) 3.

41. Johnson, G. B., "A Study of the Relationship that Exists Between Physical Skill and Intelligence as Measured by the General Intelligence of College Students," *Research Quarterly*, XIII (1942), 57–59.

42. Kagerer, R. L., "The Relationship Between the Kraus-Weber Test for Minimum Muscular Fitness and School Achievement," Unpublished Master's thesis, Purdue University, 1958.

43. Keeler, L. D., "The Effect of Maturation on Physical Skill as Measured by the Johnson Physical Skill Test," *Research Quarterly*, IX (1938), 54–58.

44. Keogh, Jack, "Motor Performance Measurement Problems when Examin-

ing Relationship of Motor and Intellectual Functioning," *A Report-Symposium on Integrated Development*, (Lafayette, Ind.: Purdue University, 1964).

45. ——, and Keogh, F. J., "Pattern Copying and Pattern Walking Performance of Normal and Educationally Subnormal Boys," *American Journal of Mental Deficiency*, in press.

46. Kephart, Newell C., *The Slow Learner in the Classroom* (Columbus, Ohio: Charles E. Merrill Books, Inc., 1960).

47. ——, "The Needs of Teachers for Specialized Information on Perception," in William M. Cronickshank (ed.), *The Teacher of Brain-Injured Children* (Syracuse, N.Y.: Syracuse University Press, 1966), pp. 171–80.

48. Klausmeier, H. J., "Physical Behavioral, and Other Characteristics of High and Low Achieving Children in Favored Environments," *Journal of Education Research*, (1958), 573–82.

49. ——, Beeman, A., and Lehmann, I. J., "Comparison of Organismic Age and Regression Equations in Predicting Achievement in Elementary School," *Journal of Educational Psychology*, XLIX (1958), 182–86.

50. ——, and Check, J., "Relationships Among Physical, Mental Achievement, and Personality Measures in Low, Average, and High Intelligence at 113 Months of Age," *American Journal of Mental Deficiency*, LXIII (1959), 1059–68.

51. Koppitz, Elizabeth M., *The Bender-Gestalt Test for Young Children* (New York: Grune and Stratton, 1964).

52. Magoun, H. W., *The Waking Brain* (Springfield, Ill.: Charles C Thomas, 1958).

53. Malpass, L. F., "Motor Proficiency in Institutionalized Retarded and Normal Children," *American Journal of Mental Deficiency*, LXIV (1960), 1012–15.

54. Namikas, G., and Archer, E. J., "Motor Skill Transfer as a Function of Inter-Transfer Test Difficulty," *Experimental Psychology*, LIX (1960), 109–12.

55. Oliver, J. N., "The Effect of Physical Conditioning Exercises and Activities on the Mental Characteristics of Educationally Subnormal Boys," *British Journal of Educational Psychology*, XXVIII (1958), 155–65.

56. Olson, W. C., *Child Development* (Boston: D. C. Heath, 1959).

57. Rarick, G. L., and McKee, R., "A Study of Twenty Third-Grade Children Exhibiting Extreme Levels of Achievement on Tests of Motor Proficiency," *Research Quarterly*, XX (1949), 142–52.

58. Reals, W. H., and Rees, R. G., "High School Letter Men—Their Intelligence and Scholarship," *School Revue*, XLVII (1959), 534–37.

59. Reynolds, W. F., and Chalmers, L. S., "Comparison of Normals and Subnormals in Mirror Drawing," *Journal of General Psychology*, LXXXVII (1955), 301–8.

60. Ryan, Dean E., "Relative Academic Achievement and Stabilometer Performance," *Research Quarterly*, XXXIV (1963), 185–90.

61. Seashore, H., "Some Relationship of Fine and Gross Motor Abilities," *Research Quarterly*, XIII (1942), 259–74.

62. Snoddy, L. M., and Shannon, J. R., "Standardized Achievement Measurements of Athletes and Nonathletes," *School Revue,* XLVIII (1939), 610–12.

63. Sloan, W., "Motor Proficiency and Intelligence," *American Journal of Mental Deficiency,* LV (1951), 394–406.

64. Sontag, L. W., Baker, C. J., and Nelson, V. L., "Mental Growth and Personality Development: A Longitudinal Study," *Monographs of the Society for Research in Child Development,* XXIII (1958), 1–143.

65. Steinhaus, Arthur, "The Role of Motor in Mental and Personality Development," *A Report-Symposium on Integrated Development* (Lafayette, Ind.: Purdue University, 1964).

66. Strong, C. H., "Motivation Related to Performance of Physical Fitness Test," *Research Quarterly,* XXXIV (1963), 497–507.

67. Teuber, Has-Lakas, "Exploring Brain Functions," National Institute of Mental Health Research Project Summaries, No. 2, Public Health Service Publications, No. 1208–2, 1965, 39–44.

68. Thurstone, Thelma Gwinn, "An Evaluation of Educating Mentally Handicapped Children in Special Classes and in Regular Classes," Cooperative Research Project Contrast #OE–SAE–6452, U. S. Office of Education, School of Education, University of North Carolina, 1959.

69. Travis, R. C., "An Experimental Analysis of Dynamic and Static Equilibrium," *Journal of Experimental Psychology,* XXXX (1945), 216–34.

70. Weber, R. J., "Relationships of Physical Fitness to Success in College and Personality," *Research Quarterly,* XXIV (1953), 471–74.

71. Woodworth, Robert S., and Sheehan, Mary R., *Contemporary Schools of Psychology* (New York: The Roland Press Corp., 1964).

MARIE R. LIBA[*]

and

MARGARET J. SAFRIT[†]

Forms and Functions
of Factor Analysis

"Order and simplification are the first steps toward the mastery of a subject—the actual enemy is the unknown." This quotation by Thomas Mann is given here not because it is unusual but because it states a belief common among those concerned with the expansion of knowledge. How is order achieved? Scientists would agree that a hypothesis can be studied experimentally and conclusions drawn about it. After many hypotheses have been tested, new hypotheses about higher-order relationships are formulated and these can be examined experimentally. In this approach, knowledge proceeds from the specific to the general. On the other hand, the general order of an area may itself be hypothesized on the basis of educated guesses. This over-all order (or orders) may be tested experimentally so that the investigator assesses the general accuracy of his ideas. This is followed by the systematic testing of many individual hypotheses to determine whether the over-all structure will survive repeated experimentation. This was Darwin's approach in formulating the theory of natural selection. Once the general theory was formulated, Darwin spent the rest of his life gathering evidence relevant to it. Significantly, Darwin's ideas are still called theories rather than laws, because of still-existing gaps in the supportive evidence. For scientific investigation which proceeds more along these lines, factor analysis is particularly well suited.

[*]Department of Physical Education—Women, University of Wisconsin.
[†]Department of Physical Education, University of Wisconsin, Milwaukee.

Centering a discussion around a particular methodology might seem to be undesirable. It may suggest too much emphasis on method and not enough on ideas. Sometimes, however, there is a class or category of problems for which a certain method is particularly suited. Should an investigator be studying a problem that falls into this category, this chapter may serve as a guide.

Factor analytic theorists have clearly established one category of problems for which factor analysis is particularly useful. Thurstone (25) described factor analysis as a method for discovering and identifying significant categories in a science. As an example, he suggested the resolution of the widely different achievements of individuals into a limited number of faculties. Holzinger and Harman (13) suggested that factor analysis is able to resolve a set of descriptive variables in terms of a small number of categories or factors in order to attain parsimony or economy of description. Thus, traditional factor analysis, which is largely exploratory in nature, can be used to arrive at substantive conclusions about important domains of individual differences. This application of factor analysis continues to be important today. And, although factor analysis can be used with other problems, this chapter will emphasize that purpose.

Since factor analysis has been used to explore the psychomotor domain, researchers in this area are aware of its value. What new ideas can a chapter such as this generate? Although the basic purpose of exploratory factor analysis remains unchanged, the methodology *has* changed. In fact, factor analysis has changed so rapidly that most of those who use it have not been able to keep up with the new developments. Recent developments in theory and method have been exceedingly fruitful in solving what were once recognized as extremely difficult problems. To some extent this can be attributed to the advent of electronic computers.

Kaiser (16) suggested that electronic computers would have great application to theoretical as well as practical problems and that the genius of such men as Guttman, Hotelling, and Thurstone might be capitalized upon more fully in the future because of the computer. His comments implied that factor analysis, which was then thought to be a mystical, half art, half science, would become a reputable method through the use of the high-speed computer. We believe that his prediction has largely been realized.

There is little doubt today that early factor analytic procedures, such as the centroid method for obtaining an initial solution laboriously computed on a desk calculator, and the graphic methods of rotation, are no longer appropriate. Walsh (26) suggests that these techniques are rapidly becoming extinct. Harman (5) points out that certain classical methods of factor analysis are now obsolete. In a discussion of recent

developments in factor analysis, Harris (10) indicated that certain procedures, although interesting in the history of factor analysis, no longer
have a substantial place in practice. It is to stress this new methodology
that this chapter is written.

Physical educators seem to hold two distinct points of view on factor
analysis. On the one hand, we have the proponents and users of factor
analysis techniques. There are a substantial number of reports in which
factor analysis was used to attack a specific problem. This group believes
that factor analysis can be used to add to scientific knowledge. On the
other hand, there are skeptics who doubt the findings because of the
method used. This group has kept up a running criticism. Their criticism
stems partly from their belief that, in order to discover new truths
about the world, one must take an inductive approach. Whether or
not any criticism of method continues to be relevant as the newer and
more sophisticated techniques come into general use remains to be seen.
It is not unlikely that the new procedures will largely vaporize the
old criticisms.

The authors wish to make two points clear. First, we wish to acknowledge our indebtedness to Professors Chester W. Harris and Henry F.
Kaiser of the Department of Educational Psychology of the University
of Wisconsin. Their influence on our thinking will become obvious as the
chapter develops. Second, the broad field of factor analysis includes many
important topics. Glass and Taylor (3) cite more than 75 books and
articles on factor analysis published since 1960. Thus, to the discerning
eye, there will be many omissions in this chapter. We hope to acquaint
the reader with some of the newer concepts, to suggest sources for fuller
treatment of these concepts, and to indicate some of the strategies that
can be used in factor analysis.

SOME DISTINCTIONS

Although many developments have taken place recently, there are a
number of traditional topics under which the newer techniques can be
included. Three of these broad topics—component and factor analysis,
derived solutions, and psychometric and statistical approaches to factor
analysis—are included here.

Component Analysis and Factor Analysis

The term *factor analysis* is often given to any multivariate model which
is applied to a large number of variables in order to obtain a parsi-
monious description of these variables. However, *factor analysis* more
accurately refers to one broad category of factor models; a second category is known as component analysis (see also Harris 1964).

The first stage of either factor or component analysis consists of determining the relationships among the variables by the Pearson product-moment correlation method. This procedure yields a correlation matrix with units ($r = 1.00$) in the central diagonal, since, except for the unreliability of measurement, any variable will correlate perfectly with itself. Factoring this matrix, or some transformation of it, is known as component analysis. In essence, all of the variance is analyzed. If, on the other hand, values known as communalities are inserted in the diagonals, the factoring is called factor analysis. This distinction is an important one (1, 10). Communality refers to the variance of the variable accounted for by all the common factors together. Usually the variance accounted for will be less than the total variance, leaving a residue to be uniquely accounted for by a specific factor.

The differences between component analysis and factor analysis are easily explained with a geometric description. Each variable is represented by a range of scores which are on a continuum. This continuum of scores can be called a vector, so that each variable is represented by a vector. If there are thirty variables, they can be identified in space by thirty vectors. The space in which these vectors lies can be called the *test space*. Let us assume that the thirty variables are being measured on three hundred individuals. Each of the individuals is also represented by a vector. These three hundred vectors form the *person space*. An excellent discussion of the geometric description is given by Thomson (24).

A component analysis is carried out within the test space, the area defined by the observed variables. The vectors which represent components exist within the test space, the vectors representing variables can be projected onto the component vectors. In this manner, component loadings (factor loadings) are determined.

Factor analysis can be described as taking place in the person space but outside the test space. Each vector representing a variable is projected onto each factor. These factors form the common-factor space.

Component Analysis

The primary objective in component analysis is to account for as much of the total variance as possible. When the observed data are reduced to matrix R, a correlation matrix with units in the diagonals, the complete set of components of R can be developed by some computing algorithm. (The components extracted by component analysis are analogous to the factors obtained in a factor analysis.) When this algorithm is a principal axis transformation the solution is known as a principal components solution of R. The data can also be linearly transformed in a particular fashion so that the component analysis on this transformation is an image analysis.

In the *principal components solution* (Hotelling, 14) successive components are extracted from the correlation matrix R. The factors are represented by the principal axes of the ellipsoids. The first general component accounts for a maximum amount of the total variance. The second component accounts for a maximum in the residual space with the first factor removed and so on, until the last component accounts for whatever variance remains. This model yields a number of factors equal to the number of observed variables.

When the data are reduced to a correlation matrix, the observed scores for the variables are scaled so that each variable has unit variance. If the data were rescaled into some form other than the correlation matrix R, the principal components model would yield a solution that is not related in any simple way to the solution obtained from R. In other words, the principal components analysis is not scale-free, which is a disadvantage of this model.

Frequently, an investigator will use an incomplete components analysis rather than the complete principal components model (17). The advantage of using an *incomplete* principal components analysis over the complete analysis is that the components accounting for only a small portion of the variance are discarded. The incomplete solution yields, for the first n components extracted, the same component scores as the complete solution and factor loadings that are proportional to those obtained in the complete solution. Although the original incomplete principal components solution ("Little Jiffy") is not scale-free, Kaiser (17) suggests a procedure by which it can be made scale-free.

Image analysis is another type of component analysis (10). According to Guttman's theory (4), any measurement can be represented by two uncorrelated parts: the image and the anti-image. The image of a variable can be predicted from the remaining n-1 variables. The anti-image is the unpredictable part.

Each image factor is represented by the projection of a variable into the subspace of the remaining n-1 variables. The anti-image is orthogonal to the image projection. The cosine of the angle between the variable and its respective projection into the space of the remaining n-1 variables is the same as the multiple correlation of that variable with the other n-1 variables.

The image model is applied to the image covariance matrix, a linear transformation of the correlation matrix. The image covariance matrix is characterized by squared multiple correlations in the diagonals and image covariances in the off-diagonals. The squared multiple correlations represent the correlation of each variable with the remaining n-1 variables. The image covariance is the amount of variance which is common to any two variables.

Image analysis is scale-free. The image matrix can be factored completely, giving as many factors as variables. Here again, the investigator may prefer to use the incomplete image model rather than the complete analysis (10). An *incomplete* image analysis à la Harris extracts m factors, m being the number of common factors determined by Guttman's strong lower bound. Incomplete image analysis, then, discards some factors which are extracted by complete image analysis.

Factor Analysis

Factor analysis models are constructed to yield a factor matrix which best fits the correlation matrix. From among the many factor analytic models, three will be discussed in this section: Rao's canonical factor analysis, the Jöreskog model, and alpha factor analysis. These factor analysis models have the advantage of being scale-free. The factor scores, however, cannot be computed exactly with these models; they can only be estimated.

Raos' canonical factor analysis model (21) is similar to Lawley's maximum likelihood solution, where the number of factors can be determined by statistical test. In fact, Rao's model is essentially the application of Lawley's factoring technique to the common-factor problem stated as a problem in canonical correlation. The canonical model involves the derivation of uncorrelated common factors which have the maximal canonical correlations with the observed variables. This model yields a scale-free solution.

In canonical factor analysis, the variables are rescaled in the unique (as contrasted to the common) portions of the data. The unique variances are estimated and then the roots are solved for, under the restriction of a hypothesized number of common factors. If the hypothesized number of factors is rejected by the statistical test, one additional factor is postulated and the process is begun again.

Since the number of common factors is determined by statistical test, this number may be a function of the size of the sample (10). Harris (7, 9) proposed a variant of the Rao solution. Guttman's strong lower bound is used to determine the minimum number of factors, rather than using Rao's statistical test. However, the form of Rao's solution is retained.

> The variant of Rao by way of Harris rescales the variables in the metric of the unique portion of the data, analyzes the rescaled data, and then transforms the results back into the original metric of the variables if that is desired, or into any other metric one wants, such as the equal-variance metric associated with standard scores. (10, p. 202)

Thus, through the Harris-Rao-Guttman solution, the number of common factors is determined by Guttman's strong lower bound, but any factor not significant by Rao's statistical test may be discarded.

In the *Jöreskog model* (15) the number of common factors is determined by a statistical test. According to Jöreskog, Lawley's general maximum likelihood solution is more efficient than the above model. However, the Lawley method is iterative, and thus involves an enormous amount of computation. Thus, the primary value of the Jöreskog solution lies in the fact that it closely approximates the Lawley solution without the use of iterative techniques.

Alpha factor analysis (19) allows one to make inferences about a population of variables from a sample of variables which has not necessarily been selected by random procedures. With this model, the variables are rescaled in the metric of the common portions of the data. This technique ensures that the factors extracted will have the maximum possible internal consistency in the classical test-theory sense. Consequently, this technique was named alpha factor analysis after Cronbach's internal consistency coefficient.

The rule for the number of factors is a psychometrically oriented one. ". . . if a common factor has nonpositive generalizability (if its associated eigenvalue is less than or equal to one), one may appropriately reject it" (19, p. 11). In other words, common factors are determined which successively have maximum reliability in the generalized Kuder-Richardson sense (17). Glass and Taylor (3) explain this characteristic of alpha factor analysis by pointing out that the factors extracted would have the maximum possible internal consistency in the classical test-theory sense. Thus, the factors that can be generalized to the universe of variables from which the sample of variables is drawn are retained. The number of alpha factors is a function of n, the number of observed variables as contrasted to statistically oriented factoring procedures where the number of factors is determined by the number of individuals in the sample.

Derived Solutions

When a factor model is applied to a set of data, an intitial solution is obtained. The factor matrix thus obtained provides a representation of the data which is at best difficult to interpret. Thurstone's criterion of simple structure (25) may be applied here—the factor pattern should consist of variables which have high loadings (or coefficients) on one factor, and low to zero loadings on the remaining factors. To approach this idea of a simple structure, the initial solution is rotated to yield a derived solution which may be either orthogonal or oblique. In orthogonal solutions, the factors are uncorrelated (axes are kept at right angles) and in oblique solutions, the factors are correlated.

The problem of orthogonal rotation has been adequately solved for some time (3, 5, 11, 18, 22). Several analytic methods for orthogonal rotations are available, however, the Kaiser varimax technique is often preferred since this is the only procedure that will not destroy the scale-free feature of an initial solution.

For the oblique case, earlier developments produced largely unsatisfactory results until a major breakthrough occurred with the developments by Harris and Kaiser (11) who showed how to obtain all possible oblique solutions by orthogonal rotations—certainly a novel idea. Their solution to the oblique rotation problem suggests that there are two classes of oblique solutions. One of these is appropriate when the common factor portions of a particular set of variables can be expressed as a set of independent clusters. Harris and Kaiser regard this type of derived solution as fundamental for every new problem since in studying various domains most research workers develop and use sets of variables in which the common portions of the variables *are* hypothesized to have the independent cluster pattern. For these, this particular procedure provides an unambiguous way to develop the information which supports or refutes the original hypothesis. This procedure will also reveal independent clusters when not originally hypothesized. For many sets of data this derived oblique solution would, therefore, provide a useful and meaningful interpretation of the data.

That the independent cluster solution for a set of data is not always a satisfactory oblique rotation was illustrated by Harris and Kaiser with the Thurstone Box problem.[1] A more satisfactory solution, however, was obtained by the application of a modified oblique procedure yielding a solution of the data which corresponded almost exactly to Thurstone's original subjective solution.

Another modification of the independent cluster procedure was illustrated by Harris (6) for a set of data originally developed and analyzed by Fleishman, Kremer, and Shoup (2). These data were reanalyzed by several factor and component models by Harris and Liba (12), and an independent cluster solution was obtained which was generally satisfactory although it contained some bipolar factors. The modification suggested by Harris, called Procrustes, fits a previously set up target matrix by a least squares procedure. The entire process can be repeated and several modifications obtained yielding eventually a derived solution that does exhibit less bipolarity and is, in this sense, a better one than that obtained by the first independent cluster solution.

Even more recently, Kaiser has developed a derived oblique solution which, for some sets of data, will yield a pattern matrix with a larger number of zero elements than the oblique independent cluster solution.

[1]The Thurstone Box Problem is a contrived example that has been used many times for "try-outs" of new procedures.

Kaiser calls this procedure Winsorizing. At the present time, no literature is available on this technique. However, the Winsorizing procedure is essentially an extension of the Harris-Kaiser orthoblique method.

One further characteristic of the oblique solutions provided by Harris and Kaiser should be commented upon. Some number of factors, depending upon the model, will be obtained for the initial solution of a set of data, and a derived solution, either orthogonal or oblique, can be obtained for that number of factors. However, it is also possible to obtain a derived oblique solution for any number of factors less than that originally obtained in the initial solution. This suggests interesting possibilities.

Consider a case in which for the alpha solution seven factors were obtained. Since the alpha solution provides either the right number of factors or possibly fewer, to rotate any number less than this is obviously inadvisable. Suppose, however, that for the same case an initial incomplete image solution à la Harris was also obtained and for that solution the number of factors was thirteen. Since this solution yields a number of factors which will be about one half the number of variables, this may be considered to approximate the maximum number desirable and a rotation of some number of factors less than this number would be logical. Thus for alpha we have seven (giving us the minimum number) and for the incomplete image we have thirteen (the maximum number) and we can now explore the factor structure for the derived solution for the number of factors ranging from seven to thirteen. For the image solution, then, the number of factors can be set at seven and a second derived oblique solution obtained; this process can be continued until the original maximum number of factors, thirteen, have been rotated. A comparison of these solutions should yield much more information about the nature of the variables studied than could be obtained without this procedure.

Psychometric and Statistical Approaches to Factor Analysis

A statistical tool is frequently used in order to make inferences from a sample to a population. Thus, a random sample of adequate size is drawn from a population of individuals. The sample is studied and inferences made. Such is the case when factor analysis is approached statistically. On the other hand, an investigator may want to make inferences about a domain of scientific content rather than a population of individuals. The psychometric approach to factor analysis consists of an attempt to infer the structure of a large battery or universe or domain of variables or tests on the basis of a limited sample of variables.

Using the statistical approach to factor analysis, the number of common factors is determined by a test of significance. Thus, one may be at the mercy of the power of this test. Harris explains,

> If [one is at the mercy of the power of this test] . . . then using the same variables but using a larger sample of individuals may lead to identifying more common factors. For some, this is an unpleasant possibility; surely the number of common factors should not be a function of the number of individuals tested but of the variables employed. (10, p. 201)

Because of this "unpleasant possibility," a great interest has been shown recently in psychometric inference.

Alpha factor analysis exemplifies a psychometric approach to factor analysis. The original Rao canonical factor analysis represents the statistical approach. However, the variant of Rao à la Harris employs a psychometrically oriented rule for determining the number of factors.

A STRATEGY

These suggestions on how to proceed in using factor analysis for the solution of particular kinds of questions are made tentatively, since the rapid increase of knowledge in this area may necessitate further expansion of the notions about strategy. Nonetheless they do now represent a major change in attack primarily in the emphasis placed on the application of more than one method to any set of data. This major change has the important concomitant of viewing the factors obtained by any one solution as interesting but unverified. The stress on comparing the results over solutions suggests greater flexibility in the interpretation of the factor structure of the variables studied. This may appear as though no definitive findings would ever result from such an approach. Quite to the contrary, we believe. This approach may finally yield the *most* definite conclusions about the underlying nature of a domain.

Selecting Initial Solutions

The data from a set of observed variables can be factored in a number of ways. In contrast to early applications of factor analysis where one method was used to analyze a set of data, the current point of view (and it is unlikely that this point of view will change substantially for some time) is that no one solution can possibly be judged as the "best" procedure. Harris (8) presents some potent arguments against advocating or using a single method. He suggests that the investigator choose among several computing algorithms that differ in principle but which can be applied objectively without undue interference in the process on the part of the investigator. Kaiser (17) expresses a clear preference for scale-free initial solutions and recommends the use of four: canonical factor analysis, alpha factor analysis, image analysis à la Harris, and principal components à la Kaiser ("Little Jiffy"). Regarding these four he says,

> I'm not going to reveal which of the four solutions discussed above is the right one; the question really is without meaning. I will say that four is a somewhat smaller number than the myriad of techniques one is confused by in the earlier literature. (17, p. 42)

Citing several writers, Glass and Taylor (3) suggest that the consensus is that four techniques (canonical and alpha factor analysis and principal components and image analysis) provide a core of methods with nearly impeccable psychometric qualifications and that at the present time the practitioner would do well to restrict his choice of an initial factoring method to this set of four.

The selection of models can be guided to some extent by the expected number of factors for particular initial solutions. Image analysis à la Harris and canonical factor analysis extract the greatest number of factors, usually about one half of the number of variables studied. Alpha factor analysis and principal components à la Kaiser, on the other hand, will yield a smaller number of factors, generally one third to one sixth of the number of variables. According to Kaiser (17), alpha (and "Little Jiffy"), in giving about the right number can sometimes give too few, and underfactoring can be a catastrophe. Harris (8) advocates the use of at least alpha and image analysis à la Harris since they differ markedly in the number of factors but tend to span whatever the unknown right number of factors is.

Present practices in the use of factor analytic methodology reflect a need for change. Glass and Taylor (3) surveyed the recent (1963–1966) factor analyses in four educational psychological research journals to determine the relative popularities of different factor analytic techniques. They found that in about one fourth of these too little information was given even to determine the techniques that were used, that the majority of the matrices were factored with units in the diagonal, and in only a few was an oblique rotation procedure used. They concluded that

> It appears that practitioners have "solved" the communality problem with a temerity that would surely make the theoretician blanch. With all due respect to the typical researcher's "no-nonsense, let's-get-the-job-done" approach, it would seem prudent to subject any collection of data to at least two different initial analyses (e.g., "Little Jiffy" and analysis of the image variance-covariance matrix or alpha and canonical factor analysis) and entertain the possibility that an oblique solution might possibly enhance interpretation of the results. (3, pp. 580–81)

Physical educators, who have had factor analyses published in the research quarterly since 1960, deserve some commendation for not being guilty of the "no information about procedures" inadequacy. Unfortunately, beyond this, the studies can be criticized on much the same grounds as those appearing in the journals reviewed by Glass and Taylor.

Once two or more models have been applied to a set of variables, the investigator can then make some comparisons over models. Three objective criteria can be used in making these comparisons. A measure of fit of the initial solution to the original correlations is determined by the average squared residual correlation. The average squared residual correlation is obtained by squaring the difference between R and FF' (excluding the diagonals), and dividing the sum of squares by the number of elements in the off-diagonals of either matrix. As FF' more closely approximates R, the better the fit. Harris (8) makes it clear, however, that none of the methods recommended so far minimizes this function. A method designed to do this (Minres) is described fully in the 1967 Harman book. A second comparison is possible for the mean communality for various methods (the well-known h^2). The mean communality refers to the proportion of the total variance extracted by any one model. Harris (8) suggests a third comparison in terms of what he calls the effective number of factors (defined arbitrarily as the number of factors for which at least one variable has a coefficient of .30 or greater). Similarly he speaks of effective common factors as factors with two or more variables with coefficients of .30 or more. In recent studies, both motor and mental performance data were analyzed by the four models recommended here and their operating characteristics were described (12, 23).

Selecting Derived Solutions

Having selected more than one method for obtaining an initial solution, the investigator is now faced with the choice of a rotation scheme to provide an interpretable analysis of a set of data. It would be more accurate to say rotation schemes, since, as in the selection of an initial model, no one rotation method can be considered most appropriate or best. Without considerable prior information about the nature of the data, it is desirable to obtain both an orthogonal and an oblique solution for each of the models selected. The selection of these should be from among the analytic procedures; the normal varimax provides a good orthogonal solution and the independent cluster procedure provides a most useful oblique solution. As a minimum, therefore, the researcher would have obtained four interpretations of a set of data—two derived solutions for each of two models. This approach would present a marked contrast to the now prevalent practice of obtaining an orthogonal derived solution for one mode of analysis and must be viewed as the single best counter-attack to some of the criticisms of factor analysis and its use in research. Thus, although, the investigator may at first balk at the vast amount of information which must now be dealt with, there is little doubt that such an attack will provide a much sounder basis for substantive conclusions about the structure of any particular domain.

As was indicated in the section on distinctions, the independent cluster oblique solution may be satisfactory for many kinds of data. It does not, however, always provide a completely interpretable factor structure, and the researcher may find it advisable to use one or more of the modifications suggested by Harris and Kaiser. At this point, we also wish to call attention again to the possibility of obtaining derived oblique solutions for factors ranging from the "minimum" number to the "maximum" number and studying these. Thus the investigator has four derived solutions which can be compared and a range of derived solutions for different numbers of factors which can also be compared. This has the distinctive feature of not only providing much more information about a given set of data but should suggest many new avenues for further study.

The most exciting possibility in this approach is the opportunity to begin to identify factors which will appear regardless of the method used. Such factors are robust or obtained independently of method and according to Harris (8) are the only ones that should be considered in making substantive conclusions about the nature of the domain. All others should remain tentative and be subjected to further study. Factors which are robust are not an artifact of the particular method used and should not be subjected to the same doubts as those obtained from one method of analysis. The ease and confidence with which such robust factors will be identified is not yet clear. Some factors will emerge that *will* be the same over all methods. As factors appear, however, which have a good bit of similarity over methods but which are nonetheless not identical in all respects, some subjectivity may enter the picture. This cannot be predicted and will not be known until such time that comparison of factors over methods becomes a common practice.

SOME CAUTIONS

Factor analysis now provides a powerful tool for studying a particular domain and its greatest justification, at least now, is as an exploratory technique. It is at the exploratory nature of factor analysis that a good many criticisms have been directed and justifiably so. How one interprets the meaning of exploratory is the crucial issue. Both Kaiser (17) and Kerlinger (20) make the following clear. The exploratory nature of factor analysis does not mean that a number of tests which are in common use are given to a group of persons yielding a "neat" correlation matrix which is then factor analyzed. The exploration of any domain begins with a set of variables which belong, at least in some logical sense, to the domain under study, but it is the precise structure of the domain that has remained obscure. Thus as Kaiser says ". . . factor analysis is an unpretentious 'bringer of order out of well-perceived chaos,' a technique which is capable of generating ideas rather than providing final answers" (17, p. 38).

The phrase "providing final answers" suggests a line of thought to be pursued briefly here. The results of factor analyses previously reported in physical education research have often been viewed as the "state of the world" for the particular area under investigation, either by the research worker himself, or, and much more frequently, by those who have attempted to summarize the results of these studies when writing articles or textbooks. Thus, the reader of the summary articles or textbook material is often "led to believe" that some particular complex behavior has been adequately dissected and described in one or more factor analyses. If this criticism has not been directed toward this state of affairs previously, it should have been. Note carefully that this criticism is not of the method but of the users and even more strongly of the second-level interpreters. As has been suggested, our confidence should be placed in those factors which are robust over methods and as yet these remain to be identified. It is certainly possible to entertain the idea that some of the results of previous factor studies will now be verified, and on this verification or on new findings will rest our more conclusive comments about the nature of the behaviors or domains investigated.

The naming of factors and the pitfalls in it now deserves some comment. Kerlinger (20) suggests that it is easy to name a factor and then to believe that there is reality behind the name. This has probably happened in physical education. We would like to suggest a healthy skepticism of entities such as "explosive strength" or "dynamic strength" to identify only two. Factor names are attempts by the investigator to focus on the essence of the variables represented in that factor and as such are very useful. They are always tentative and should be so viewed and should not in any sense be taken to describe a "real" phenomenon. We might adopt a policy of calling the factors A, B, and C (if this did not seem to be outlandish) or utilize any other systematic designation until such time that a factor has repeatedly emerged in various factor studies and has shown to be robust over methods. Then, and only then, might a label be applied and still with some degree of tentativeness. It is not the label that is important but the underlying grouping of variables, and the precise nature of this grouping is not always readily discernible. Finally, it might be cheekily suggested that when a factor emerges from a study of a particular domain and to it is attached the label of original domain investigated not only has a desperation label been applied but the basic rationale for the exploration of a domain must be somewhat faulty.

As the closing section to this discussion, we might turn our attention to one last criticism of factor analysis which many have heard expressed frequently—you only get out of it what you put into it. Fortunately, this is true, and we hold that no procedure should be deprecated on this account. Getting more out of something than one puts into it has the flavor of the unacceptable. Suppose a researcher designed a study to determine the effect of manipulating variables a and b upon some characteristic. There is no way for that researcher to make any generalizations about the effects of variables c to z on that characteristic, nor does the competent investigator attempt to do so. How does factor analysis differ in its scope from such a study? A study is delimited no matter what the particular design and method employed to analyze the data. Of course, the exploratory nature of factor analysis, wherein one attempts to study the nature of a domain, might be the reason for the critical comments. Yet this is unjustified. There is still a particular domain or aspect of the domain, some behavioral attribute to be studied and the investigator makes no claims beyond this. There must be a beginning and since, in general, there is no complete a priori information about the nature of the domain or there would be no need for factor analytic exploration, whatever small segment is chosen for study should begin to add to substantive knowledge about the larger domain of concern. Thurstone (25, pp. 53–54) expresses this point eruditely, providing an appropriate ending to this chapter.

> Each generalization in the scientific description of nature results in a loss in the extent to which the ideal constructs of science match the individual events of experience. This is illustrated by simple experiments with a pendulum, in which the mass, the period, and the locus of the center of gravity with reference to a fulcrum are involved in the ideal construct that leads to experimental verification. But the construct matches only incompletely the corresponding experimental situation. The construct says nothing about the rusty screw and other extraneous detail. From the viewpoint of immediate experience, scientific description is necessarily incomplete. . . .
>
> Every scientific construct limits itself to specific variables without any pretense of covering those aspects of a class of phenomena about which it has said nothing.

REFERENCES

1. Cattell, Raymond B., "Factor Analysis: An Introduction to Essentials I. The Purpose and Underlying Models." *Biometrics*, XXI (1965), 190–215.

2. Fleishman, Edwin A., Kremer, Elmar J., and Shoup, Guy W., *The Dimensions of Physical Fitness—a Factor Analysis of Strength Tests.* Office of Naval Research, Contract Non R. 609(32) Technical Report 2. (New Haven: Yale University, 1961).

3. Glass, Gene V., and Taylor, Peter A., "Factor Analytic Methodology." *Review of Educational Research,* XXXVI (1966), 566–87.

4. Guttman, Louis, "Image Theory for the Structure of Quantitative Variates." *Psychometrika,* XVIII (1953), 277–96.

5. Harman, Harry H., *Modern Factor Analysis* (Chicago: The University of Chicago Press, 1967).

6. Harris, Chester W., "A Modified Harris-Kaiser Oblique Solution for Factor Analysis." Paper presented at Research Section, AAHPER Meeting, Las Vegas, Nev., March, 1967.

7. ———, "Canonical Factor Models for the Description of Change," in Chester W. Harris, (ed.), *Problems in Measuring Change* (Madison, Wisc.: University of Wisconsin Press, 1963).

8. ———, "On Factors and Factor Scores." *Psychometrika,* in press.

9. ———, "Some Rao-Guttman Relationships." *Psychometrika* XXVII (1962), 247–63.

10. ———, "Some Recent Developments in Factor Analysis." *Educational and Psychological Measurement,* XXIV (1964), 193–206.

11. ———, and Kaiser, Henry F., "Oblique Factor Analytic Solutions by Orthogonal Transformations." *Psychometrika,* XXIX (1964), 347–62.

12. ———, and Liba, Marie R., *Component, Image and Factor Analysis of Tests of Intellect and of Motor Performance.* Cooperative Research Project No. S-192-64, Office of Education, Department of Health, Education and Welfare, 1965.

13. Holzinger, Karl J., and Harman, Harry H., *Factor Analysis.* (Chicago: Chicago Press, 1941).

14. Hotelling, Harold, "Analysis of a Complex of Statistical Variables into Principal Components." *Journal of Psychology,* XXIV (1933), 417–41.

15. Jöreskog, K. G., *Statistical Estimation in Factor Analysis* (Stockholm: Almqvist and Wiksell, 1963).

16. Kaiser, Henry F., "The Application of Electronic Computers to Factor Analysis." *Educational and Psychological Measurement* XX (1960), 141–51.

17. ———, "Psychometric Approaches to Factor Analysis," in *Invitational Conference on Testing Problems,* (Princeton, N.J.: Educational Testing Service, 1964), pp. 37–45.

18. ———, "The Varimax Criterion for Analytic Rotation in Factor Analysis." *Psychometrika,* XXIII (1958), 187–200.

19. ———, and Caffrey, John, "Alpha Factor Analysis." *Psychometrika,* XXX (1965), 1–14.

20. Kerlinger, Fred N., *Foundations of Behavioral Research* (New York: Holt, Rinehart, and Winston, Inc., 1965), chapter 36.

21. Rao, C. R., "Estimation and Tests of Significance in Factor Analysis." *Psychometrika,* XX (1955), 93–111.

22. Regan, Mary C., "Development and Classification of Models for Multivariate Analysis." *Educational and Psychological Measurement* XXV (1965), 997–1010.

23. Safrit, Margaret J., *The Structure of Gross Motor Skill Patterns,* Cooperative Research Project No. S-397, Office of Education, U.S. Department of Health, Education, and Welfare, 1966.

24. Thomson, Geoffrey H., *The Factorial Analysis of Human Ability* (New York: Houghton Mifflin Co., 1951).

25. Thurstone, L. L., *Multiple Factor Analysis* (Chicago: University of Chicago Press, 1947).

26. Walsh, James A., "Review of Baggley's 'Intermediate Correlational Methods.'" *Educational and Psychological Measurement* XXV (1965), 925–27.

ROBERT M. MALINA*

An Anthropological Perspective
of Man in Action

Movement is a distinguishing characteristic of life. Physical educators have usually been chiefly interested in the processes and products of movement. They haven't considered its impact on the individual himself or on man as a biocultural organism shaped by and adapted to cultural influences.

It is first necessary to consider some of the concepts of current anthropological theory, and to define physical activity and physical education. *Physical activity* and *physical education* are frequently treated as synonyms, but they are not. *Physical activity* is defined as the movement of the body in the context of voluntary free exercise, play, games, sports, or dance. *Physical education,* is defined as the use of physical activity for the achievement of educational objectives, either directly or indirectly. Two of the most frequently cited objectives of physical education fall within the category of organic fitness—the ability to meet the physical stresses of daily living without undue fatigue, and the development of a repertoire of neuromuscular skills.

Anthropology can be divided into two categories, physical and cultural, both of which represent extremes of a continuum—man. The former concentrates on the biological, organic nature of man, and the latter on his

*Department of Anthropology, University of Texas. I am grateful to Dr. Wilton M. Krogman and Dr. Loren S. Eiseley at the University of Pennsylvania for their critiques and suggestions in the preparation of this paper, written while I was an NIDR trainee, under grant No. USPHS 5 T1 DE109-04.

nonbiological nature, his unique capacity for culture, which is derived essentially from his ability to handle symbolism and language. Since man is the object of study in both categories, the line of demarcation between the two cannot be neatly drawn. Instead, they are interrelated and interdependent, a fact clearly evident because they share the same basic aim: an understanding of man's adaptation to, and control of, his natural, man-made, and social environments (8, 39).

Since the biological and cultural aspects of man have the same ultimate function, they are integral to human evolution. Man's evolution, however, is unique in the "man and culture originated simultaneously" (39, p. 5). With the emergence of language and culture man branched into a societal type of evolution different from that of the animals around him and different from that of his ancestors the primates.

Current biological evolutionary theory is synthetic and essentially genetic, viewing evolution as changes in the genetic composition of populations (16). Modern cultural evolutionism divides these changes into the general and the specific, the latter, with which we are more concerned, being a series of adaptive sequences in particular cultures (28). The similarity of biological and cultural evolution suggests that a comparison of the two will aid our understanding of the complexities and mechanisms of human evolution. There are four primary organic evolutionary processes: natural selection, mutation, gene flow (migration), and genetic drift (16). These four processes have strikingly similar counterparts in culture change: cultural selection, invention and discovery, diffusion and acculturation, and cultural drift (14, 28). These processes are essentially mechanisms for introducing variability into populations and cultures. They do not, however, act in isolation, but constantly interact to bring about the adaptation of man to his environments. For example, the Alakaluf Indians of Tierra del Fuego, with a slight material culture, adapt to the rigors of their cold climate primarily by an increased metabolic rate (7). On the other hand, the Eskimos adapt to the cold with a slightly increased metabolic rate but also have special clothing, a cultural feature. Incidentally, among some Eskimo peoples the motor skill of sewing a parka is an important selective factor in the choice of wives by the males. The variability caused by the interaction of biological and cultural mechanisms is of major concern to anthropologists for it represents the essence of human evolution.

Human variation, both biological and cultural, is continuously distributed over the globe. Anthropologists attempt to organize this diversity in a meaningful manner, both biologically and culturally. Both types of organization must reflect reality, be it genetic or cultural, and take into account man's ability to symbolize, his biological make-up, his basic needs for maintenance and survival, and his social structures, political organizations, and the like.

Man's biological and cultural heritage is adaptive, permitting him to interact with his environments and thus become fitted to them. The adaptive process obviously has a genetic component since all organisms are adapted for a mode of living characteristic of their particular species or subspecies and suitable to their environmental conditions. On the other hand, adaptation is also plastic since individuals and populations encounter environmental fluctuations to which they must adapt. Modifications in the organism caused by this plasticity are no less adaptive than genetic adaptations. Nevertheless, the genetic and plastic components of adaptation are intimately related, for an organism can adapt itself only within the limits set by its genetic endowment.

Culture, sometimes called the extrabiological method of adaptation, plays an extremely important role in man's adaptability to his varied environments. Culture itself, however, has a biological basis, since "there is no culture without human genes" (9, p. 93), and since it is the biological organism, regardless of his cultural heritage, that must adapt. Culture, with its greater flexibility and capacity for rapid change, is probably a more potent and efficacious mechanism than genetic change in meeting the adaptive challenges presented by man's environments (9).

It is within this perspective of man as a biocultural organism that the role of physical activity, as a part of man's adaptive apparatus, must be understood. The physical activity of man, however, is dependent upon, conditioned by, and adapted to cultural influences. Activities are performed within the local cultural pattern, which, as the consensus of individual behavior patterns, has coherence, continuity, and distinctive form. It must be recognized that such patterns have multiple dimensions, representing both overt and covert behavior. In addition, the conditions that maintain these cultural codes of physical activity, and the means by which they operate in different cultures, must be determined if the role of physical activity as a part of man's adaptive apparatus, must be properly understood. Similarly, it is essential that physical educators realize that whatever talents or skills a performer may have, his ability and creativeness will express itself within the limits laid down by his culture. Thus, the role of physical activity must be understood in terms of the traditions and sanctions (essentially standards) laid down by a particular culture.

Although all sciences have traditional methods of gathering, organizing, and analyzing data, the manner in which a science uses the available data to solve problems and indicate directions for new research is a measure of its effectiveness. Most physical educators have usually not made complete use of their resources and potential in the anthropological realm. Several researchers (17, 20) have attempted so-called cultural anthropology studies, only to fall short because they used the extremely narrow approach of treating culture more in the sense of the fine arts or the "cultured" person, and trying to equate art and sport, rather than treating culture as a societal phenomenon. According to Maheu (20, p. 31), for example, "The first thing to be said is that if we take culture in the sense of any of its forms of expression, present contacts between it and sport are extremely slight, in fact practically nonexistent." Sport, however, is accepted by society almost to the point of ritual as can be seen in the opening of the Olympic Games, on football weekends, and in television coverage. Certainly sport is a part of our cultural pattern. Sports, games, dance, and their varied forms of expression in different cultures *are* culturally acceptable.

Several researchers have approached the cultural manifestations of physical activity more comprehensively. Stumpf and Cozens (33, 34) and Dunlap (10) analyzed the role of games, sports, and recreational activities in three Pacific cultures, the New Zealand Maoris, the Fijians, and the Samoans, and clearly illustrated the vital role of these activities in the total cultural patterns of these societies. Although these earlier studies, essentially descriptive, have shown both generalized and specific roles for physical activities in the three cultural settings, further studies of different populations and studies using updated techniques of data collection and analysis are necessary. If physical education is to take its place among the scientific and social disciplines that study man, the need for the study of man in action in a variety of cultural settings is apparent. Such cross-cultural approaches must take into consideration as many aspects of the population under study as possible. They must realize that groups exist in unique sets of conditions, each one shaping the total adaptation of the individual and his society to their environment. Furthermore, all the facts about the population and its environmental setting should be considered if reasonably accurate conclusions are to be drawn. Researchers must also realize that alternate paths of adaptation are frequently open to different cultures as well as to individuals within these cultures, so that variability is the rule rather than the exception. In addition, if it is desirable to study the role of physical activity in the varied cultures of the world, especially those preliterate cultures still in existence, such studies must necessarily proceed rapidly.

The spread of technological advancement into areas populated by indigenous peoples will eventually result in genetic and cultural amalgamation. This applies not only to the spread of Western culture, but also to the breakdown of social and geographical barriers, between and among indigenous peoples. These advances have lessened the impact of the natural environment and are creating perhaps the most dynamic civilization man has ever known. The vast and interconnected technology of our times, a structure created essentially by science, is sweeping into itself, like a whirlpool, all the different societies and cultures of the world. What is the impact of technology on other cultures? What is its impact on our American culture? How can we best adapt programs of physical education to meet the demands imposed by technology. These and other questions are of prime concern, and physical education is in an ideal position to seek answers.

THE PHYSICAL STATUS OF MAN—AN EVOLUTIONARY VIEW

The human body is essentially a complex of bone levers whose position and movement is controlled by muscular actions integrated by the central nervous system. The physical structure of man has not materially changed since the early days of human evolution. Except for the remarkable expansion of the skull to house the rapidly developing brain and related structures, the limb skeleton of man has not changed markedly over time. In fact, the limb bones of pre-sapiens man (*Homo erectus*) had already achieved the morphology and proportions of *Homo sapiens* (6). However, although man's biological evolution has apparently decelerated, his sociocultural evolution has proceeded very rapidly with little sign of deceleration so far. This rapid continuation of man's sociocultural progress with little if any change in his physical mechanism poses an important question: How long can man sustain his rapid sociocultural advancement on the same biological base? Do the diseases of modern society, especially cardiovascular disease, suggest signs of breakdown in man's physical machinery? The increasing frequency of degenerative heart disease, obesity, anxiety syndromes, and the like undoubtedly reflect the change in our way of life imposed by rapid technological advance. For example, in the United States the amount of food consumed per capita far exceeds the amount of energy expended, which means either that the population is overfed or underactive. Perhaps one of the chief means of countering the diseases of modern society is with regimes of sensible living in which physical activity is an integral part. Although genetic factors are implicated in many of the prevalent diseases, the available evidence suggests that a reasonable regime of daily physical activity coupled with moderation in food intake will aid in the prevention of at least degenerative heart disease and obesity, not to mention built-up anxieties and tensions.

To view physical activity as a panacea for all the ills of modern technological society, however, is myopic. What is needed instead, is a careful consideration of how physical activity can offset the deleterious effects of the sedentary way of life imposed by scientific advances. The problem is where to start!

The notion that regular participation in physical activities during childhood tends to persist into the activity patterns of adults is reasonably well established. Although adults can develop new activity habits, the overwhelming tendency is a reversion to familiar activities, most of which are team sports cast in interscholastic settings. Consequently, it is essential to be concerned with the determinants of physical activity during the growing years, for it is at this level that the roots of many of our adult problems lie.

MOTOR DOMAIN OF PHYSICAL EDUCATION

The vast majority of the child's early experiences with his environment are mediated primarily through motor channels, and it is within this motor sphere that the principal domain of physical education lies. Motor activities are too often seen only in terms of their products and processes. Equally important are the determinants of such motor acts, both biological (genetic) and cultural, as well as the interaction and interrelation of the two within the developing biocultural individual. Take, for example, the skill of walking, which is the base upon which many more highly refined patterns of movement are superimposed. All children, barring significant developmental retardation, learn to walk within relatively narrow age limits without specific training practices and in spite of the restriction of being cradled for long periods of time. Thus there appears to be some inborn control over the child's motor development. What are these controls or determinants?

Unfortunately, we cannot yet observe and isolate specific genes. Instead we must use indirect evidence from twin studies, parental relationships, and population differences to infer the genetic controls of motor development. Evidence from twin studies (11) suggests a greater similarity in early motor behavior as measured by the Bayley scales among monozygotic (identical) twins than among dizygotic (fraternal) twins. Studies of parent size and build (12) show these to be significant factors in the early motor development of the child. Children born of large parents, both in size and build, tend to be not only larger and heavier, but also advanced in skeletal ossification status as well as in the development of gross motor and manipulative skills during the first three years of life. As for population or racial differences, Negro children both in the United States and Africa show an acceleration in skeletal maturation status and in motor development during the first year or two of life (37). Some evidence among American Negroes suggests that this advancement persists through three years of age in gross motor skills and four years of age in manipulative skills (31). Eventually, however, Negro children decelerate or white children accelerate in their rates of skeletal and motor development so that there is little if any difference between the groups. The basis for these results is not clear. Undoubtedly a genetic factor or factors operate since these motor differences appear at or soon after birth. As postnatal growth and development proceeds, however, child-rearing practices must be considered, and are probably extremely important in directing the motor pursuits of children. Perhaps homes with more permissive atmospheres provide the child with greater freedom to exercise his newly acquired and rapidly developing motor powers.

It is apparent, therefore, that the child's motor development has in part a genetic basis. It is equally apparent, however, that cultural influences become increasingly more important as the child grows. For example, Scarr (29) noted a relatively high heritability estimate (40 per cent) for number of activities selected by monozygotic over dizygotic twin girls 6 through 10 years of age, suggesting that activity motivation in terms of activities selected is in part determined by genetic factors. No such concordance, however, was evident in the specific kinds of activities selected, such as sedentary versus active, indicating the operation of nongenetic factors. These influences operate only within the limits and sanctions of the specific cultural pattern (in the case of peer-group standards, for example, a subcultural pattern), and within the limits and potential established by the child's genetic endowment.

No one will deny that children have the potential to learn and develop a series of fundamental motor skills. To what extent are these skills genetically based and to what extent are they influenced by the cultural pattern in which the child is reared? What are the influences of different child-rearing practices on subsequent motor development and performance? These are problems which need careful consideration if physical education is to be effective in developing a repertoire of neuromuscular skills. These skills are related not only to the child's developmental status, which itself has a genetic basis, but also to his cultural background. Styles of balance development, for example, vary with cultural settings. Among the mountain dwelling, land-locked Fore and Gimi of the Eastern Highlands of East New Guinea, balance develops differently than it does among the coastal Asmat and Kayagar on the southern tidal plain of West New Guinea. The coastal people have a canoe-dependent culture and children learn to balance at an early age standing upright in the long, narrow, canoes (32). Although this example is an extreme situation, it illustrates the cultural dependence of some types of motor activities.

Similarly, patterns and techniques of jumping, running, climbing, throwing, tumbling, and activities incorporating complex sequences of these skills vary from culture to culture, from age group to age group, and between the sexes. How are these skills learned in different cultural settings? How do age and sex differences affect their performance? How do local cultural factors influence performance? Which of the motor skills are standardized across cultures and which are not? What are these activities used for—subsistence, free play, games, sports, ritual? To what extent do the limits imposed by various cultural sanctions permit varied expression of such skills? These questions and many others should be of concern to those interested in the motor development of children, particularly if cross-cultural studies are to be considered.

Physical educators have not studied motor performance cross-culturally, except for several comparisons of "fitness" between American, European, and Japanese children (4, 15, 18). In these studies, the tests of performance were developed for American children. In addition, the samples were drawn from technologically advanced, or "westernized," cultural backgrounds. There have also been some studies on comparative physical education, but they were aimed primarily at program differences, in spite of the fact that many primitive cultures have no formal schooling and no programs of physical education.

Many of the studies in physical education have been narrow in approach, concerned primarily with some measurable product of motor performance, such as the distance jumped under rigorously controlled conditions. No one will deny the value of such rigorously controlled studies, especially in our standard-conscious American culture, a veritable "cult of the average." Nevertheless, more attention should be devoted to the cultural context within which activities are performed and to the development of culture-free (if such a concept exists) tests of performance. Certainly, more adequate methods of studying cross-cultural motor performance are needed. Perhaps physical educators and anthropologists should adopt the techniques of cross-cultural studies of personality development, such as the strategy of convergent validation suggested by LeVine (19).

In the matter of method, the motion picture is a potent tool for cross-cultural studies of motor development and performance. Sorenson and Gajdusek (32) highly recommend the use of films in ethnopediatric research as way of providing a permanent record for future study and for identifying universal styles or unusual components of child behavior in various cultural settings. A number of studies in which the motion picture technique was used to examine patterns of development in fundamental motor skills were recently summarized by Glassow, Halverson, and Rarick (13). For the most part, these studies were limited to small samples of midwestern white children, but the method should certainly be applied in different cultural settings if a complete understanding of motor development is to be achieved.

Although cinematographical procedures are currently popular in physical education research, they have been used primarily to analyze various athletic skills. Although they have undoubtedly contributed much to the development of improved techniques of athletic performance at highly specialized levels, physical educators should realize that their prime responsibility is to the child. It is during the growing years that those differences which characterize adults as well as different populations make their appearance.

CULTURAL UNIVERSALS

Play, games, athletic sports, and dances have been recognized as universal to cultures the world over (23), as have been the elements of education, social organization, technology, economics, and the like. It appears, however, that in some culture complexes, the universals recognized as play, games, sports, and dance are intricately woven into the total cultural pattern so that they are essential to the realization of other elements classified as universal. Yet in some societies, exercise for the sake of exercise is nonexistent among adults. Instead, work is the only exercise. In such cultures, usually subsistence economies, physical activity is not artificial, but pragmatic. Even these cultures, however, do include physical activity in the form of dance or athletic activities as integral parts of other elements in the culture complex.

Before discussing physical activity relative to other cultural elements, it is necessary to consider first the possible role of geographical and ecological factors as conditioners or determinants of physical activity pursuits. Obviously, geographical barriers are no longer as important as they were in the earlier history of mankind. Nevertheless, the setting in which a people lives does exert an influence on the activities of that society. Some evidence suggests a possible relationship between physical environment and activity patterns in the form of games. Roberts, Arth, and Bush (27), in an analysis of game types (physical skill, strategy and chance) in 50 societies throughout the world, report a relationship between geographical location and the number of games of physical skill. The authors observed that of 23 tribes inhabiting territories within 20° latitude of the equator, 18 had fewer than five games of physical skill, while of 24 tribes residing more than 20° latitude north or south of the Equator, only 9 had fewer than five games of physical skill. A preliminary analysis of the relationship between dietary composition (especially protein and fat) and mean annual temperature suggests a possible association between environment and physical activity as expressed in games of physical skill. Similarly, terrain and altitude are possibly factors of importance in the remarkable physical endurance of Tarahumara Indians as demonstrated in their kickball racing activities (1). Thus, geographical and ecological factors, though frequently passed-off as unimportant, remain potentially influential and deserve further study.

It is interesting to observe that man, during the course of his evolution, has spread into a wide range of environments, including the extremes of heat, cold, and altitude. The climatic stresses, primarily physiological, imposed by these environmental extremes have been and still are potent forces guiding the direction of ongoing human evolution. In fact, it is within the limits of these three environmental extremes that land mammals, including man, are rather rigorously selected for their abilities to resist climatic stress (7). However, cultural attitudes and values, as well as patterns of behavior, are influential in determining the tolerance of a population to these environmental stresses. This tolerance, in turn, undoubtedly influences the activity patterns of the residents.

Cultures the world over perform certain functions essential for their survival. Biological adequacy is essentially a fitness to perform the tasks necessary to maintain the society. In other words, people must be healthy enough to meet the rigors of daily life and to perform the functions necessary for survival. It is in this context that many forms of physical activity derive their basis, so that the activity patterns meet the needs of the culture. In some settings, as a matter of fact, the ideal of physical fitness is related to the maintenance of leadership within the group. Among the Chiricahua society, for example, the theme of "validation by participation" predominates (24). A leader's role among the Chiricahua is related to his actual performance in warfare, hunting, and raiding, and he maintains this position so long as he is physically fit and active. When old age and reduced health and deterioration in fitness set in, the leader's position and effectiveness is challenged (regardless of the wisdom of old age) and someone younger and more fit for the task takes over. Thus, the organic fitness of group members is universally essential to fulfilling the needs of the society.

Perhaps the simplest way to evaluate the place of physical activity in a particular culture is to check the items of their material culture (technology) that are devoted to games, sports, and similar activities. Osgood (25), for example, classified 22 of 339 elements (approximately 6.49 per cent) of Ingalik Indian material culture as items for "toys and games." It should be noted however, that one of the 22 categories, that classified as "miscellaneous game implements," contained 20 specific game items. Such figures may be misleading since elements classified for other aspects of the culture, such as weapons and travel, ceremonial, and puberty paraphernalia, may be important elements in the physical activity pursuits characteristic of the people. Although the use of such elements may be inferred from their presence in the material culture, this does not tell us anything of the frequency or manner of use, the intensity and duration of participation, or related factors. Along similar lines, the use of archaeological techniques and data as a way of discovering the history of sports, games, and other activities in earlier cultures is highly promising (21).

Physical activity has great relevance in the dynamics of social organization and education in many cultural settings. Imitative play is the way children in most primitive, preliterate cultures acquire proficiency in motor skills, many of which reflect the domestic tasks, interest, and needs of the particular society. The play activities of the Mbuti pygmies, for example, are essentially an imitation of the society's hunting and gathering activity (38). In many societies, it is largely through imitative play that the individual is patterned for the culture he lives in, in contrast to the formal educative schooling of Western societies.

Play is a universal aspect of development, although it is highly dependent on the cultural setting in which the child is reared. As children develop, play behavior becomes more highly refined and may take the form of games of varying complexity. It is beyond the scope of this chapter to define games; suffice it to say that games are not equivalent to play (26, 27), and are an integral part, not only of play, but also, in many societies of the dynamics of socialization and child rearing.

In a cross-cultural study of 56 societies, Roberts and Sutton-Smith (26) noted a relationship between child-rearing practices and game patterns. Using a threefold division of games into those of chance, strategy, and physical skill, the authors showed that games of physical skill were significantly related to child-training practices that emphasized reward for and frequency of achievement, and that such games of physical skill were frequently used on the tribal level as training techniques in hunting activities. Although many cross-cultural and intracultural differences were apparent in their analysis, games of physical skill were definitely related to training for achievement, with games of strategy and chance related to training in obedience and responsibility respectively. Such observations certainly emphasize the interrelatedness of game behavior, variations in child-training practices, and general cultural demands. Of particular concern in this regard is the highly competitive nature of our success-oriented American culture. Early in the life of American children, the spirit of competitive self-enhancement and success styles are well engrained. Boys 8 through 12 years of age, the age during which competitive activities predominate, are already able to distinguish various success styles, that is, success through strategy, power, or a combination of the two. Girls, on the other hand, tend to distinguish only between those who succeed through good fortune and those who fail (35).

Further, these success styles are related to the patterns of child-rearing, and to the games played, especially in the case of boys. Other evidence from the same authors (36) demonstrates similar interrelationships of child-training variables, game-playing behavior, and general cultural variables in the game involvement of adults.

The role of play, games, sports, and dance as media for socialization and as channels of expression is obvious enough. More important is the relationship of such activities to group loyalty and solidarity, a sort of collective societal identity, intricately related to theories of ritual, rites of initiation, and training for survival and war in many primitive societies.[1] The use of athletic activities in puberty rites is well documented. Monge's illuminating account of natural acclimatization in the Andes (22) clearly illustrates the role of running events and training in running in the initiation rites of the Highland Indians. Similarly, feats of courage and strength, drills in dancing, hunting, and warfare, as well as demonstrations of remarkable physical endurance are characteristic of puberty rites in many societies the world over. The vast majority of such demonstrations of athletic prowess are restricted primarily to males, indicating perhaps the need for the male to prove himself since he lacks a clearcut physiological indicator of adulthood, as menarche is in females. It must also be recognized that such "rites of passage" are intricately related to the educative process, the transmission of cultural heritage and cultural expectations to the future societal leaders. Many of these rites last several months, a reasonably good indicator of the degree and severity of the training involved. It may be speculated that the great emphasis on junior and senior high school athletics in contemporary American society represents a sort of "rite of passage" for adolescent males, an opportunity for them to prove their manliness.

The preparation for war among many primitives involved an athletic type of training regime for the development of the skills necessary in battle and in fitness for survival, accompanied by numerous ceremonial events geared to the development, maintenance, and arousal of tribal loyalty. If one observes the preparation for an American football game, the highly secret preparation of game plans and tactical maneuvers, community pep rallies, and so forth, one can easily notice many patterns of behavior analogous to tribal preparations for war. In fact, the role of games and sports as a medium for the resolution of conflict has not been thoroughly explored. Similarly, with intertribal warfare practically extinct in most corners of the world, the rise of games and athletic events as war surrogates in some societies is remarkable. Perhaps with the warpath eliminated as a way to demonstrate prowess, status, and prestige, as well

---

[1]In this context, it is interesting to note that Neanderthal Man apparently utilized the highly refined motor skill of tossing clay pellets at a target as a "magic ceremony" (3).

as a medium for the release of out-group aggression, games and sports provide socially acceptable avenues for such achievement and tension release. Among the modern Zulu (30), for example, older patterns of war organization, sorcery, and magic have been superimposed on the sport of soccer, a relatively recent import, so that an entire cycle of ceremonial activity surrounds its adoption into the modern Zulu way of life. The position of games and sports as potential conflict surrogates in many societies is clearly expressed by Chapple and Coon (5, p. 635):

> A game canalizes potential conflict . . . by bringing about interaction at a high frequency but within the rhythmic order imposed by the techniques. Games thus prevent conflicts; they provide regular opportunities for interaction within habitual techniques by using well-known symbols, and this provides a constant framework for interaction. In this way games provide one of the most important means of preserving equilibrium in a society . . .

Although play, games, sports, and dance are cultural universals in their own right, their interrelationships with other facets of the cultural pattern is indeed remarkable. It is beyond the scope of this chapter to discuss sport and dance in the aesthetic aspects of community life. Suffice it to say that in many cultures the dance forms, as well as the artistic depictions of motor feats, are dynamic expressions of the place of such activities in the total cultural complex. Physical activities as manifested in free play, games, sports, and dance are not only integral parts of the cultural pattern of most peoples, but also provide an ideal tool for the study of such problems as: culture change in light of increased culture contact throughout the world; games as war surrogates in the problem of conflict resolution; theories of ritual and initiation rites; the dynamics of social organization involving educational practices and personality development; and, in view of the rise in professional sports and international athletic competition, their role in contributing to the economic development of the people. Nevertheless, it is imperative that such studies consider as much of the total setting of the people as possible.

Studying the physical activity for its own sake is basically sound, but to fully elucidate its role in preliterate and modern societies requires a global view. With the widespread popularity of Western sports and the rapidity with which they are being incorporated into a variety of cultural patterns the world over, the time is more than ripe for interdisciplinary study. It must be cautioned, however, that many aboriginals are at home in their own cultural setting and may lose interest when their culture is displaced, as occurs in instances of rapid technological turnover. Games, sports, and dance can help preserve native forms of activity and recreation which can be beneficially adapted to the alterations in daily life and cultural patterns induced by technological change.

CONCLUSION

Considering that man's capacity for culture is derived from his ability for symbolic thought and language, what is the meaning of movement and performance to man? Or, why do men pursue physical activities? To attribute such pursuits to innate "drives" is insufficient and narrow. No human activity is undertaken unless human beings are motivated to perform the activities in question. The source and definition of motivation for physical activity lie within the multidimensional cultural complexes erected by man. Hence, specific physical activities are meaningful primarily within the cultural context within which they are performed, or more specifically, within the cultural perception of physical activity. Perhaps skills and activities frequently taken for granted have different meanings in different cultures or subcultures, for example, age and sex groups, or the adolescent subculture in the United States.

It is apparent from the preceding discussion that viewing man in action from an anthropological perspective has raised questions rather than provided answers to current problems for both physical educators and anthropologists. Part of the answer undoubtedly lies in the value systems of the specific cultural complexes, as well as in the methods of study used by both disciplines. Physical educators, on the one hand, have generally been busily engaged in defending the relative merits of physical activity as an educational medium rather than as a part of the total cultural pattern, while anthropologists have been busily engaged in describing cultures. Perhaps a joint effort at understanding the intra-cultural as well as the cross-cultural significance of physical activities will take place in the future so that both anthropology and physical education can truly achieve their objectives as sciences of man.

REFERENCES

1. Balke, Bruno, and Snow, Clyde, "Anthropological and Physiological Observations of Tarahumara Endurance Runners." *American Journal of Physical Anthropology,* XXIII (1965), 293–302.
2. Bennett, John W., and Tumin, Melvin M., *Social Life* (New York: Alfred A. Knopf, 1948).
3. Blanc, Alberto C., "Some Evidence for the Ideologies of Early Man," in Sherwood L. Washburn (ed.) *Social Life of Early Man,* (Chicago: Aldine Publishing Co., 1961), pp. 119–36.
4. Campbell, William R., and Pohndorf, Richard H., "Physical Fitness of British and United States Children," in L. A. Larson, (ed.) *Health and*

Fitness in the Modern World (Chicago: The Athletic Institute, 1961), pp. 8–16.

5. Chapple, Eliot D., and Coon, Carleton S., *Principles of Anthropology* (New York: Holt, Rinehart & Winston, Inc., 1942).

6. Clark, W. E. LeGros, *The Fossil Evidence for Human Evolution*, 2nd Ed. (Chicago, University of Chicago Press, 1964).

7. Coon, Carleton S., *The Origin of Races* (New York: Alfred A. Knopf, 1962).

8. Dobzhansky, Theodosius, *Mankind Evolving* (New Haven: Yale University Press, 1962).

9. ———, "Culture and the Direction of Human Evolution—a Summation," in Stanley M. Garn (ed.), *Culture and the Direction of Human Evolution* (Detroit: Wayne State University Press, 1964), pp. 93–98.

10. Dunlap, Helen L., "Games, Sports, Dancing, and Other Vigorous Recreational Activities and their Function in Samoan Culture." *Research Quarterly*, XXII (1951), 298–311.

11. Freedman, D. G., "Inheritance of Personality in Infants." *Science*, CXL (1963), 168–98.

12. Garn, S. M., "Determinants of Size and Growth During the First Three Years," in *Modern Problems in Pediatrics* 7:50–54, S. Karger, Basel/New York, 1962.

13. Glassow, Ruth B., Halverson, Lolas A., and Rarick, G. Lawrence, *Improvement of Motor Development and Physical Fitness in Elementary School Children*, Cooperative Research Project No. 696 (Madison, Wisc.: The University of Wisconsin, n.d).

14. Herskovits, Melville J., *Cultural Anthropology* (New York: Alfred A. Knopf, 1964).

15. Ikeda, Namiko, "A Comparison of Physical Fitness of Children in Iowa, U.S.A., and Tokyo, Japan." *Research Quarterly*, XXXIII (1962), 541–52.

16. Johnston, Francis E., "Racial Taxonomies from an Evolutionary Perspective." *American Anthropologist*, LXVI (1964), 822–27.

17. Jokl, Ernst, *Medical Sociology and Cultural Anthropology of Sport and Physical Education* (Springfield, Ill.: Charles C Thomas, 1964).

18. Knuttgen, Howard G., "Comparison of Fitness of Danish and American School Children." *Research Quarterly*, XXXII (1961), 190–96.

19. LeVine, R. A., "Toward a Psychology of Populations: The Cross-Cultural Study of Personality." *Human Development*, IX (1966), 30–46.

20. Maheu, Rene, "Sport and Culture." *Journal of Health, Physical Education and Recreation*, XXXIV (1963), 30–32, 49–50, 52–54.

21. Masterson, D., "The Early History of Ball Games." *Medical and Biological Illustration*, XV (1965), 259–65.

22. Monge, Carlos, *Acclimatization in the Andes: Historical Confirmations of "Climatic Aggression" in the Development of Andean Man*, Donald F. Brown (trans.) (Baltimore: Johns Hopkins Press, 1948).

23. Murdock, George Peter, "The Common Denominator of Cultures," in Ralph Linton (ed.) *The Science of Man in the World Crisis* (New York: Columbia University Press, 1945), pp. 123–142.

24. Opler, Morris Edward, "Themes as Dynamic Forces in Culture." *American Journal of Sociology*, LI (1946), 198–206.
25. Osgood, Cornelius, "Ingalik Material Culture." *Yale University Publications in Anthropology*, No. 22, (1940).
26. Roberts, John M., and Sutton-Smith, Brian, "Child Training and Game Involvement." *Ethnology*, I (1962), 166–85.
27. ———, Arth, Malcolm J., and Bush, Robert R., "Games in Culture." *American Anthropologist*, LXI (1959), 597–605.
28. Sahlins, M. D., "Evolution: Specific and General," in M. D. Sahlins and E. R. Service (eds.) *Evolution and Culture* (Ann Arbor, Mich.: University of Michigan Press, 1960), pp. 12–44.
29. Scarr, Sandra, "Genetic Factors in Activity Motivation." *Child Development*, XXXVII (1966), 663–673.
30. Scotch, N. A., "Magic, Sorcery, and Football among Urban Zulu: A Case of Reinterpretation under Acculturation." *Journal of Conflict Resolution*, V (1961), 70–74.
31. Sessoms, Janet E., "Common Motor Abilities of Negro Preschool Children. Unpublished Master's thesis, State University of Iowa, 1942.
32. Sorenson, E. Richard, and Gajdusek, D. Carleton, "The Study of Child Behavior and Development in Primitive Cultures: A Research Archive for Ethnopediatric Film Investigations of Styles in the Patterning of the Nervous System." *Pediatrics*, XXXVII (1966), 149–243.
33. Stumpf, Florence, and Cozens, Frederick W., "Some Aspects of the Role of Games, Sports, and Recreational Activities in the Culture of Modern Primitive Peoples. I. The New Zealand Maoris." *Research Quarterly*, XVIII (1947), 198–218.
34. ———, and Cozens, Frederick W. "Some Aspects of the Role of Games, Sports, and Recreational Activities in the Culture of Modern Primitive Peoples. II. The Fijians." *Research Quarterly*, XX (1949), 2–20.
35. Sutton-Smith, Brian, and Roberts, John M., "Rubrics of Competitive Behavior." *Journal of Genetic Psychology*, CV (1964), 13–37.
36. ———, Roberts, John M., and Kozelka, Robert M., "Game Involvement in Adults." *Journal of Social Psychology* LX (1963), 15–30.
37. Tanner, J. M., *Growth at Adolescence*, 2nd Ed. (Oxford, Eng.: Blackwell Scientific Publications, 1962).
38. Turnbull, Colin M., "The Mbuti Pygmies of the Congo," in James L. Gibbs, Jr. (ed.) *Peoples of Africa* (New York: Holt, Rinehart and Winston, Inc., 1965), pp. 279–317.
39. White, Leslie A., *The Evolution of Culture* (New York: McGraw-Hill Book Company, 1959).

GERALD S. KENYON*

A Sociology of Sport:
On Becoming a Sub-Discipline

Although not a new idea, the sociology of sport has at present neither
a substantial body of knowledge, nor a clearly defined domain of inquiry.
Questions of definition, orientation, and method have hardly been raised,
let alone answered. However, recent developments suggest that there is
a mounting interest in the sociology of sport which promises to be more
than fleeting. The quantity of literature has been increasing steadily during the past few years. There have been discussions at several professional meetings. In Europe, where there is the greatest activity, the
International Committee for Sport Sociology was recently formed as an
affiliate of two UNESCO organizations—the International Council of
Sport and Physical Education, and the International Sociological Association. The Committee, which held its first international seminar in
April, 1966, in Cologne, represented interest from a wide range of countries; from the Soviet Union to the United States, from Japan to Cuba.
The English language *International Review of Sport Sociology*,[1] became
a reality in 1966. Insofar as they will encompass the social psychology
of sport, the recently formed International and North American Societies
for the Psychology of Sport could make additional contributions. More-

*Department of Physical Education—Men, University of Wisconsin. This is a
revised and extended version of a paper read at the History and Philosophy Section
of the AAHPER National Convention, Chicago, March 18, 1966.
[1]*International Review of Sport Sociology* (Vol. 1, 1966, 265 pages) distributed by
"ARS POLONA", Krakowskie Przedmiescie 7, Warsaw, Poland. Edited by Andrzej
Wohl, Akademia Wychowania Fizycznego, ul. Marymoncka 34, Warsaw, Poland.

over, it is now possible in the United States, to pursue the Ph.D. degree with a specialization in the sociology of sport.

Such an upsurge of interest in a relatively undelineated subject area calls for the consideration of certain conceptual and methodological issues that invariably confront workers in any new field. With this in mind, the purpose of this chapter is to identify, illustrate, and comment upon a few of such issues, with the hope that, if nothing else, some much-needed debate will be stimulated. The discussion is divided into three parts: first, an attempt to place the sociology of sport in a particular frame of reference; second, to consider some prerequisites to the development of a substantial sociology of sport; and third, to discuss some implications for physical education. The treatment of each of these questions will necessarily be brief.

A FRAME OF REFERENCE—THE LOCUS PROBLEM

Any new field has as its origin some already established field or fields. To date, interest in sport sociology has come from both sociology and physical education. However, physical educators, particularly those writing a decade or two ago, seemed to conceive of sport sociology as the study of ways to increase the efficiency of "social development," that is, the development of certain "desirable" social behaviors through school physical education programs. This "mission-oriented" approach is certainly an understandable one, since it came from dedicated members of a *profession*. The outlook of sociologists, particularly those in the Western countries, as members of a *discipline*, has been somewhat different. Thus, a choice can be made between the two approaches based on the direction of one's sympathies. Unfortunately, the issue is not as clear cut as this.

Recently an old debate was revived by Henry (1964), namely, the question of whether physical education ought to be a discipline, a profession, or both. In the fact of the complexity of this issue, and, admittedly, on a somewhat authoritarian note, the following statements are presented for the readers' consideration.

To be a discipline implies among other things, having as an objective the *understanding of some portion of reality*—that is, *its description, its explanation, and sometimes its prediction*. A profession, on the other hand, has as its fundamental goal, the *altering of some aspects of reality* with a view to *improving the lot of mankind*. If the motivation of a discipline is curiosity, that of a profession is service, the welfare of humanity. It is simply a matter of "what is" vs. "what ought to be." It follows, therefore, that arguing that a given field can be simultaneously a profession and a discipline is little else save a logically invalid contradiction of terms. The only solution to this dilemma would be to recognize that, while it is possible for the same phenomenon to serve as the focal point of both a profesion and a discipline (subject matter for one, a medium for the other), it is there that the similarity ends. Thus, the expression "physical education" with its obvious professional connotations, is not a suitable label for both the professional *and* disciplinary aspects of human physical activity. However, because of its widespread currency, and despite the semantic difficulties long alluded to, the term might be retained, but in a restricted sense. Those who would use physical activity to change behavior—whether it be cognitive, affective or psychomotor— we may term *physical educators*. On the other hand, those whose objective is to understand the phenomenon, we may consider members of a discipline, the name of which is still a topic of much debate.[2]

Regardless of the label that meets with the greatest favor, there is no logical reason why the study of all the various manifestations of sport, exercise, and dance cannot be put under a single umbrella, one that could include the traditional approaches, whether they be scientific or humanistic. It is conceivable that certain subfields would emerge, based primarily on different approaches to truth, and perhaps to some extent, on interest in particular forms of physical activity. Thus, one major classification may be the *sport sciences*, which in turn could be subdivided into the physical science of sport, the biological science of sport, and the social science of sport. Most existing scientific approaches could logically be placed within one of these subfields without doing too much damage to their traditional characteristics.

It follows that the *sociology of sport* would be subsumed under the social science of sport and as such may be defined as the study of the underlying regularity of human social behavior within situations involving sport. Such a definition places the field within the confines of a discipline; in this case one committed to the extension of knowledge about a phenomenon as old as man, his physical activity or movement.[3]

[2]If "physical education" is to designate a profession—or better—a component of the teaching profession, what term should be used to designate the discipline? Several labels have been offered, but, there appears to be little agreement at the moment. The point of departure for Morehouse and the group at UCLA has been "kinesiology." Larson has suggested "the activity sciences." The University of Illinois is developing a curricular option in "exercise science." At Laval University in Quebec their science of man in motion is "kinanthropology." Although in a more limited sense, Hubbard (1960) talks about "Homokinetics." Stish (1963) and others, avoiding the mixing of Latin and Greek roots, have used the term "anthropokinetics." Since "ology" is the Greek suffix meaning "the study of", the study of moving man actually should be "anthropokineticology" (an-throp'-o-kin-et-i-col'-o-gy).

[3]It should be clear then, that a *sociology of physical education*, is closely akin to the already established *sociology of education* and as such has not too much in common with the sociology of sport.

Whether sport sociology becomes part of an already emerging sport sciences field,[4] or, as more sociologists become interested in the phenomenon, as part of sociology, perhaps closely related to the sociology of leisure, it is too early to say. So long as it continues to attract scholars and researchers with a wide variety of backgrounds the "locus" of sport sociology is not a crucial issue. Its orientation is crucial, however. Thus, for reasons already stated I cannot conceive of sport sociology and physical education as one and the same thing. I firmly believe that, if we seek a social scientific understanding of sport, we cannot play two roles at the same time. Just as sociology is not social work, neither is sport sociology motor therapy.

In the present context the question arises as to whether the subject matter of the sociology of sport is simply a part of sociology or some other social science, or whether it is sufficiently independent to warrant separate attention. For example, Henry (1964) has argued that exercise physiology is not *applied* physiology, but physiology *per se*. I would argue that it is neither, rather it is *exercise physiology*. This apparent tautology can be understood if we consider that the distinction between two fields of inquiry is based primarily on the nature of the phenomenon to which workers in those fields devote their attention. I would suggest that the exercise physiologist seeks to understand the physiology of exercise stress, while the goal of the physiologist is not to understand physical activity as such, but to understand the function of the organism or one of its systems. Similarly, the sociologist, insofar as he might wish to study the social aspects of sport, hopes to be able to understand the structure and function of social systems in general, using sport as a means, not an end.[5] The sport sociologist, on the other hand, has the understanding of sport per se as his goal, albeit with the help of sociological theory and method. Borrowing from set theory, the various subfields, each with human physical activity as its subject of inquiry, are not *subsets* of existing disciplines, but *intersect* with them.

Thus it follows that research in sport sociology could contribute to both an understanding of sport as a particular social phenomenon, and, at the same time, to knowledge about social systems in general.

> In short, questions initially restricted to a particular institutional sphere have a double objective. On the one hand, they direct attention to what may be distinctive to the particular class of institutions or organizations under study. These distinctive characteristics are not at once swallowed up in generalities that deliberately neglect them. On the other hand, these questions of restricted scope can often be extended to wider classes

[4] An International Congress of Sport Sciences was held in conjunction with the 1964 Tokyo Olympics. In 1967, the Canadian Association for Sport Science was formed.

[5] The orientation found in much of the published research in sport sociology.

of situations. Neither the more general nor the more specific version of the originating questions claims exclusive value; each has its use in augmenting knowledge of differing kind. The focus on a particular institutional sphere, with its characteristic statuses, social structure, and value-system, results in findings that illuminate its distinctive character; it curbs that kind of premature generalization that loses sight of what is peculiar to an institution by attending only to what it shares with other institutions." (21: xvii)

PREREQUISITES TO A SOCIOLOGY OF SPORT

Given a frame of reference, there remains a need to establish some more or less mutually acceptable principles upon which a meaningful body of knowledge can be based. Three of these appear critical: first, the need for a *workable conceptual system*; second, the need for, and implications of, a commitment to *value-free inquiry*; and third, the need for a *theoretical-empirical balance*. Obviously, the application of such principles, and the subsequent development of the field, depends on the availability of well prepared investigators together with adequate media for the dissemination of current thought and research. These will not be considered here, however.

A Workable Conceptual System

No science can proceed without a clearly formulated set of theoretical and operational terms.[6] They are essential prerequisites to clear and unambiguous communication, and thus permit the formulation and testing of useful hypotheses and theories. What is needed at the outset is the identification of those concepts and constructs that reflect the structure of, and processes within, various phenomena of concern to the sociologist of sport. We must begin by selecting, defining, and organizing our basic terms of reference—the precursors of both good description and adequate explanation. For example, at the descriptive level, biology has been greatly aided by the classification of organisms into phyla, classes, orders, families, genera, species, etc. More recently, the development of a Taxonomy of Educational Objective (3, 14) promises to serve as an important catalyst to successful inquiry into learning and socialization.

Fortunately, the bastardized nature of sport sociology permits the use of many already well defined and well understood concepts—those already well established within existing social sciences. But there remains

---

[6]For a discussion of the role of concepts in the sociology of sport, see "The Sociology of Sport as an Area of Specialization," a report of the Sub-Committee for the Sociology of Sport, Western Conference Physical Education Meetings, Chicago, 1966.

a need for the identification and clear definition of the concepts peculiar to sport as a social phenomenon. The task is not a simple one, however. For example, the word "sport" itself still lacks a generally accepted definition.[7] Certainly the operational definition, "Sport is that which is reported in the sport pages," is hardly adequate. The word "game" is another term difficult to define once and for all. We are not alone, of course, in having to deal with such problems; for example, exercise physiologists have been forced to deal with such concepts as "second wind" and "physical fitness," the definitions of which are still the subject of much debate.

However tentative the definitions of concepts useful for inquiry in sport sociology may be, it is important also to show how they are related to each other. The result is a conceptual framework or paradigm which should permit far greater precision in communication, and consequently, a clearer context within which research problems may be cast.

For example, suppose a sport sociologist is interested in explaining *involvement in sport*. Early in the process of developing a definitive statement of the problem, and certainly before he can formulate testable hypotheses, he would require some conceptual framework.[8] Hopefully an existing one is available. If not, he would need to develop one, a major project in itself. Since sport per se is too gross and complex a concept, it would need breaking down into its elements. One such paradigm is as follows:

Sport may be considered institutionalized, competitive, gross physical activity. Its major elements are its *form*, its *participants*, its *facilitators*, and the *situation* in which it occurs. (See Figure 1.)

Any sport has a *form*, the details of which distinguish it from other sports. It has an *explicit form* including specified goals (the object of the game and the criteria for winning), and the specified rules governing the pursuit of such goals; and an *implicit form*, including the acquired characteristics of the particular sport that help to give identity to the activity—such as the ritual of player dress and of behavior.

Obviously, any particular form of sport requires *participants*. These

[7]For an analysis of what constitutes sport, see Loy and Kenyon (1968).

[8]An investigator must decide whether to use existing conceptual frames of reference or to develop new or modified ones. For example, if sport is taken to be a social institution, or a social system, the nomenclature and theory associated with institutions or social systems in general could be extremely useful as a basis for analysis, if the objective is to determine the degree to which sport as a social system can be explained (serves the same function) in terms consistent with other social systems. If, however, the object is to dwell upon the phenomenon itself, then regardless of the utility of existing knowledge of other social phenomena, that which is unique to the phenomenon must be taken into account (21). I would argue that both approaches are legitimate for the sport sociologist, so long as the worker using one approach does not overlook work employing the alternative approach.

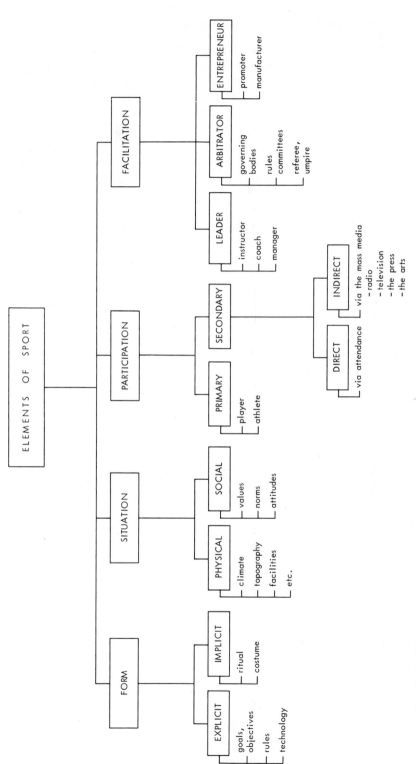

Figure 1. *The Major Elements and Subelements of Sport.*

are of two types. The *primary participant* is actively involved in the activity as a player or athlete. The *secondary participant's* involvement can be either direct through attendance as a spectator, or indirect through the consumption of one or more forms of the mass media, such as radio, television, the press, or the arts.

Any particular form of sport requires a setting or milieu—its *situation*, which possesses both physical and social characteristics. The prevalence or incidence of the activity frequently depends on or is related to environmental factors ranging from climate and topography to social values and attitudes.

Although a particular *form* of sport may be established, its *situation* receptive, and a variety of *participants* ready to become involved, an additional impetus is required for a particular form of the activity to become operational. A *facilitator* is required to cause an event to occur. Facilitators are usually nonparticipating decision-making persons who are one of three types: the *leader*, who for the most part is the instructor or coach for a particular sport; the *arbitrator*, the rule-maker—the rules committee of sports governing bodies, and the rule enforcer—the referee or umpire; and the *entrepreneur*, the person whose primary interest in the activity is commercial, but nevertheless may facilitate the activity itself or some form of it. Such persons include the manufacturers of sporting goods and sporting goods dealers, the promoters of sport for entertainment or for the consumption of secondary participants, and the various ancillary enterprises that surround a given physical activity, from the sale of food and drink to the publication of newspapers, magazines, and books.

Given the elements of sport, and at least within the context of the above paradigm, *involvement* can be of several types. It can be as a primary or secondary participant or as one type of facilitator. All are involved but in different ways. Moreover, involvement can be further differentiated on the basis of its level, degree, and pattern. There are three gross phases of involvement in sport: the period of socialization, the period of sustained involvement, and the period of withdrawal. Obviously, to research the phenomenon of involvement in sport calls for a consideration of many concepts together with their operational definitions.

In general, if we wish to explain one or more *patterns* of involvement an important first step would be the identification of various existing patterns, followed by their careful description.

Upon an adequate identification and description of certain patterns of involvement any attempt to *explain* these would call for a careful consideration of sociological and social psychological theory, which in turn would lead to the introduction of new concepts, greater in number and complexity than those considered thus far. Some might be borrowed, some would need to be specially formulated. In any case, a conceptual system sutiable for the study of sport would begin to emerge. It follows that the greatest impetus comes from the need created by research. Thus, however handy some well developed conceptual systems might be for the growth of sport sociology, their appearance, at least in a satisfactory form, will depend upon those able and willing to generate data called for by carefully conceived research problems.

As concepts are chosen and constructs invented, lurking in the background is the related question of whether those employed by sociologists should be reduced to those of psychology, which in turn should be reduced to those of biology, and so on, until ultimately the entire realm of social reality is explained in terms of certain subatomic particles—the so-called *problem of reduction*. Social reality however is not necessarily physical reality. Although it could be argued that any object, whether it be a large stone to a 250-pound tackle, is almost entirely space, approaching either head first with considerable momentum is likely to suggest something otherwise. Moreover, a consequence of reducing one field to another, is that the constructs of the former field are eliminated. Are we ready to eliminate the several useful social and psychological concepts such as attitude, self-esteem, achievement motivation, mobility, social system, socialization, stratification, etc.?[9]

If social reality is considered to have some uniqueness and therefore can be distinguished from physical or biological reality, it follows then, that the time is long overdue for challenging the long-held myth that exercise physiology is the primary source of explanation of sport, i.e., the queen of sport sciences. The writer is yet to be convinced that any amount of physiology will fully explain sport. Luckily, for both sides, many physiologists feel the same way.

Value-Free Inquiry

My business is to teach my aspirations to conform themselves to fact, not to try to make facts harmonize with my aspirations.
— Thomas Huxley

However worthwhile dance, games, aquatics, or calisthenics might be, it is not the role of the sport sociologist to promote them, for his in-

[9]"Consider your instructor's chair. If a specialist in the branch of physics called mechanics were to study it, he would see it as a combination of weights and balances; a biologist specializing in anatomy would see it as a receptacle for the human form and might assess its effect on the spinal column; an economist might see it as a product of mass production, a unit cost and price; the psychologist might see it as a part of the perceptual frame of the student; and the sociologist might see in the chair a symbol of status. Like any field of inquiry, sociology is selective in its approach." (4: 3).

quiries are not based upon the assumption that physical activity is a priori "good." Sport sociology, if conceived of as a value-free social science, does not endeavor to influence public opinion or behavior, nor attempt to find support for the so-called "social development" objective of physical education. Thus, the sport sociologist is neither a spreader of gospel, nor an evangelist for exercise. His function is not to shape behavior, attitudes, and values, but to explain them.[10]

More specifically, an argument for a value-free or value-neutral stance for the sport sociologist has three aspects to it. First, is the basic question of a value-free method. Here the researcher who allows his personal values or social philosophy to influence his observation (he sees what he wants to see) or color his interpretations is simply engaging in bad science, by definition. Since the goal of science is to achieve a semblance of lawfulness or agreement about the nature of physical and social reality, this goal can be greatly delayed by the use of contaminated mehods, since it would be largely by chance that any consistency would be reported among observers of the same phenomenon.

A second aspect of the value-free argument concerns the choice of subject matter. Regardless of the "freedom" enjoyed by the investigator, certainly many factors, from the desires of a funding agency to those of the investigator's wife, may influence his choice of phenomena for study. However, if he is limited to problems reflecting current social problems or some practical need, the development of the very knowledge upon which social action depends could be greatly delayed. This is simply the old "basic" vs. "applied" research argument. Experience, in the United States at least, has shown that the large scale "crash program" has not been particularly successful despite large expenditures in federal funds.

A third dimension of the concept of value-free inquiry is the restrictions placed on the theoretical frame of reference which provides a basis for formulating hypotheses and for explaining the findings. Limiting the researcher to a single social, religious, or political philosophy could prevent the discovery of new and often more elegant explanatory systems. If Darwin and his supporter Huxley had yielded to the pressures of the Christian church of their time, the world would have been deprived of some ideas that have since proven to be far-reaching.

That the researcher commits himself to a value-neutral attitude while conducting research does not imply that he is free of opinions, values, or aspirations. Indeed, he may be highly active in one or more ideologi-

---

[10]For a position somewhat opposed to that presented here, see Trogsch, Friedrich, "Forschungsergebnisse im Bereich der Körperkultur und der Formierungsprozess von Sportgruppen," *Kölner Zeitschrift für Soziologie und Sozialpsychologie,* X (1966) 268–72; and Erbach, Günther, "The Science of Sport and Sport Sociology—Questions Related to Development—Problems of Structure," *International Review of Sport Sociology,* I (1966), 59–73.

cally based social movements. However, the degree to which his research is fruitful, that is, to which his findings are capable of replication by others, will depend in no small degree upon the extent to which he can hold in abeyance his personal values and perhaps even prejudices. This is particularly true when dealing with social phenomena, since there is often considerable emotional content in both the observer and the observed.

It would be well to acknowledge the fact that every scientist, prior to conducting a particular investigation, *has* made a value judgment, over and above his choice of subject matter. He has committed himself to a particular logic for ascertaining the "truth," namely, the scientific method. Beyond this point on, however, the objectivity of research becomes crucial for the discovery of new and valid explanatory principles. The point in belaboring this issue stems from the fact that sport in many of its manifestations is highly value-charged, and as such becomes most difficult to study objectively. Moreover, there is ample evidence in the research literature of studies that were obviously contaminated by researcher bias.

One of the first consequences of embracing a value-free approach for sport sociology is the casting aside of some long-held "self-evident truths" in the realm of sport. Among these is the intuitive belief that sport is sport regardless of who is perceiving it. Closer to the truth is that sport is seen differently by different people; that is, it depends on, in Thomas' terms, one's "definition of the situation." It is unrealistic to believe that the athlete, his parents, his coach, his principal, the local newspaper reporter, the sporting goods manufacturer and dealer, the promoter, or network television announcer, all view the game in quite the same way. As Berger points out, in a deterministic sense, "Most of the time the game has been 'fixed' long before we arrived on the scene" (2: 87). Accepting a "situation-dependent" hypothesis raises questions about the other long-held intuitive truths, for example, the often-heard suggestion that sport, in and of itself, is a prophylaxis to deviant behavior.

As a value-free science, then, sport sociology has as its objectives to describe, to explain, and even to predict. Descriptions, explanations, and predictions of what?

Description. The widespread prevalence of sport in all of its manifestations in American society is hardly news to anyone. Clearly, we have entered the era of *megasport.* However, despite the appearance of the obvious, together with the availability of certain gross information, good descriptive data are not always available. Statistics describing the distribution of sport and physical activity by region, sex, age, social class, religious preference, education, occupation, etc., are not readily available.

Nor has the relative interest in, and attitude toward, sport been clearly enumerated. Although gathering such information is a somewhat pedestrian task, the data acquired could be a useful adjunct to the generation and testing of theories explaining the significance of sport.

Explanation. However interesting or dull a particular collection of facts may be, to stop at this point is to be vulnerable to the frequently-voiced criticism of sociologists, namely, that their efforts merely substantiate the already obvious, probably at considerable expense to a Federal grant-giving agency. Much more interesting questions are, "How is it that someone thinks such 'trivia' are important," "What needs are met for individuals through actual or vicarious participation in sport," or "What function does sport serve in a given society or subsociety?"[11] Questions in this vein are only now being adequately formulated. In spite of some excellent thinking on such subjects during the past two decades, notably by Huizinga (1960), Reisman and Denny (1954), Stone (1957), Caillois (1961), and McIntosh (1963), relatively few empirical studies have been reported. An important exception, of course, is the work of Roberts and Sutton-Smith (1962), who have postulated, and to some extent verified, their "conflict-enculturation hypothesis." Other studies, on a lesser scale, show promise as well (Anderson *et al.*, 1956; Helanho, 1957; Luschen, 1962; and Vlot, 1964).

Prediction. The final test of scientific explanation, and closely connected with explanation, is, of course, prediction. Thus far, the social sciences do not have an enviable record in this regard. Without raising the difficult question of *causality* at this point, it seems important that, difficult as it is, the notion of prediction should not be dismissed too quickly. By this it is not meant that five or six quick studies will enable us to predict the name of the winning pitcher in the third game of the 1984 World Series two years before the game is played. It is believed, however, that through an imaginative combination of theory and empirical findings, prediction, at least in a gross and statistical sense, is in the realm of possibility, particularly if we employ certain mathematical models, some of which are already available.

A Theoretical-Empirical Balance

Students of social phenomena fall somewhere on a methodological continuum whose extremes are occupied by either strict theorists or strict empiricists. Insofar as they compete with one another, we have the rationalist vs. the positivist. It would be valuable to distinguish between the two, in the context of sport sociology.

The empiricist often seems preoccupied with methods and techniques,

[11]See the Chapter by John Loy elsewhere in this volume.

despite Claude Bernard's observation of many years ago, "Method itself gives birth to nothing." Nevertheless, empirical observation is fundamental to science. By empirical, we do not mean the sudden seizing upon what one can remember of his past experiences, but rather, the careful acquisition of sense-data, capable of verification with other sense-data, acquired under similar circumstances. This method, although not an end in itself, often determines both the conditions under which observations are made, and the nature of the conclusions ultimately drawn. For example, to begin to appreciate the multidimensionality of small group behavior requires not only the development of adequate tools or instruments to make all the necessary observations, but also a knowledge of procedures of organizing and processing data. Fortunately for the social sciences, powerful tools are now becoming available for the empirical testing of hypotheses about social phenomena. Several mathematical models, such as multiple discriminant analysis and improved factor analytic procedures, are available for handling many variables simultaneously. Stochastic models permit the study of the dynamics of various individual and social phenomena. These, together with now readily available computers, for the first time provide the investigator with a capacity to deal with the mountains of data necessary for adequate tests of social theory.[12]

In the final analysis, however, it is not finding the techniques, but finding the problem that is most difficult (21). Yet those who have studied exercise and sport frequently have been long on technical sophistication and short on adequate reasons for making their careful observations in the first place. For the most part the results have only increased the chaos in an already-chaotic brickyard (8). As has been pointed out on several occasions, we hardly need further evidence that during vigorous exercise the heart rate often increases. Moreover, there must be a more imaginative strategy for studying the isometric phenomenon than by observing, almost at random, all possible combinations of load, joint angle, number of repetitions, and duration of rest periods. Such an approach is theoretically empty. Despite great toil, it is likely that nothing of significance will be found.[13]

[12] A word of caution is appropriate at this point, however. In this electronic age, now more than ever before, there is a danger of becoming preoccupied with technique, but of a special kind. It is rather easy today to hide in or near a university's sleek, air-conditioned computing center, amusing oneself with punched cards, magnetic tapes, and the latest version of Fortran. The danger lies in allowing the sterility of such an environment to create a situation wherein the objectives of research are lost by confusing technology with science. We must not lose sight of the fact that measuring instruments and data-reducing procedures are tools, not ends. Never before have so many investigators been in a position to make so many mistakes so fast.

[13] Or as Berger has put it, in science as in love, a concentration on technique is quite likely to lead to impotence (2).

Theory, then, can help in finding the problem by giving rise to the right questions—not trivial ones, but questions of some scientific consequence.[14] Our theories will need to be modest, and perhaps only partial at first, whether they be borrowed or whether they be specially created. For an example, if certain units or modules of a social system can be adequately understood, eventually it may be possible to put these together into a larger, more inclusive system that would provide a more general explanation (28). In this regard, one potentially useful approach is the linking of mathematical models with discursive theory. For example, McPhee (1963) has postulated a model showing how the concept of addiction can be applied to a wide variety of human activities, including involvement in sport.

Returning to the phenomenon of involvement in sport, existing social psychological and sociological theory, together with a variety of available observational and data-processing techniques, could be expected to aid immeasurably in getting research underway, leading ultimately to the formulation of new propositions unique to sport. For example, social learning theory could be expected to be useful in studying the period of socialization; role theory, conformity-deviance theory and certain theories of motivation, would be relevant for understanding sustained involvement; and theories of social change and of attitude change would certainly be pertinent in researching the period of withdrawal.

Given a firm theoretical base, viable hypotheses could be deduced that would begin to explain the particular aspects of involvement that may be of interest. By way of illustration, suppose that *patterns* of involvement are the focus of attention. Such a situation is one involving choice (24). We can set out to discover the properties of the choosing organism, or we can inquire into the environment of choice. Since both are likely to generate factors influencing the pattern of involvement, the best strategy would be to include both. As a result, we are confronted with a system in which there is a continuous interplay among several variables—some providing stimulation to consumption ("stimulants") and others providing resistance ("resistants").

Although verbal theories may be useful in identifying appropriate constructs and hypothetical relations among them, mathematical models can be employed to increase the precision with which statements can

[14]Just as our emphasis upon technique may hamper discovery, so does our reliance upon the arm chair. Those who theorize need to know what the empiricist is up to, even if he never dirties his hands with raw data. To theorize in a vacuum is to risk arriving at a situation whereby "explanations are sometimes provided for things that never were" (21). Skinner (1963), not one to get overly excited when it comes to theory, argues that they can create a false sense of security, an unwarranted satisfaction with the status quo, with a failure to recognize that most theories are eventually overthrown, resulting in the greater part of the associated research being discarded.

be made, and to gain power in the analysis and interpretation of data. Traditionally *static models* have been chosen to describe the various aspects of human physical activity. For example, when several variables are to be considered simultaneously, a common practice is to study their interrelationships using various multivariate statistical models, such as discriminant functions, multiple regressions, and factor analysis. Since the problem here is concerned with changing amounts of involvement (or "levels of consumption" in McPhee's [1963] sense) over time, whether a few weeks or a lifetime, a *dynamic model* would be more appropriate. Of the several models (5, 7, 24) in contemporary use, which one might fit our data best? Strictly deterministic approaches such as the generation of a set of differential equations or the employment of game theory, are probably not suitable for our purposes. The former is unsuitable because it is doubtful that we would have any high correlations among our determinants. Consequently, there is likely to be considerable error. Since game theory assumes the presence of rational choice for each decision made, this doesn't seem to be appropriate either.[15] If we accept the argument that the choice to participate is based on a combination of both rational and nonrational decisions, it would follow that a stochastic model would be most appropriate for our purposes. Models of this type allow us to attach probability values to each hypothesized variable at various points in time. Insofar as the probability of an event at one point in time has some influence upon the probability of that event occurring sometime later, a Markoff chain approach is called for. In the final analysis, determining the best techniques, whether they be for collecting of data or for treating them, will depend upon considerable trial and error.

Clearly then, for a meaningful contribution to knowledge in sport sociology as in any other science, research must be characterized by sophistication in both theory and method. After first rejecting authoritarianism and mysticism, the sociologist of sport should strive for a judicious combination of the rational and the empirical. He can afford neither soft theory nor soft procedure.

> Researchers plod on, often ignoring the complexity of behavior, in their task of finding simple, isolated relations, while discursive theory soars even higher, constructing more and more elaborate verbal systems to describe behavior. At best, these verbal systems have provided us with a vivid heuristic image of a system of behavior in operation. At worst, they have led us into flights of fancy, and even further into a morass of words. In any case, they are hardly translatable into research terms. Yet, if our discursive theory is often too broad to be usable, our research is often so pedestrian that it offers no aid to the theorist.

[15]Game theory might be useful for describing certain aspects of the system, however. For example, the competition among entrepreneurs for clients is a complex n-person game.

Ordinarily, concerned with single relations, inferred from correlations, most social research fragments behavior, leaving it like Humpty Dumpty, never to be put together again. (7: 92)

IMPLICATIONS FOR PHYSICAL EDUCATION

Lest the sport sociologist be accused of an unconscious or conscious desire to ignore reality, I would like to make some reference to the implications of sport sociology for physical education, keeping in mind that for purposes of this paper and hopefully beyond, one is not a subset of the other. As the sport sociologist seeks to understand the situation as it really is, it is conceivable that some of his findings might well be useful to the physical educator who, in practicing a profession, needs to be armed with as much of the latest knowledge as he can possibly muster. For example, if people tend to behave the way they are expected to behave, it is conceivable that their motor behavior, that is, how, or even whether they play the game, is largely determined by those social norms embraced by the members of his reference group. A clear understanding of this and other relevant sociopsychological phenomena could assist the physical educator in meeting the goals of contemporary American education. It's not that Gulick or Wood or Hetherington or Williams were wrong; it's just that times have changed. As McCormack (1966) has observed, it's no longer "survival of the fittest," but "survival of the brainiest." Today, in answering the question, "Who needs fitness?" sociological factors are likely more important than any other.

Thus, it seems to me that the physical educator needs substantial knowledge of the social significance of sport, at least to the same extent that he has a grasp of its biological, or physical, aspects. To suggest that physical educators need sport sociology as one of their foundational subjects is nothing new, with the possible exception that in former times the suggestion implied a sport sociology in a more value-oriented or "social development" sense. Regardless of the orientation, few professional schools have had available qualified personnel. What is needed are more graduate programs providing academic opportunities in the social science of sport. Such programs might be offered by departments of sociology or academically oriented departments of physical education. At present, probably the best arrangement would be a joint program in which both departments in a given institution would cooperate to provide the best set of experiences possible. Although the need has prevailed for many years, only recently has it become possible to pursue a graduate degree with a concentration in the social science of sport.[16] To some extent the sport sociologist cannot help but benefit from an exposure to a wide

[16]Although several universities in the United States are offering course work in the social science of sport, only a few, such as the Universities of Illinois and Wisconsin, and Michigan State University, have inaugurated Ph.D. programs designed to prepare sociologists of sport.

array of physical activities and sport. There is a limit, however. If through such exposure one becomes a devoted apologist for exercise, as-appears to be the objective of some professional preparatory programs for physical educators, there is a danger of contaminating one's objectivity—a fundamental prerequisite to scientific inquiry.

SUMMARY

In summary some attempt has been made to place the sociology of sport in a particular frame of reference—a subdiscipline pursuing knowledge in the tradition of the social sciences. In addition, comments upon what is considered to be three of several factors upon which the development of the field depends have been advanced, namely, a value-free orientation, a workable conceptual system, and a theoretical-empirical balance. The list was not meant to be exhaustive. For example, no reference has been made to the important question of what constitutes the best preparation for the sport sociologist. Finally some implications for physical education were touched upon briefly.

In conclusion, if we want to become serious about the sociology of sport we need to go beyond such interesting reflections as the observation that some churches sponsor extensive sport programs while others do not, and begin to consider what the church does to sport, what sport does to religious practice, and even preference, and ultimately, the place of church sport in a theory of sport. Work of this kind requires both vigor and rigor, particularly rigor—we need to be rigorous in our definitions, in the formulation of our constructs, hypotheses, and theories, in selecting measuring devices that have some semblance of validity, in treating our data, and in interpreting our findings.

As sport sociology becomes more fashionable, it is possible that we will witness a "bandwagon" effect. That is, in a Parkinsonian sense, orchestra size increases to meet tune popularity. If excellence is our goal, pursuing it is one thing, achieving it another. Pursuing mediocrity, however, and achieving it are the same thing. If we fail, at least we should have given rise to a successor—the sociology of sport sociology.

REFERENCES

1. Anderson, Helge, *et al.*, "Sports and Games in Denmark in the Light of Sociology." *Acta Sociologica*, II (1956), 1–28.
2. Berger, P. L., *Invitation to Sociology* (Garden City, N.Y.: Doubleday (Anchor), 1963).
3. Bloom, B. S., *et al.*, *Taxonomy of Educational Objectives—Handbook I: Cognitive Domain* (New York: David McKay, 1956).
4. Broom, L., and Selznick, P., *Sociology* (Evanston, Ind.: Row, Peterson, 1958).
5. Bush, R. M., and Mosteller, F., *Stochastic Models for Learning* (New York: John Wiley and Sons, 1955).

6. Caillois, Roger, *Man, Play, and Games* (Glencoe, Ill.: The Free Press, 1961).

7. Coleman, J., *Introduction to Mathematical Sociology* (Glencoe, Ill.: The Free Press, 1964).

8. Forscher, B. K., "Chaos in the Brickyard." *Science*, CXLII (1963), 2590.

9. Helanko, R., "Sports and Socialization." *Acta Sociologica*, II (1957), 229–40.

10. Henry, F. M., "Physical Education: An Academic Discipline." *Journal of Health, Physical Education, and Recreation*, LXIX (1964), 32–33.

11. Hubbard, A. W., "Homokinetics: Muscular Function in Human Movement," in Johnson, W. (ed.), *Science and Medicine of Exercise and Sports* (New York: Harper and Row, Publishers, 1960).

12. Huizinga, J., *Homo Ludens* (Boston: Beacon Press, 1960).

13. Kenyon, G. S., and Loy, J. W., "Toward a Sociology of Sport." *Journal of Health, Physical Education, and Recreation*, XXXVI (1965), p. 24.

14. Krathwohl, D. R., *et al.*, *Taxonomy of Educational Objectives—Handbook II: Affective Domain* (New York: David McKay, 1964).

15. Larson, L. A., "Professional Preparation for the Activity Sciences." *The Journal of Sports Medicine and Physical Fitness*, V (1965), 15–22.

16. Loy, J. W., and Kenyon, G. S., *Sport, Society and Culture* (New York: The Macmillan Co., 1968).

17. Lüschen, G., "Sport et Stratification Sociale," *Revue de l' Education Physique*, II (1962), 1–6.

18. McCormack, T., "Changing Social Structure and the Concept of Fitness," paper read at YWCA Consultation on Fitness for Women, Geneva Park, Ontario, January 4-8, 1966.

19. McIntosh, P. C., *Sport in Society* (London: C. A. Watts & Co., Ltd., 1963).

20. McPhee, W. N., *Formal Theories of Mass Behavior* (Glencoe, Ill.: The Free Press, 1963).

21. Merton, R. K., "Notes on Problem-Finding in Sociology," in Merton, et al. (eds.) *Sociology Today* (New York: Basic Books, 1959).

22. Riesman, D., and Denney, R., "Football in America: A Study in Culture Diffusion," in David Riesman (ed.) *Individualism Reconsidered* (Glencoe, Ill.: The Free Press, 1954).

23. Roberts, J. M., and Sutton-Smith, B., "Child Training and Game Involvement." *Ethnology* Vol. I (1962), 166–85.

24. Simon, H. A., *Models of Man* (New York: John Wiley and Sons, 1957).

25. Skinner, B. F., "The Flight from the Laboratory," in Marx, M. H. (ed.) *Theories in Contemporary Psychology* (New York: The Macmillan Co., 1963).

26. Stish, E. E., "Anthropokinetics and Physical Education." *Newsletter: The Wisconsin Association for Health, Physical Education and Recreation*, XXXIII (1963), 1–4.

27. Stone, G. P., "Some Meanings of American Sport," *Sixtieth Annual Proceedings*, College Physical Education Association, Columbus, Ohio, 1957, 6–29.

28. Zetterburg, H. L., *On Theory and Verification in Sociology* (Totowa, N.J.: Bedminster Press, 1963).

JOHN W. LOY*

Game Forms, Social Structure, and Anomie

Although sport is an important part of American society the social significance of sport has received little serious study. The social scientists have taken it for granted, and the physical educators, in general, have overlooked it. Physical educators may be too involved in and too close to sport to stand back and assess its role in society. The social scientists may have feared the loss of academic status that would come with investigating an insignificant subject.

It can of course be argued that the social scientists' inattention to sport is justified because the influence of sport, although profuse, is not profound. This, however, does not seem valid. As Boyle succinctly states in his book, *Sport—Mirror of American Life*:

> Sport permeates any number of levels of contemporary society, and it touches upon and deeply influences such disparate elements as status, race relations, business life, automotive design, clothing styles, the concept of the hero, language and ethical values. For better or worse, it gives form and substance to much in America. (2)

Accepting Boyle's thesis that sport mirrors American life, it is the pur-

*Department of Physical Education, University of California at Los Angeles. This article is a greatly modified version of a paper titled "Sport and Social Structure" presented at the History and Philosophy Section, National Convention of the American Association of Health, Physical Education and Recreation, Chicago, Illinois, March 18, 1966. Appreciation is accorded to Dr. Gerald S. Kenyon, University of Wisconsin, who provided the author with much encouragement and constructive criticism in the preparation of this paper.

pose of this paper to postulate a number of relationships, both manifest and latent, between sport styles and life styles within different segments of American society. A tentative theoretical account of these hypothesized relationships is also provided by means of a paradigm resulting from the merger of two seemingly unrelated sociological typologies.

The ensuing discussion has three primary focal points. First, a brief overview of Caillois' structure and classification of games is given. Second, a description of Merton's theory of social structure and anomie is presented. Third, in view of Merton's theory, a paradigm is developed, positing where in the social structure each of the game categories given by Caillois may be expected to predominate.

CAILLOIS' PARADIGM

Roger Caillois (3), a French sociologist, has undertaken the development of both a sociology of games and a sociology derived from games. Although he recognizes that it would be rash and probably fallacious to define a culture from its predominate game forms alone, he nevertheless contends that the choice of game categories does reveal ". . . the character, pattern, and values of every society" (3: 66). Moreover, he contends that it is not unreasonable to consider that the very destiny of cultures may be determined by their preference for one of the four fundamental game forms he gives in his classification scheme (3: 66).

Caillois classifies all forms of play and games into four categories— *agón, alea, mimicry,* and *ilinx*—representing competition, chance, simulation or pretense, and vertigo. These categories are based on what Caillois believes to be the basic psychological attitudes governing play, namely, ". . . the desire to win by one's merit in regulated competition (*agón*), the submission of one's will in favor of anxious and passive anticipation of where the wheel will stop (*alea*), the desire to assume a strange personality (*mimicry*), and, finally, the pursuit of vertigo (*ilinx*)" (3: 44).

In addition to his major classification of game forms he recognizes four subclassifications based on certain combinations of the four categories: (a) competition-chance, (b) competition-simulation, (c) vertigo-simulation, and (d) vertigo-chance. Combinations of competition and vertigo or simulation and chance are not possible, he argues, because of their basic contradictory elements (3: 71–79).

A further distinction in Caillois' classification is that each category may be placed on a continuum going from *paidia* to *ludus* (3: 27–36). *Paidia* is the spontaneous, nonregulated, informal type of play associated with a given game category; *ludus* is the rule-bound, formal, institutionalized aspects of a specific game form. For instance, in games of competition, informal footraces among children are at one end of the continuum, and formal contests such as national track and field championships are at the other. For the reader's benefit an outline of Caillois' paradigm is given in Figure 1.

Figure 1. *Caillois' classification of games.*

Agôn (Competition)	Alea (Chance)	Mimicry (Simulation)	Ilinx (Vertigo)	Paidia
Footraces	Spin the bottle	Children's initiations	Swinging	
Jumping contests	Heads or tails	Games of illusion	"Rocket" rides	
Arm and leg wrestling	Bingo	Acting out sport stars	Horseback riding	
Fishing	Craps	Charades	Water skiing	
Hunting	Faro		Parachute jumping	
Sandlot ballgames	Bunko		Sky diving	
Interscholastic basketball	Lotteries	Water ballet	Ski jumping	
Collegiate football	Slot machines	Horse shows	Bobsledding	
Professional baseball	Roulette	Sport spectacles	Automobile racing	Ludus

FROM: Spontaneous, informal, nonregulated activity

TO: Formal, organized, regulated activity

Adapted from Roger Caillois, *Man, Play, and Games* (New York: The Free Press, 1961), p. 36.

From his paradigm Caillois works toward a sociology derived from games. First, he presents the cultural forms of each game category that can be found at the margins of the social order. As illustrations he provides sports for *agôn*, lotteries for *alea*, hero-worship for *mimicry*, and tightrope walking for *ilinx*. Second, he postulates that the fundamental game categories are reflected in everyday social life in institutionalized forms. Economic competition, for example, represents *agôn*; speculation on the stock market represents *alea*; ceremonial etiquette represents *mimicry*; and occupations such as flagpole painting represent *ilinx*.

For Caillois games are ". . . accompanied by a special awareness of a second reality as of a free unreality, as against real life (3: 10)." When game forms are transposed to reality they often become corrupted. The corrupt form of *agôn* is an obsession with success in which the end justifies the means. Corruption of *alea* stems from excessive superstition, which leads to a fatalistic disposition. The corruption of *mimicry* is alienation, which comes about when an individual accepts his disguised role as the real one. Finally, the corruption of *ilinx* is madness resulting from the use of drugs, alcohol, or similar substances to induce a state of vertigo (3: 43–55). The social ramifications of Caillois' paradigm are schematically summarized in Figure 2.

Figure 2. *The corruption of games.*

Game Category	Cultural Forms Found at the Margins of the Social Order	Institutional Forms Integrated into Social Life	Corruption
Agôn (Competition)	Sports	Economic competition Competitive examinations	Violence Will to power Trickery
Alea (Chance)	Lotteries Casinos Hippodromes Parimutuals	Speculation on stock market	Superstition Astrology, etc.
Mimicry (Simulation)	Carnival Theater Cinema	Uniforms Ceremonial etiquette	Alienation Split personality
Ilinx (Vertigo)	Mountain Climbing Skiing Tightrope walking Speed	Professions requiring control of vertigo	Alcoholism Drug addiction

Adapted from Roger Caillois, *Man, Play, and Games* (New York: The Free Press, 1961), p. 54.

In discussing the structure of his game categories Caillois states that the key characteristics of games of *agôn* or competition are perseverance, equality, and merit. Competition requires assiduous training and necessitates discipline and hard effort in the midst of battle. Contests can occur only among equals, even if equality must be artificially created, (for example, as in designating weight classes for boxers and wrestlers). The winner is the athlete or team demonstrating the greatest merit. Chance elements of the contest are reduced to a minimum so that victory will be beyond debate (3: 15).

In games of *alea* the participants are passive, employing neither brawn nor brain. A player has recourse only to "mother luck." Games of chance

... are based on a decision independent of the players, an outcome over which he has no control, and in which winning is the result of fate rather than triumphing over an adversary. More properly, destiny is the sole artisan of victory, and where there is rivalry, what is meant is that the winner has been more favored by fortune than the loser. (3: 17)

Games of *mimicry* or simulation are characterized by the fact that ". . . the subject makes believe or makes others believe that he is someone other than himself. He forgets, disguises, or temporarily sheds his personality in order to feign another" (3: 19). Simulation as a game form can often be seen in the play of children. In their imitation of adults little boys and girls assume a variety of roles such as mother, husband, policeman, fireman, space cadet, and the like. An example of a diluted form of *mimicry* is the person who becomes so identified with a champion athlete during a sport performance that he loses himself entirely in the game as a vicarious participant.

Games of *ilinx* ". . . consist of an attempt to momentarily destroy the stability of perception and inflict a kind of voluptuous panic upon an otherwise lucid mind" (3: 23). Games of vertigo typically have elements of daring, speed, and temporary loss of control often associated with dizziness.

On the basis of his fourfold classification of games, Caillois has made a number of exciting, if at times speculative, suppositions about the relationships between various game forms and certain cultural elements. Applying his paradigm to games in American society one can readily hypothesize that the predominant game form in our society, *agôn*, reflects the major value orientations of our culture, such as equality, achievement, rationality, and fair competition (3: 23). But as Florence Kluckhohn has cautioned: "However important it is to know what is dominant in a society at a given time, we shall not go far toward the understanding of the dynamics of that society without paying careful heed to the variant orientations."[1]

MERTON'S PARADIGM

Merton's paradigm of social structure and anomie (13) is relevant to Kluckhohn's admonition, for it reveals how ". . . some social structures exert a definite pressure upon certain persons in the society to engage in nonconforming rather than conforming behavior" (13: 132).

According to Merton, among the many elements of social and cultural structure, two are of primary importance. "The first consists of the culturally defined goals, purposes, and interests, held out as legitimate ob-

[1]For discussions of the major value orientations of American culture see Dubois (6), Grahm (7), Kluckhohn (10), and Williams (17).

jectives for all or for diversely located members of society" (13: 132). The second element consists of the acceptable ways of obtaining such goals (13: 132). It is observed that some individuals, because of their position in the social structure are not functionally able to fully assimilate either cultural goals, or institutionalized means for reaching these goals, or both.

A classical sociological typology has been constructed by Merton showing how individuals may adapt to the two primary elements of social and cultural structure in five different ways. These modes of adaptation, which he calls *conformity, innovation, ritualism, retreatism,* and *rebellion,* are shown in Figure 3. In brief, they may be characterized as follows:

Figure 3. *A typology of modes of individual adaptation.*

Modes of Adaptation	Culture Goals*	Institutionalized Means*
I. Conformity	+	+
II. Innovation	+	−
III. Ritualism	−	+
IV. Retreatism	−	−
V. Rebellion	±	±

*(+) = acceptance; (−) = rejection; (±) = rejection of prevailing values and substitution of new values.

Adapted from R. K. Merton, *Social Theory and Social Structure,* rev. ed. (New York: The Free Press, 1957), p. 140.

In the case of *Adaptation I—Conformity,* an individual accepts both the culture goals and the institutionalized means for achieving them.

In *Adaptation II—Innovation,* an individual ascribes to the culture goals, but does not accept the preferred means of reaching these goals.

In *Adaptation III—Ritualism,* an individual limits his horizons by not aspiring to lofty goals such as monetary success, but compulsively abides by institutionalized norms.

In *Adaptation IV—Retreatism,* an individual rejects both the culture goals and the institutional means. Merton remarks that: "People who adapt (or maladapt) in this fashion, are strictly speaking, *in* society, but not *of* it."

In *Adaptation V—Rebellion,* an individual is virtually alienated from current values and means and considers them purely arbitrary. Individuals using this mode of adaptation are physically *in* society, but sociologically *outside* it. In rebellion, especially at the stage of political action, allegiance is transferred to "new groups possessed of a new myth." "The dual function of the myth is to locate the source of large-scale frustrations in the social structure and to portray an alternative structure which would not presumably give rise to the frustration of the deserving (13: 156).

For each mode of adaptation, Merton postulates where in society the greatest pressure is exerted upon individuals to adapt to cultural goals and institutionalized means in a specific manner.

A MERGER

In the discussion to this point synopses have been given of the paradigms of Caillois and Merton. It has been shown how Caillois believes that all games can be subsumed under a fourfold classification, and that there are definite relationships between each of these categories and various social structures. It has also been shown that Merton believes that some social structures exert pressures on selected individuals to adapt to the means and ends of a culture in deviant ways.

Accepting Caillois' premise that the predominant game forms of any social group reveal its values and reflect its basic behavior patterns; and accepting Merton's premise that different modes of adaptation are characteristic of individuals in different segments of society; an effort is made in subsequent sections of this paper to develop a paradigm illustrating how given game categories may be associated with one or another of the modes of adaptation. Furthermore, because Merton has observed that any specific mode of adaptation is, in general, more characteristic of individuals from one social stratum than another, the analysis that follows will deal with social classes as well as game categories and modes of adaptation.

Social class is defined for the purposes of this paper as "a division of a society, made up of persons possessing certain common social characteristics which are taken to qualify them for intimate, equal status relations with one another, and which restrict their interactions with members of other social classes (11: 338). It should be recognized that social class is a multidimensional construct. The more basic dimensions of social class include personal prestige, occupation, income, personal possessions, education, class consciousness, power, value orientations, and types of personal interaction. "The pivotal meaning of social class . . . is that an individual's social-class position largely determines his social environment (11: 338).

An analysis of the dominant profile of American culture, as reflected in the value system of the upper-middle class, *conformity* as a mode of adaptation, and *agôn* as a game form, provides the first section of the paradigm.

Conformity, Agôn, and the Upper-Middle Class

Conformity is of course the most common and widely diffused mode of adaptation in American society. Without commitment to the basic goals and institutionalized means by a large proportion of the population, society as a social organization would cease to exist. This mode of adaptation, however, is perhaps most characteristic of middle- and upper-middle-class people. According to Kahl:

> The upper-middle class believe in themselves and in the American way of life, and they are devoted to their careers. They stress planning for the future and not too much regard for the past; they stress activity, accomplishment, practical results; they stress individualistic achievement within the framework of group cooperation and collective responsibility. (9: 193)

In view of the preceding statements it is postulated that the most predominant game form in America is *agôn* and that the frequency of participation in competitive games is greatest among middle- and upper-middle-class people. Intuition and common sense may suggest that such a postulation is both obvious and trivial. Since, however, there is not much empirical evidence about the frequency of participation in competitive activities by members of the different social classes it is argued that the above hypothesis is worthwhile.

Because our interest centers on variant profiles and deviant behavior little more need be said at this point regarding conformity and *agôn*. In view of the great stress placed on the interdependence of games of *agôn* and *alea* by Caillois (3: 114) we next take up games of chance as related to *innovation* and the lower class.

Innovation, Alea, and the Lower Class

From his analysis of the social structure Merton finds that the greatest pressure to accept innovation as a mode of adaptation is on the lower strata (13: 114). Many lower-class people, although they accept the success-oriented goals of our society, do not have access to the institutionalized means to reach these goals.

> Recourse to legitimate channels for "getting in the money" is limited by a class structure which is not fully open at each level to men of good capacity. Despite our persisting open-class ideology, advance toward the success-goal is relatively rare and notably difficult for those armed

with little formal education and few economic resources. The dominant pressures lead toward the gradual attenuation of legitimate, but by and large, ineffectual strivings and the increasing use of illegitimate, but more or less effective expedients. (13: 144)

In a similar vein, Caillois writes:

Wealth, education, training, family background are all external and often decisive conditions which in practice may negate legal equality. Several generations are sometimes necessary for the underprivileged to catch up to the rich. The promised rules for true *agôn* are flouted. (3: 112)

In both Caillois' treatment of *agôn* and *alea* and in Merton's treatment of *conformity* and *innovation* we find the dichotomy of merit and chance. Thus it is hypothesized that games of chance are associated with *innovation* as a mode of adaptation and that lower-class people engage in games of chance more often than those in the middle class. Both Merton and Caillois have made some critical observations relevant to the preceding hypothesis. For instance, Merton suggests that individuals exhibiting *innovation* as a mode of adaptation are not always consciously aware of the discrepancy between individual worth and societal rewards, and often explain their situation in terms of fate or luck.

For the unsuccessful and particularly for those among the unsuccessful who find little reward for their merit and their effort, the doctrine of luck serves the psychological function of enabling them to preserve their self-esteem in the face of failure. It may also entail the dysfunction of curbing motivation for sustained endeavor. (13: 149)

Caillois likewise observes that "recourse to chance helps people tolerate competition that is unfair or too rugged" (3: 115).

Merton, as well as Caillois, seems to be aware of the linkage between the doctrine of luck and the game context, for he reports:

This orientation toward chance and risk-taking; accentuated by the strain of frustrated aspiration, may help to explain the marked interest in gambling—an institutionally prescribed or, at best permitted rather than preferred or prescribed mode of activity—within certain social strata. (13: 149)

As a final comparative contrast between Caillois and Merton as regards chance and the lower strata of society, it is interesting to observe that Merton quotes Gilbert Murray as saying: "The best seed-ground for superstition is a society in which fortunes of men seem to bear practically no relation to their merit and efforts" (13: 147). It will be recalled that Caillois listed excessive superstition as the corruption of the play form of chance.

Having treated *Adaptation I—Conformity* as related to games of competition and the upper-middle class, and having dealt with *Adaptation*

II—Innovation as related to games of chance and the lower class, let us now turn to *Adaptation III—Ritualism*, games of simulation and the lower-middle class.

Ritualism, Mimicry, and the Lower-Middle Class

According to Merton, *ritualism* can be readily identified and is most likely to be found among lower-middle-class Americans. "For it is in the lower-middle class that parents typically exert continuous pressure upon children to abide by the moral mandates of the society, and where the climb upward is less likely to meet with success than among the upper-middle class" (13: 151).

In view of the implied value system of the lower-middle class the proposition is made that *ritualism* as a mode of adaptation is associated with the game category of *mimicry* and that lower-middle-class people more frequently engage in vicarious sport participation than members of other social classes. Whereas the emphasis of former propositions was placed on involvement in games as an actual participant, the stress here is given to vicarious involvement in competitive games as a spectator. It is suggested that within the lower-middle class one can find the loyal and rabid fans of our major professional sport teams. Within the ranks of the lower-middle class are the Monday morning quarterbacks and hero-worshippers of major athletic figures among the adult population. Such *sportniks* may be characterized as having a "vicarious success" syndrome; that is by identifying with a successful sport star or team, they experience the success they themselves would like but can never obtain. They are "in season"[2] all year long at the local bar or similar social setting.

The relation of these observations to games of *mimicry* may be discerned from the following commentary of Caillois:

> Identification is a degraded and diluted form of mimicry, the only one that can survive in a world dominated by the combination of merit and chance. . . .
>
> Everyone wants to be first and in law and justice has the right to be. However, each one knows or suspects that he will not be, for the simple reason that by definition only one may be first. He may, therefore, choose to win indirectly, through identification with someone else, which is the only way in which all can triumph simultaneously without effort or chance of failure. (3: 120)

[2]A physician friend of my colleague Professor Kenyon has noted that no matter what time of year he frequents a certain local bar he finds the same groups of men arguing over the finer points of the current sport in season. Accordingly, he has concluded that some vicarious sport buffs must be "in season year round."

Identification and the Lower Class

The process of identification in the sports context is not limited to the lower-middle class, but can be found in segments of the lower strata as well. In the former, identification seems to center on our so-called national team sports; in the latter it seems to center on the individual, combative sports of boxing and wrestling. Identification with sport stars such as championship boxers on the part of some lower-class people may express an unconscious desire to fight back at an unjust society; or it may be an emotional identification with an individual of one's own class (and perhaps ethnic as well) background who has "made it."

This latter viewpoint is given support by the reflection of Olmsted in her treatment of gambling among the urban proletariat. She reports:

> There is often considerable emotional identification with the actual winners on the part of other players. It is apparently reassuring to feel that one of one's social class, with almost insuperable educational, ethnic, and social handicaps, can become *rich* without overcoming these handicaps. (15: 82)

Caillois also observes that "chance, like merit selects only a favored few:"

> The star and the hero present fascinating images of the only great success that can befall the more lowly and poor, if lucky. An unequaled devotion is given the meteoric apotheosis of someone who succeeds only through his personal resources—muscles, voice, or charm, the natural inalienable weapons of the man without social influence. (3: 120–21)

In our discussion of identification and the lower class we have deviated from the outline of our paradigm. Earlier, each game category was treated in terms of its relationship to a given mode of adaptation and given level of social class. This deviation indicates that there may be a common behavior pattern shared by people from the lower-middle and lower class even though the basic mode of adaptation is different for each.

This shared behavior characteristic may be a passive orientation toward life. Regarding the value orientations of the lower-lower class Mott writes that "the core of the prevalent value system is based on a choice of two types of behavior: withdrawal from the participation in the affairs of society or fighting back. The more common choice is withdrawal" (14: 216). Such withdrawal indicates a passive orientation toward life among some members of the lower strata. The complete abandoning or scaling down of success goals by lower-middle-class people also illustrates a passive orientation toward life.

Having entered the domain of the speculative, let us pass on to the realm of fantasy.

Pseudo-Rebellion, Mimicry, Ilinx, and Youth

As noted earlier people who use rebellion as a mode of adaptation are alienated from the values and standards of society and are encompassed in their "new myths." The role-playing of such renegades of the social order results in a "monopoly of the imagination" (13: 156–57). It may also be recalled that Caillois listed alienation as the corruption of *mimicry*, in which an individual accepts his disguised role as the real one. Thus it is hypothesized that games of virtually pure simulation may be found among individuals displaying very mild forms of *rebellion*, or *pseudo-rebellion* if you will, as a form of adaptation.

It is suggested that pseudo-rebellion is typical among young children. Pure simulation or pretense is often seen in the games of young children and who would deny that their idealized play world is a utopia wherein there exists a ". . . closer correspondence between merit, effort, and reward" than in "reality."[3]

In order children we often find a diluted form of *mimicry*—identification that is encouraged by the mass media. The younger teenagers copy the hair and clothing styles as well as other tastes and gestures of their idols. Such simulation among the younger generation sometimes leads to contagious hysteria (3: 122) as seen at Beatle performances and during tense, emotion-packed interscholastic ballgames. This hysteria induces alienation and is thus a corruption of *mimicry*; but it is also akin to *ilinx* in that stability of perception is momentarily destroyed and ". . . a kind of voluptuous panic upon an otherwise lucid mind" (3: 23) is inflicted.

Among still older youth such as late teenagers and undergraduates we also find an emphasis on simulation and vertigo: hot rod racing, contemporary dances, surfboarding, sky diving, and the recent drug crazes.

Caillois has set forth the interesting hypothesis that in primitive societies games of *mimicry* and *ilinx* are pronounced, whereas in advanced or complex societies games of *agôn* and *alea* predominate. In writing of the two types of societies he states:

> In the first type there are simulation and vertigo or pantomime and ecstasy which assure the intensity and, as a consequence, the cohesion of social life. In the second type, the social nexus consists of compromise,

[3]This quotation, from Merton (13: 155) is slightly out of context. The quotation in full reads: "In our society, organized movements for rebellion apparently aim to introduce a social structure in which the cultural standards of success would be sharply modified and promises would be made for a closer correspondence between merit, effort and reward."

of an implied reckoning between heredity, which is a kind of chance, and capacity, which presupposes evaluation and competition. (3: 87)

Without resorting to G. S. Hall's recapitulation theory, it is conjected that the social reality of youth is greatly characterized by simulation and vertigo, but the reality of the adult world has place for only competition and chance.

Having rebelled, let us retreat.

Retreatism and Social Isolates

Merton regards retreatism as probably the least common mode of adaptation and points out that "in this category fall some of the adaptive activities of psychotics, autists, pariahs, outcasts, vagrants, vagabonds, tramps, chronic drunkards, and drug addicts" (13: 153). He also points out that *retreatism* is ". . . a privatized rather than collective mode of adaptation" (13: 155).

Because of the nature of individuals anticipated to adjust by means of *retreatism* one might not expect games of any category to be associated with this mode of behavior. However, each of the game forms in Caillois' classification do have variates which are suitable for social isolates. In view of the type of persons listed above, alcohol and drug use can be cited as a form (albeit a corrupt one) of *ilinx*. In the case of the corrupt form of *mimicry* one may point to the individuals who take on the Charlie Chaplin bum role.[4] An illustration of an *agôn* variate for the social isolate is ice-fishing. While an example of *alea* might be solitaire. Perhaps a better example of *alea* is given in Olmsted's analysis of the lonely track bettor. She writes:

> Horse racing also appeals to the social isolate, since to play the horses "seriously" requires many hours of solitary paper work—very congenial to such a person—and a minimum of contact with others. The horse player, even more than most gamblers, lives in a dream world of his own, far removed from everyday life. (15: 63)

She continues her analysis with reflections which fit in well with Merton's treatment of maladaptive persons.

> He lives at two removes from reality—he displaces his own sexuality on the horse, and then has little contact with the horse—he merely bets on it at a distance. Because of the vicarious nature of this activity it appeals to people with a rather tenuous contact with reality. The proportion of psychotics and near-psychotics among horse players seems to be higher than among other gamblers. (15: 63)

[4]Merton treats the hobo as one type of person who uses retreatism as a mode of adaptation and observes that ". . . if this deviant is condemned in real life, he may become a source of gratification in fantasy-life" (13: 154). Drawing upon the insight of Kardiner he deals with the matter in more detail in terms of Charlie Chaplin's bum (13: 154–55).

Our paradigm is now almost fully developed. We have considered all modes of adaptation to cultural elements given by Merton and all game categories presented by Caillois as related to members of different social classes in American society. Moreover, we have related these factors to certain age groupings and have dealt with the matter of direct versus vicarious participation. The attentive reader, however, will note that we have avoided any discussion of the upper strata. This fact might be explained away on the ground that the upper class contains such a small percentage of the population that it is not worthy of treatment as regards the game situation. But frankly, it must be admitted that any analysis of the social elite involves a number of complexities which are difficult to resolve satisfactorily.

The Upper Class

The fact that members of the upper class have virtually achieved the culture goals of success probably precludes the description of their basic behavior patterns in terms of any one mode of adaptation. Likewise they cannot be characterized by any one predominant game form. Accordingly there is much room for analysis and speculation.

For example, it can be pointed out that the attainment of monetary success by members of the upper class is often based on chance as much as merit because of inheritance. This observation may help explain the fact that gambling in different forms is quite pronounced among selected segments of the upper strata. As Merton states: ". . . both the eminently 'successful' and the eminently 'unsuccessful' in our society not infrequently attribute the outcome to 'luck'" (13: 148). And as Olmsted observes:

> The very bottom ranks or outcasts in most societies and the top ranks of a hereditary aristocracy share a common faith in the importance of "fate," since they are aware that their position owes far more to accident of birth than to any characteristic of their own. (15: 74)

Previous citations of Caillois have revealed his recognition of the linkage of *alea* and heredity.

Alternative game forms associated with the upper class are suggested by its major value orientations, which include belief in tradition, graceful living, familism, and dilettantism (15: 74). First, members of the upper class may be more traditional and inner-directed in Riesman's terms[5] than persons from other social levels and thus prefer participation

---

[5]Baltzell (1: 77) in his treatment of the Philadelphia gentleman states: "Following Riesman, it is our hypothesis that, in contrast to the prevailing 'inner' and 'other' directedness of the contemporary American social character, the members of the upper class, even in 1940, still retained a blend of the 'tradition' and 'inner-directed social character.'"

in competitive games of an individual rather than a team nature. Illustrations which come readily to mind include tennis, sailing, squash, fencing, and big-game hunting.

Second, the emphasis on etiquette, ceremony, and protocol by upper-class people indicates that simulation may be a predominant game form. The emphasis on correct behavior in sporting activities and the stress on amateurism at all costs is perhaps a reflection of *mimicry* and pretense. Examples include the mandatory white dress for participants and quiet applause by spectators in tennis; and all the etiquette, ceremony and protocol associated with gambling in a world-famed casino by members of the social elite. Baltzell in his analysis of upper-class society notes the importance of ritual as a mechanism of social cohesion (1: 73) and observes that "where most Americans value the doer and idealize the engineer-entrepreneur, the older ideal of the well-rounded gentle-amateur still exists as the upper-class ideal" (1: 71).

Finally, for good measure, the observation is made that there are elements of rebellion among some segments of the upper strata that are suggestive of games of vertigo. Perhaps the frenetic activities of certain playboys and members of the "jet set" are indicative of *ilinx*.

In summary, because of their unique position in the social structure as regards the assimilation and access to culture goals and institutionalized means, a variety of game forms may be displayed in the sporting activities of the members of the upper class. This treatment of the upper class concludes the construction of the proposed paradigm relating game forms (as given by Caillois) to American social structure in terms of anomie theory (as given by Merton). A schematic outline of the paradigm developed herein is presented in Figure 4.

POSTSCRIPT

No real effort has been made to support the preceding suppositions with empirical evidence. This does not imply, however, that such support is entirely lacking. For instance, Sutton-Smith and others (16) studied game involvement in adults by analyzing the data from 1940 and 1948 national survey polls and found that games of strategy and physical skill are preferred by high status groups and games of chance by low status groups. Their findings lend support to the hypotheses made previously that games of *agôn* are associated with the upper-middle class and games of *alea* with the lower class.

An example of research supporting the hypothesis that vicarious participation is most pronounced among members of the lower-middle class is Clarke's study (4) of "the use of leisure and its relation to levels of

Figure 4. *A paradigm of game forms, social structure, and anomie.*

Mode of Adaptation	Culture Goals	Institu- tional Means	Social Position	Game Form
I. Conformity	+	+	Upper-Middle Class	*Agôn* (Competition)
II. Innovation	+	−	Lower Class	*Alea* (Chance) Diluted *Mimicry* (Identification)
III. Ritualism	−	+	Lower-Middle	Diluted *Mimicry* (Identification)
IV. Retreatism	−	−	Lowest Societal Positions	Solitary Variates of *Agôn, Alea, Ilinx* and *Mimicry*
V. Rebellion	±	±	Outside Society	Corrupted *Mimicry* (Distorted simulation)
A. Pseudo- rebellion	(±)	(±)	Youth Society	*Mimicry* and *Ilinx* (Simulation and Vertigo)
B. Admixture	=	=	Upper Class	*Agôn Ilinx* *Alea Mimicry*

occupational prestige." He discovered that the greatest percentage of respondents devoting most of their time to spectator activities came from prestige level III, which ". . . includes sales and clerical workers as well as white-collar employees generally" (4: 302).

Although studies such as those just cited provide some evidence for the relationships between certain game categories and membership in selected social classes, they do not give much empirical insight regarding the associations between game forms and modes of adaptation. Perhaps sociological data of a historical nature would be relevant in this case. For example, common sense suggests that gambling would be an infrequent social activity during periods of depression because of the severe socioeconomic situation imposed upon people from all social levels. But the paradigm outlined above suggests the contrary, for it is in periods of great financial strife that large proportions of men of good merit are denied legitimate means to success and must rely on fate. Johns discussing the British situation states that "Orwell noted, during the Great Depression, how the incidence of betting, far from declining

in the period of unemployment, actually increased" (8: 145). If such was
the case in America as well, it would seem that indirect empirical support is given to the postulated interdependence between games of *alea*
and *innovation* as a mode of adaptation to cultural goals and institutionalized means.

Other evidence similar to that just cited can no doubt be found and
brought to bear on the other hypotheses made in this chapter; however,
it must be granted that if one casts his nets far enough and long enough
he can gather data to bulwark almost any kind of theoretical framework.
Thus the reader should be cautioned about certain limitations of the
paradigm presented. First, there are inherent problems in the typologies
of Caillois and Merton which do not readily permit the paradigm resulting from the merger of their works to be soundly grounded in "reality."
Caillois, for example, writes that ". . . to the degree that I will try to
establish the classification to which I am committed, each concept chosen
will not relate too directly to concrete experience, which in turn is to
be divided according to an as yet untested principle" (3: 13). And it has
been said of Merton's theory that "the dichotomy of cultural goals and
institutional means, basic to anomie theory, may be so artificial as to
have little meaning, since both are linked in reality" (5: 55). Second,
various critiques of the work of both Caillois and Merton[6] reveal major
weaknesses in their theories, and these weaknesses have likely been
compounded by the writer in his juxtaposing of the two typologies.
Square pegs can be put in round holes but, something is lost in the
effort and the "goodness of fit" is left in doubt.

On the other hand, due to the paucity of conceptual frameworks permitting an analysis of game forms in society the present paradigm is at
least heuristically useful. First, the paradigm points out the potential
sociological importance of the serious study of the role of games in
American culture. Second, it makes clear that if such a study be undertaken, then some sort of classification of game categories must be used.
Third, the paradigm indicates that if one is to examine various modes of
gaming in society, then he must pay heed to the degree, kind, and manner of participation, and give careful attention to certain sociological
parameters of the participants, such as age, sex, and social class. Fourth,
and perhaps most important the paradigm makes explicit the fact that
knowing with whom individuals interact in a game situation and under
what game categories such interaction takes place does not provide a
profound picture of social reality—one must know the *why* or the *how*

---

[6]For various critiques and modifications of Merton's theory the reader is referred
to Clinard (5), especially pp. 10–56; for a critique of Caillois see Peter McIntosh,
(12).

and *what* of such interaction. Finally, it may be noted that the major weaknesses of the paridigm may also be heuristically useful. The fact that the conceptual framework given here cannot easily account for the diffusion of certain game forms from one social strata to another raises problems worthy of investigation. For example, how can one best explain upper class, made prominent by the middle class, and is now largely the phenomenon of baseball which was introduced to America by the associated with the lower class? Perhaps a conflict theory focused on the antagonistic interests of different social classes can promote a better explanation of the matter than the consensus-oriented paradigm treated here.

In conclusion, the writer suggests that the usefulness of his paradigm will be validated if it is in any way instrumental in stimulating research into the role of games and sports in society, even if the research is designed to deconfirm it.

REFERENCES

1. Baltzell, E. Digby, *An American Business Aristocracy* (New York: The Free Press, 1962).

2. Boyle, Robert H., *Sport—Mirror of American Life* (Boston: Little, Brown and Co., 1963).

3. Caillois, Roger, *Man, Play, and Games,* trans. Meyer Barash (New York: The Free Press, 1961).

4. Clarke, Alfred C., "The Use of Leisure and its Relation to Levels of Occupational Prestige." *American Sociological Review,* XXI (1956), 301–307.

5. Clinard, Marshall B., ed., *Anomie and Deviant Behavior: A Discussion and Critique* (New York: The Free Press, 1964).

6. DuBois, Cara, "The Dominant Profile of American Culture." *American Anthropologist,* XV (1955), 1232–39.

7. Grahm, Saxon, *American Culture* (New York: Harper and Row, Publishers, 1957).

8. Johns, E. A., *The Social Structure of Modern Britain* (London: Pergamon Press, 1965).

9. Kahl, Joseph A., *The American Class Structure* (New York: Holt, Rinehart & Winston, Inc., 1959).

10. Kluckhohn, Florence R., in *Personality in Nature, Society and Culture,* eds. Clyde Kluckhohn *et. al.,* 2nd ed. (New York: Alfred A. Knopf, 1963).

11. Krech, David, *et. al., Individual in Society* (New York: McGraw-Hill Book Company, 1963).

12. McIntosh, Peter, *Sport in Society* (London: C. A. Watts and Co., Ltd., 1963).

13. Merton, Robert K., *Social Theory and Social Structure*, rev. ed. (New York: The Free Press, 1957).

14. Mott, Paul E., *The Organization of Society* (Englewood Cliffs, N.J.: Prentice-Hall, Inc., 1965).

15. Olmsted, Charlotte, *Heads I Win, Tails You Lose* (New York: The Macmillan Company, 1962).

16. Sutton-Smith, Brian, *et. al.*, "Game Involvement in Adults." *Journal of Social Psychology*, LX (1963), 15–30.

17. Williams, Robin M., Jr., *American Society* (New York: Alfred A. Knopf, 1960).

LAWRENCE F. LOCKE*

Movement Education—
A Description and Critique

INTRODUCTION

In the past decade the word "movement" has achieved a remarkable currency among physical educators in the United States. Some of the diverse implications of this recent interest in movement have been discussed elsewhere (29). The purpose here is to examine the particular concept of "movement education."

Although the phrase "movement education" has been used along with "kinesiology," "motor learning and performance," and several permutations of "the art and science of human movement" to designate a body of knowledge or a discipline of movement, it is *not* used here in that sense. "Movement education" is used here as the generic label for all of the recently evolved physical education programs that use exploration and problem solving as a teaching method; that provide an array of experiences such as running, jumping, climbing, and swinging as lesson content; that use some portion of the language and theory of Rudolf Laban to organize content; and that have as an objective the improvement of the student's capacity to move.

Among physical educators, there has been a recent note of urgency ing numbers of teachers, mostly men, were being urged to support cur- in attempts to understand movement education. In the past year increas- riculum changes that are called movement education without themselves

*Department of Health Education, Physical Education and Recreation, Teachers College, Columbia University.

having a satisfactory understanding of what movement education is or why the change was urged. It seems important to aid this group by providing a definition and discussion of movement education.

It is the latter consideration along with the unique nature of the topic that makes this document a more personal statement than is customary in scholarly writing. To those who resent the absence of consistent bibliographical citation, I apologize. They will find appended a substantial bibliography that is organized to facilitate further independent investigation.

Whether by carelessness or naiveté, hyperbole has been a common form of expression for many people committed to the concept of movement education. As consistently as possible I have chosen to ignore this fact and attend instead to the ideas that seem to lie behind the written words wherever the two can be disentangled.

I am most directly indebted to the writing of A. D. Munrow who, were his works more readily available in the United States, would have made much of this essay redundant (37). I also wish to acknowledge the influence of my colleagues Muska Mosston and Bryant Cratty who, in speaking and writing about issues bearing upon movement education, have powerfully shaped my own views (36, 9, 10).

THE ORIGIN AND GROWTH OF MOVEMENT EDUCATION

No comprehensive source exists to provide details concerning the growth of movement education. One approach is to regard the history of movement education as the personal history of Rudolph Laban. In England, between 1937 and his death in 1958, Laban refined a comprehensive theory of movement. His small body of published work included one short speculative essay on the possible use of his theory in dance (27). It was from this seed that movement education was to grow and take root in English schools.

By 1952 the movement-education-oriented syllabus *Moving and Growing* (32) had replaced England's 1933 *Syllabus for Physical Training* (6). This event marked the end of a period in which traditional methods of teaching and rigidly prescribed physical training dominated English physical education.

A second stage in the history of movement education begins after 1952. In this stage, Laban's system, originally intended as technical training for modern dance, was elaborated in the colleges of physical education until it emerged as Women's Gymnastics. This prototype of movement education exercised progressively greater influence over some sectors of English physical education.

A third stage began perhaps as early as 1958, certainly by 1960, with the entry of movement education into the mainstream of physical education in the United States. Some aspects of the language of movement education had been present much earlier. Several prominent American physical educators had been interested in some of the methods of movement education for many years. Nonetheless, it would be difficult to maintain that movement education in the United States is anything other than an imported product, manufactured in England.

Movement education in England seems to have been set up in opposition to traditional physical training. The history of movement education in the United States seems rooted in the same conflict. Movement education has been, until quite recently, the exclusive project of women's physical education. Men have not been much involved and have frequently looked upon movement education with some hostility. The association of movement education with dance and with the elementary school program (more a female than a male domain) would have been sufficient grounds for suspicion. The general neglect, if not outright antipathy, of many movement educators for traditional objectives of sport skill and physical fitness, proved to be anathema for the men of the profession.

It is important to note that movement educators have never proposed replacing sports and games in the curriculum. They have argued that movement education is the necessary foundation for any skill instruction. This implies a reduction in the time devoted to skills instruction and some delay in the introduction of competitive sports. They further argue that skills might better be taught less by command and imitation and more by involving the student's intelligence and insight. Any fear of an attack on the secondary school sports tradition is not supported, however, by what movement educators have actually proposed.

It was the women at the college level who showed the most immediate interest in movement education. Lacking the institution of varsity sports to distract them from considering the average student, women college instructors had long been convinced of the general failure of American physical education to produce physically educated adults. This has been especially true where women have insisted that more than mastery of sports skills must be involved in a proper physical education. They propose that such an education must produce a "readiness" to continue to learn movement skill. Such readiness is compounded, they say, out of a mastery of fundamental skills plus the procedures for self-tuition and must be backed by a positive attitude toward movement as an experience.

From the viewpoint of critics of traditional physical education the situation is roughly as follows. Sports skill instruction *as* physical education has failed because real mastery of a particular skill is exceedingly difficult if it is not preceded by a thorough mastery of the basic patterns of movement that are foundational to all skills. When traditional programs do provide students with some skill in a sport the skill is often isolated, surrounded by a wasteland of personal awkwardness, inhibition, and insensitivity to the experience of movement. Because sports skill instruction is thus handicapped, the result has been, say the critics, generations of adults who move poorly and dislike movement activities. These adults are the products of attempting to thrust one skill after another upon students who have yet to achieve any real command over, or insight into, their movement capacity. Hunt has called the result of this additive procedure "summated failure" (23). Whether this picture is accurate or not, it has been widely accepted by women in the profession and has proved to be fertile soil for the concept of movement education.

A DEFINITION OF MOVEMENT EDUCATION

Movement education, defined in its most generic form, is a prescription for the *kind* of gross motor skills that are to be taught to school children and for *how* such instruction is to be accomplished. Such a prescription, whether that of movement education or some other system, must lie at the heart of any physical education program.

Any attempt to produce a more specific definition must first confront the great variety of movement education programs described in the literature. Even the small number of programs that are in actual operation display a surprising lack of homogeneity. If one were to seek the essential elements that identify a school physical education program as "movement education" one might quickly be led to the conclusion that movement education is any physical education program that a teacher chooses to call movement education.

The majority of programs are designed for elementary school children (2, 5, 14, 15, 20, 21, 30, 32, 35, 41, 44, 47). Programs that seem related to movement education occur as specialized dance training programs (13, 26, 27, 43, 44), in various clinical settings as diagnostic and therapeutic programs (3, 11, 42), in community agencies for adults (31), and as physical education in secondary schools and colleges (12, 21, 24, 34, 38, 39, 40, 46).

School programs in England and in the United States provide two of the fundamental styles of movement education. There are, however, an additional host of relatives. Some of these are offshoots of movement education and others are parallel developments. Among the many related programs are educational dance, basic movement, fundamental movement, movement exploration, movement gymnastics, educational gymnastics, and developmental movement. To further confound the matter any one author or teacher may use any one of these labels as a synonym for movement education or as a designation for an entirely dissimilar program. One note of consistency is the fact that the vast majority of movement education teachers are women and most programs are intended for women or children.

Movement education may occur as physical education itself or as an element within physical education. Both situations may be found in a single school system. In the elementary grades children may, in their physical education period, receive movement education in terms of both method and content. In the higher grades children may receive a more traditional program of physical education (sports skills, self-testing, fitness activities, and gymnastics) with no more than an occasional use of teaching methods identified with movement education. At the secondary level special units (frequently considered remedial in function) concerned with selected aspects of movement education may be introduced.

Lest the reader be overwhelmed by such diversity let us turn now to a brief catalog of the movement educator's procedures with regard to method and content. While no definitive frequency count is implied, each of the following occur often enough to be characterized as typical of many movement education programs.

A DESCRIPTION OF METHOD

The method of instruction ranges the entire breadth of what Mosston has called the "spectrum of styles" (36). Individual teachers may, from time to time, engage in direct instruction or act in the most indirect kind of facilitating roles. However, in the majority of prescriptions, the teacher is cast in the role of a leader in exploration, problem-solving, and movement analysis.

Exploration

The teacher encourages the child to try out new movements, new apparatus, new patterns of movement, and new relationships with moving people and objects. In these the child is the explorer. The teacher provides only the environment and the set for activity. Exploring a piece of gymnastic apparatus may, at first, involve no more than supervised free play. Exploration often does involve more structured experiences. The teacher may give a series of challenges that are linked together so as to provide a variety of experiences with one aspect of movement.

1. Can you turn in your own space?
2. Can you turn around something on the floor?
3. Pretend some part of you is attached to the floor. How can you turn around it?
4. Sit on the floor. Can you turn in one place?
5. What are some other ways to turn when you are on the floor?
6. Try any turn you like. Can you make it go fast? Can you turn in a lazy circle?
7. Try your favorite turn. Make it high, low, big, little.
8. Can you turn as you move around the room?
9. Can you change the shape of your body as you turn?
10. Take a tiny turning movement and make it grow until your whole body follows in a turn.
11. Can you turn with a partner? Can you turn one way and your partner another?
12. Can you move around the room while turning with your partner?
13. Can you turn fast and your partner slowly?

The teacher does not demonstrate and seeks appropriate rather than particular answers to the challenges.

Problem-Solving

The teacher sets a problem requiring movement as an answer. The problem may require a particular accomplishment, such as getting over a barrier, or running in a particular manner. For example: How can you get over this box and still keep moving straight ahead? The problem may involve the generation of a particular quality of movement within a designated performance such as height in vaulting, speed in turning around an obstacle, or flowing transfer of weight in a balance task. The student is expected to generate a variety of solutions and to select one of these, on the basis of his own evaluation, for practice and mastery.

Class Atmosphere

The teacher typically acts in an atmosphere of considerable informality. The children are limited as to their operating space but are rarely restricted to formal rows or lines. The fact that children are exploring or improvising individual (and simultaneous) answers to problems leads to a considerable sense of freedom from regimentation and prescription.

Demonstration

The teacher rarely demonstrates a movement. The teacher does not function as a model to be imitated. Students do not look to her for the "correct" movement. In a typical program the central objective is to encourage the student's personal familiarity and facility with the production of movement. Thus, the imposition of the teachers' facility is regarded as contrary to the purpose of the lesson.

Correction, Refinement, and Mastery

Students are encouraged to develop personal standards for judging whether movements are effective, efficient, and satisfying. The teacher does not regard "any" solution as a good solution and will encourage each student to perform at a level consonant with his ability. The teacher does not hesitate to suggest modes of exploration or particular classes of solution. She will often closely question students concerning judgments about what is effective and what is not.

Correction and refinement often take the form of a Socratic dialogue in which the student makes both verbal and physical responses. For example: When did you let go of the bar in that swing? (Student demonstrates.) What would happen if you let go sooner? Later? (Student experiments.) Which is best for dropping down lightly? (Student answers orally.) Concentrate on trying to feel the exact place in the swing to let go. (Student practices.)

Some movement problems permit only a small range of solutions. In these cases all of the students in the class will be practicing the same movement. Given, however, the unbridled propensity of young children to improvise, the range of solutions is often much larger than the teacher expects and may take directions the teacher could never have anticipated. This lends a delightful air of genuine adventure to some movement education classes. Whatever the nature of the material, it is general practice to spend some time in each lesson on the task of selecting, revising, and perfecting the solutions that students generate in response to problems and challenges.

Individualized Learning

In movement education an attempt is made to individualize, to a degree at least, the rate of learning and the degree of difficulty represented by the movement tasks. The teacher rarely attempts to hurry a student in solving a problem or in mastering a movement. Because practice is frequently decentralized into small groups, some students may, with full encouragement and approval, be working to achieve mastery of one kind of movement while other children are moving ahead to a higher level of difficulty. One child may achieve an elaborate and difficult solution while another masters no more than a very simple answer to the same problem.

Teacher and students regard both responses as correct. This makes success relative to the unique meld of task requirements and student ability.

Evaluation

In movement education, the process of evaluation is never an obvious factor in instruction. Although the teacher is concerned with estimating student progress toward program objectives, she rarely makes relative evaluations public with regard to particular performances ("This movement is the best. That is a poor movement," etc.). Experienced teachers often seem to possess a behavioral model of the movement patterns that are typical for particular age levels. This model serves as a reference point for subjective evaluation of behaviors that deviate markedly. The teacher uses such private and subjective evaluations to guide her instruction with respect to the needs of individual pupils.

Evaluation is a concern for the teacher in an unusual sense. The ability to appraise movement is viewed as an ability to be acquired by the child through his experiences in the program. Thus, the teacher chooses methods of instruction intended to help the child evaluate the effectiveness of his own movement or that of others. The child must come to recognize an unsatisfactory or cumbersome solution when he encounters it.

The teacher frequently employs the process of observing movement as a tool in shaping the child's ability to evaluate movement. One member of the class will produce a performance while the other children observe. The teacher may then ask pointed questions about the nature of the performance. "Why do certain movements occur? How could the movement be altered? How is direction changed within the movement? What would happen if . . . ?"

A persisting theme in movement education is that evaluation is to be treated as a device for providing "information" to the student about his performance. Public evaluation that places a relative value on performance is not regarded as a necessary or desirable instrument by which to manipulate student motivation.

Pattern of Instruction

Most frequently the class responds as a unit to the teacher's directions. The teacher may use long sequences of challenges or only one problem designed to initiate prolonged exploration. Dialogues with individual students are punctuated by periods in which the class gives attention to the movement of one child. In order to help a student become aware of a particular quality of movement, he may be instructed to imitate the movement of another child. Frequently children work in small groups, and interaction between students is encouraged. Formal verbal instructions involving the entire class are kept to a minimum and activity is as continuous as possible. The teacher observes students closely, giving individual help when appropriate.

Frequently the teacher will move the locale of the lesson from a particular problem encountered in free movement to the counterpart or extension of the same problem involving apparatus (balls, ropes, balance beams, vaulting boxes, obstacle courses, or overhead rings).

A DESCRIPTION OF CONTENT

In movement education, it is difficult to separate method from content in the usual sense. The method of exploration, problem-solving, and challenge, as a teaching style, *is content*. However, certain additional aspects of content can be identified. While the child's own movement responses are the content of the lesson, it is the phrasing, sequence, range, and organization of the problems presented by the teacher that give shape to that content.

For example, the language used in a typical movement education class reflects the teacher's way of organizing the subject matter. It is common in movement education to use language and consequently concepts that reflect the particular theory of movement created by Rudolf Laban. Within Laban's system of analysis four basic aspects of movement are recognized. To some degree these aspects represent different ways of viewing movement—foci for attention—rather than four exclusive categories of events. Laban's four aspects of movement are:

1. *The Body: What moves?* This includes: (a) the activity of the body, locomotion, gesture, manipulative transport, (b) the body parts involved, limbs and trunk, (c) the degree of symmetry in the movement of body parts, and (d) the flow of body movement—the degree to which movement is simultaneous or successive.
2. *Effort: How does the body move?* This includes the organization of basic effort elements: (a) weight (force), (b) time (speed), (c) space (path), and (d) flow (constraint or freedom).
3. *Space and Shape: Where does the body move?* This includes: (a) size or extent of movement (large or small), (b) level of transit (high or low), (c) direction (high-right-backward, low-forward-left, etc.), and (d) pattern through the air or over the floor (straight, angular, curved, twisted, etc.).
4. *Relationship: With what does the movement occur?* This includes: (a) relation of movement in one body part to another body part, (b) relation of one moving individual to another, and (c) relation of one moving group to another group. (26, 27, 28)

Laban's model serves as a way of thinking about movement. It serves as the framework within which the teacher observes movement. The system indicates what the essential events and qualities are, and how they relate to each other. The central theme of any one lesson and the progression of themes through an entire program are determined by the movement educator's unique way of thinking and talking about movement.

Using Laban's analysis, the teacher decides what must be taught and the order of presentation. For example, this structure dictates that the ability to produce movement with deliberate control over the effort element of weight (force) is a major objective of the curriculum. The child must, for example, master control of how forcefully he executes a jump turn. He must sense the possible range of force and be able to select the particular degree of effort suited to the task. To this end a wide range of experiences are provided in which controlled force can first be explored and then manipulated with reference to particular needs.

Laban's system also dictates the nature of progression. Simultaneous control over several movement qualities follows practice and control over one. Individual problems precede group problems. Problems involving flow and transition are preceded by problems calling for short, discrete responses.

In some movement education programs the teacher encourages the student to use Laban's concepts in analyzing his own learning problems or in observing the movement of others. Thus, both student and teacher attend to those elements in movement which Laban has identified as important.

Methods of analyzing movement that are different from Laban's model have been used to determine content in some movement education programs (1, 7, 8, 46). Although these programs may differ in such details as the inclusion of games or the words used for the elements of movement, they seem otherwise to have similar central concerns.

The scope of content will be as great as the range of factors encompassed in the analysis. In some programs this is a very great range indeed. Within the one content area of "space" a child might encounter experiences and problems in the following simple to complex sequence:

1. Distinguishing personal space from common space.
2. Producing straight and curved movement both in the air and over the floor.
3. Learning the concept of "level" as an element in space and practicing the use of a variety of levels in movement.
4. Translating from various forms of spatial notation to activity in real space.
5. Locating and utilizing unoccupied space in a continuously varying array of moving humans.

A DESCRIPTION OF INTENTIONS

Putting aside for the moment the matter of intentions that may be implicit or covert, the explicit objectives of the movement education program can be identified. These seem to be quite consistent across a range of programs that vary in the details of method and content. Nevertheless, the list presented below would not appear in any one movement education syllabus. The items are comprehensive statements which condense detailed intentions into a brief series of general objectives. Those objectives which are most abstract and thus least open to direct pedagogical manipulation and empirical observation have been placed at the beginning of the list. Those objectives which are most concrete and thus open to some manipulation, observation, and evaluation appear toward the end.

1. *Pleasure in Movement*

Many of the decisions made in movement education with regard to method and content are made with the intention of maintaining and cultivating the sense of joy and satisfaction that can accompany human movement. Informality, freedom, individual pacing of learning, relative rather than absolute standards for success, absence of coercion, absence of stress on competition, the excitement of exploration, and the powerful personal satisfaction of discovery, are all directed as much by the desire to create a love for moving as they are directed by any consideration of pedagogical efficiency.

2. *Freedom from Unnecessary Inhibition in Movement*

Many children acquire, as they grow, a terrible accretion of inhibition that smothers the spontaneity and verve with which they can move. In this way their repertoire of responses to the movement demands of life become progressively more stilted and thus less adjustive. In movement education every effort is made to prevent self-consciousness, restriction of the creative impulse, and debilitating dependence upon the teacher. This may be seen, for example, in the careful way teachers nurture the student's sense of freedom in creating potential solutions to movement problems.

3. *Awareness of the Elements in Movement*

Although consciousness of movement is not emphasized with very young children it is axiomatic that, at appropriate times, the capacity to be aware of how and where one moves is a desired goal. The awareness sought extends beyond conscious monitoring of the sensory experience of performance to more general awareness of limits (what cannot be done), possibility (what could be done), and personal resources (repertoire of skill). English movement education programs, particularly, place great emphasis on learning to be aware of kinesthetic sensation during movement.

4. Developing a Pool of General Movement Ability

Movement educators sometimes treat movement ability as if it were a unitary human trait. At other times they treat movement ability as a series of separate faculties (agility, coordination, creativity). In either case the goal of training movement ability, in a nonspecific sense is maintained throughout the literature. The purpose of attempting to improve general movement ability is to provide, via transfer of training, for all future movement contingencies. The presumption is thus that the student can acquire a general fund of movement capacity which will facilitate the learning and performance of new motor skills.

5. Understanding Movement

The movement educator believes that the child not only must know how to move but why movement occurs as it does. With older children this belief leads to the inclusion of "intellectual" content, including instruction in movement theory. The extreme form of this is apparent in college physical education programs for women in the United States. In these programs, or program units, principles relevant to movement are drawn from mechanics, anatomy, and physiology. Mastery of these scientific principles and their applications is a major course objective. More typically, instruction directed toward understanding movement proceeds with much less verbalization (particularly with younger children) and depends more upon the manner in which day to day lesson content reveals the nature of movement.

6. Attaining Self-Direction in Learning to Move

The child is expected not only to learn movement skills but to acquire methods for generating and refining new skills for as yet unencountered tasks. The teacher tries to provide an analytic set for observing and understanding movement. The student is encouraged to be his own tutor even to the extent of learning how and when to seek the tuition of others.

7. Acquiring Specific Skills

Some movement education programs use organizations of subject matter that involve Laban's analysis less extensively (at least less overtly). They use instead some collection of pragmatically determined skills. These often include running, jumping, throwing, receiving, stopping, turning, climbing, swinging, etc. To some extent, however, the goal of mastery of specific fundamental skills is present in all movement education programs. Fundamental locomotor skills and the transferring of body weight are concerns in all programs.

The reader now has a description of some of the objectives of movement education as well as an outline of method and content. Before moving on to a critique I want to set forth my conclusion as to which point in the preceding description most sharply distinguishes movement education from other forms of physical education.

No single element of method of content in movement education is completely new or unique. Some portions of content or method do receive unusual stress or are conceived of in unusual ways. On balance, however, much in movement education would be familiar to many elementary school physical educators. Aside from matters of emphasis, the real difference seems to be in the objectives. In movement education the performances that represent the achievement of program objectives will occur in the future. The performances used in the program have only an indirect resemblance to the future performances.

This situation is very different from the usual model in physical education in which the performances used as content for the program are, in part at least, identical to the performances that will be required in the future. This is the case with instruction in sport and recreational skills.

Objectives such as understanding, self-tuition, general movement ability, awareness, and pleasure in movement, indicate that movement education differs from traditional physical education more sharply in terms of the objectives that are taken seriously than in terms of the method of instruction.

A CRITIQUE OF MOVEMENT EDUCATION

In the field of education no widely accepted, comprehensive theory of instruction exists. Therefore, criticism of a particular instructional system must proceed from a corpus of maxims about the conditions that will optimize learning. Such standards are usually disconnected and open to considerable subjective interpretation. My criticism of movement education is no less unscientific and certainly no more free of caprice than other armchair attempts to evaluate educational methods without a full arsenal of empirical evidence.

Before discussing the strengths and weaknesses of movement education, let us first establish a basis for comparison. For the purpose of convenience, programs of physical education which are *not* movement education will be referred to here as "traditional" programs. While the creation of such a category does violence to some genuine differences among various American programs the notion of an average or modal program would probably be supported by any survey of physical education in the United States. Such a program would center upon teaching sports skills. In it the teachers would show the student how to perform and then guide his practice through correction. The elementary school program would consist largely of teaching simplified elements of the sports skills and practice in "lead-up" games. The secondary school program would consist of instruction and practice in some sequence of sports. Physical fitness activities might be added for the boys and dance instruction for the girls.

The critique will begin by noting some of the special strengths of movement education. Most of these assets can best be presented in terms of what they suggest for improving procedures in traditional physical education.

The Strengths of Movement Education

Movement education stresses teaching method. Whether all of the behavioral rules for teachers established in movement education texts are (or ever could be) acted out by real teachers is open to some question. There can be no question, however, that the teacher's behavior in making a vast range of decisions forms the bridge between the subject matter tasks of the curriculum and the learning processes of the student. Teaching methods *are* those decisions and teaching method does matter. More to the point, movement education has provided the first stimulating, nonpedantic break with a long tradition of slighting or mistreating teaching method, both in physical education textbooks and in professional preparation programs. Exploration, problem solving, and all that these imply for the teacher's behavior are sharp breaks with an undistinguished tradition.

Movement education focuses upon children and the teachers of children. For a variety of reasons elementary physical education has not always been taken seriously by people inside or outside the profession. This is largely a matter of the sociopolitical structure of physical education as a profession and is not the result of logic. Physical educators generally acknowledge that the early elementary school years are a crucial period for developing readiness for sports skill instruction. Yet, by junior high school many members of a typical physical education class appear unable to profit from skill instruction without extensive remedial effort. It is too simple to claim that these children have poor motor ability.

Although movement education has been used with students at all age levels it is particularly well designed to fit the characteristics of young children. Movement education makes great use of the enthusiasm, creative potential, and curiosity that are the hallmarks of children. Further, movement education tries to take into account what young children cannot do, what they fear, and the importance of their own peculiar pacing for learning.

By emphasizing the crucial importance of experience in the lower grades movement educators have contributed a small nudge toward toppling the disastrous structure of contemporary physical education. In this structure, with rare exceptions, the outstanding teachers are promoted to higher grade levels in the school system. They move upward to where the rewards are found. Unfortunately, this is also where their talents often can make not a larger but a smaller contribution to the objectives of physical education.

Movement education encourages self-directed learning. Movement education stresses the attitudes and cognitive abilities necessary for the acquisition and performance of new skills beyond the school years. Few physical educators would argue that this stress is misplaced. Traditional methods of teaching sometimes make it difficult to encourage and reward the kind of analytic set that is necessary for self-tuition. Each time we demand only imitation, each time we provide a needed correction without giving the student access to how the correction was derived, we make the student more dependent upon cues emitted by the teacher. Such a process is correctly called training. Only when the student is required to add his own creative insight and skill can it be called education.

Movement education emphasizes the process of observing movement. The process of closely observing the movement of others and one's self can be a valuable aid in learning complex skills. Traditional physical education has given astoundingly little attention to instruction and practice in observing and analyzing movement. This has even been true in the preparation of physical education teachers themselves. Movement education provides much guided practice in the intelligent observation of movement.

Movement education stresses appropriate introductory experiences to movement skills. In traditional physical education programs the children are sometimes thrust forward into complex games and into demanding situations long before they have oriented themselves. In order to learn effectively a child must be familiar and comfortable with the learning situation. By providing for exploration, familiarization, and some individualization of the rate of learning, movement education has a powerful advantage over some traditional programs.

Given the great stress on appropriate introductory experiences, movement education may be regarded as *precurriculum*—as readiness training. Something of this sort is at least implicit in the movement education literature. Like the proponents of some of Bruner's theories, the movement educators do not want to teach before the child is ready. On the other hand they do not want to wait until the child is ready. They intend to teach readiness.

Movement educators recognize the importance of theory in organizing subject matter and selecting methods of instruction. Despite internecine squabbles over Laban's theories, leaders in movement education have persistently stressed the need for using *some* theoretical structure as a reference point in determining content and method. Traditional physical education has, too often, been governed by expediency. Methods of instruction have been selected because they could be made to work in a given situation. Such collections of pat techniques for specific situations produce a kind of educational low gear. The teacher has no guiding principles by which to make rational decisions and lacks any basis for constant self-criticism and improvement.

A good theory provides a matrix of propositions stating the way in which teaching method relates to actual changes in various kinds of learners. The propositions are anchored in carefully collected data. Movement education offers no such comprehensive theory and its supporters have largely ignored the matter of empirical data. On the other hand, movement education does provide a workable taxonomy of subject matter and at least a rough way of systematically relating content, methods, and particular kinds of learners. The importance of the theories of movement education is not so much that they are perfect or universally applicable but rather that they set a rationale for practice that is explicit and examinable.

Teachers directly involved in movement education have related to me several miscellaneous assets that seem worthy of note. Teachers have a more practical eye than authors of textbooks. Their observations thus provide a different flavor.

1. Movement education, when good teachers are available and there are small classes with adequate equipment, provides an immense amount of very genuine pleasure for children.

2. Movement education has proved to be an ideal setting in which to identify children who can profit from remedial physical education. Such children often can slip by in an ordinary physical education class.
3. Movement education has proved to be an ideal setting for identifying the quick learner and facile performer. These are the individuals destined for dance training and varsity sports.
4. Movement education has had a facilitating effect upon dance and gymnastic programs, leading to the development of suitable teaching space and the purchase of a wider range of equipment. Movement education has had a direct effect upon gymnastics in that it encourages tumbling, free exercise, and apparatus routines that are less preconceived, and which are often exciting and highly adventurous.

The Problems Presented by Movement Education

Any system of education will present some disadvantages. Armed with an understanding of advantages and strengths let us now turn to the problems that give many physical educators serious reservations about movement education. Problems that I judge to be most important appear at the beginning of the list.

Movement education emphasizes an ultimate objective that may be impossible to attain. Movement education is a complex system which proposes to accomplish many things. Some of its objectives are immediate but most are long range. The objective that seems to me to come closest to serving the purpose of an "ultimate objective" is the intention *to teach children to move well in all activities.* More specifically, many movement educators expect to facilitate, if not accomplish, the learning of sports skills.

Movement educators either directly or by implication propose to develop a general capacity for movement that will facilitate subsequent skill learning. Whether a given educator stresses transfer to sports skills or to the more general sort of movement requirements found in adult living is an individual matter. The essence of the intention remains the same. The identification of this objective is a significant point and calls for documentation. While the following quotations are specifically selected to illustrate the point at hand, they are, I think, a reasonable representation.

> Basic movement skills are designed to increase the range and effectiveness of general movement patterns fundamental to the development of highly specialized skills. (12: 1)
>
> The purpose of these skills (educational gymnastics) is to give the individual mastery over himself in a wide variety of situations. The experience of solving problems and moving in many different ways develops kinesthetic consciousness and feeling for movement. This forms

a pool of general skill which probably contributes to the learning of any physical skill. (34: 8)

As a child progresses in experiences in movement, he will be better able to achieve mastery in a variety of activities if he has been encouraged to explore his own movement from a great many different approaches and to discover for himself satisfying movement patterns. (14: 3)

It is to be hoped that through the training in these movement-qualities and through movement education generally, individual standards of body coordination may be raised so that a skill learner while still having to learn a new skill, does so without the clumsy, jerky, wasteful movements that characterize unskilled performances, with the result that learning occurs much more quickly and happily. (44: 30)

What, then, are the potential benefits from such an experience (movement exploration)?

  1. To develop skill in and knowledge of movement through progressively designed experiences which later can be applied to all phases of life. (2: 5)

One cannot learn to play tennis without playing tennis. However, the learning of tennis can be facilitated . . . through the application of previously learned patterns and knowledge of the way the body produces and controls force. (7: 364–65)

. . . the exercise of the flow of movement will enable a child to use his mobility for all practical purposes in everyday life. (27: 96)

People trained in the performance of the eight basic actions, combined with bound and fluent flow, will be more able to choose the appropriate movements for any tasks they face than those who rely entirely upon their natural gifts or intuition. (28: 18)

Movement education thus proposes to teach readiness for future movement demands. Whether it is called the pool of general movement ability, good body coordination, kinesthetic sensitivity, effective general movement patterns, a feeling for movement, or simply skill in movement, the words add up to a concept of general ability that will persistently transfer so as to facilitate learning and performance in new skills.

Can movement education accomplish what it thus proposes to do? Only two things are sure in regard to this question. *First: no reliable empirical data dealing with movement education has been published to make such a judgment possible.* Movement education was initially the product of data-free theorizing. This is an acceptable and sometimes necessary process. That movement education has so far remained in the schools as data-free practice is less fortunate and not acceptable. The only empirical information we have that concerns the achievement of objectives comes from movement education teachers. The difficulty here is that the teacher's judgment can be a defective source. Long-term successes of a particular practice are not observable, and short-term results are not easily traced to the teaching methods from which they presumably arose.

Second: while the evidence presently available concerning general motor factors is not in complete agreement, it does not support the existence of unitiary faculties such as coordination, kinesthesis, or general movement ability. A movement educator must presume not only that general human faculties exist but also that he can train them so that transfer will occur in a variety of specific tasks.

The questions of transfer of training in motor tasks and general versus specific models for the organization of human motor ability have been much discussed and will not be examined in detail here. Readers interested in the substance of recent discussions in these areas should see: Battig (4), Fleishman (17, 18), Fitts (16), Cratty (9, 10), Knapp (25), and Munrow (37).

It seems likely that Cratty is correct in his observation that it is indefensible (and unhelpful) to declare perceptual-motor skills either specific or general (10). A learner can possess both kinds of ability with regard to a given task. One suspects, however, that such general factors as do exist are relatively unmodifiable. At the very least we can expect these to have been largely determined by middle childhood. Intelligence, characteristic level of arousal, persistence, and such perceptual abilities as spatial visualization are probably not open to any substantial manipulation. The remaining factors seem likely to be skills that are closely tied to the tasks in which they were acquired and between which we would expect little transfer. If these assumptions are even partly true then the movement educator may be falling between two stools.

No one, not even the most ardent supporter of movement education, would claim that a general movement lesson is a better way to learn tennis than a tennis lesson. The movement educator would argue that a child must come to the tennis lesson *ready* to learn. He must possess the necessary strength, attention span, psychological readiness for competitive sport, positive attitude towards movement activities, confidence in his own capacity to master movement skills, and some ability in the fundamental elements of running and striking. All of these are factors to which movement educators claim to make some positive contribution. It would be difficult to disagree although I am sure that normal maturation plus a traditional program of lead-up games, rhythmics, dance, and tumbling would produce the same kind of minimal readiness.

The difficulty arises when movement educators claim that movement education will provide a pool of general skill or a superior kinesthetic sense that will make the student of tennis learn faster or to a higher level of proficiency. It is much more difficult to agree with this assumption. Much in the research literature of motor learning argues against such a possibility. I grant that a skillful tennis teacher could rebuild some of the cognitive connections between tennis and what was learned in movement education. One must ask: Why bother? Why bother with movement education at all? What does it offer that a sound traditional program could not offer? No one knows the answers to these questions. We have only the raw data of limited personal observation—and our prejudices.

Understanding movement is neither as useful nor as desirable as movement educators sometimes insist. There is some risk that too much stress on problems, analysis, and intellectual content can undermine the element that makes movement such a source of pleasure. Those who truly love to move do not always insist on knowing how or why. The fresh joy of a child's running is best preserved by doing it—not by talking about it. Many physical educators would here stand with Keats.

> *Do not all charms fly*
> *At the mere touch of cold philosophy?*
> *There was an awful rainbow once in Heaven:*
> *We know her woof, her textures; she is given*
> *In the dull catalogue of common things.*
> *Philosophy will clip an Angel's wings.*

In focusing upon the superiority of their method when contrasted with traditional procedures movement educators have seriously misidentified and underestimated the central problems in physical education. The acceptance and enthusiasm that movement education has found in the United States is based only in part on its virtues. Many supporters are responding to the belief that traditional methods have failed to produce a sufficiently high proportion of physically educated students. The movement educator's enthusiasm, however, has led him to misidentify the source of the problem. There seems to be more reason to believe that there has been a failure of teachers and "teachers of teachers" than to believe that there has been a failure of traditional method and sports skills content. If the problem has been a failure of teachers, then administrators of movement education programs will face the same dilemma they faced in hiring traditional teachers. Where will they find good teachers? If generations of physical education teachers have abused skills teaching, nothing in movement education makes it "fail-safe" against the same teachers. Much the reverse seems to be true.

The debate between movement educators and traditional physical educators cannot become a "war of methods" because there are few facts to serve as ammunition. Both traditional methods and movement education could conceivably produce acceptable results if the teaching were in capable hands. The real problem for any instructional system remains unchanged. How to recruit, train, and retain outstanding teachers for the task of elementary school physical education?

In no sense do I mean to deny the importance of teaching method. Mosston has argued convincingly that a particular style of teaching may include a particular style of learning (36). Some styles of learning are inextricably bound to the educational goals towards which we project our students. Nonetheless, it is unreasonable to expect superior teaching methods to produce superior teachers.

The teacher's role in movement education is deceptively simple. Some popularized accounts of movement education appearing in the United States have openly or by implication stated that:

1. it is easy to teach movement education (in terms of the teacher's time and effort).
2. little training is required—a few in-service sessions will do.
3. the teacher need not be skilled in movement.
4. any intelligent teacher can master the method required.
5. movement education makes possible, if not more reasonable, the continuing use of classroom teachers in elementary school physical education programs.

In terms of my understanding of movement education, *these are dangerously inaccurate conclusions.* Movement education presents a difficult teaching task. It requires more extensive and intimate involvement of the teacher in planning and conducting each lesson than is typically the case with traditional methods.

Munrow's observation that a movement education program truly centered upon the growth of individual children, would require teachers possessing ". . . the intelligence of a genius, the insight of a poet, and the patience of a saint" (37: 262) comes close to the mark. A good movement education class is not easy to conduct, and the training necessary to teach such a class is not readily obtained or absorbed.

There is a common fallacy to the effect that what an outstanding teacher can do, an average teacher can do. It is inconceivable to think that a teacher who is not a "problem-solver" himself could teach by the problem-solving method—to say nothing of producing problem-solving students. Teachers' colleges have despaired of attempts to produce such fundamental alterations in the personal style of teacher trainees as is required by the concept of "being a problem solver."

It is important that the teacher understand what the implications of teaching method are for the process of learning. A teacher can, with practice and guidance, learn to alter his style to better meet some situations. Nonetheless, teachers are sometimes tempted or pressured into using a style not in harmony with their own personalities, with unhappy results. It seems far better to use a method of teaching that is familiar and natural than to flounder with one which is awkward and artificial. For many elementary school physical education teachers presently in the field, it is my impression that the particular methods of movement education will prove unnatural.

If the goal is to be the best possible physical education for elementary school children and if, as seems to be the case, physical educators are unsure about the role to be played by the classroom teacher, then we must vigorously resist any attempt to escape the issue by recourse to the disarmingly simplistic notion that movement education can be "do-it-yourself" physical education for untrained classroom teachers. If movement education is a demanding task for the specialist it can not be other than doubly demanding for the nonspecialist.

Movement education may not be the best method of instruction for all students. For all the emphasis on individual differences little has been said about the fact that movement education provides but one alternative route among possible types of curriculum and instruction. It is sure to be a fine route for some children. Most young children will find movement education attractive. As the program is applied to progressively older groups for whom the task of physical education is better defined in terms of the acquisition of fundamental skills than in terms of the exploration of the wonders of movement, the number of students who can efficiently learn through problem-solving and discovery will grow smaller.

It seems probable that the child who learns for the sheer joy of manipulating and mastering movement would be capable of learning under any method of instruction. Those children who are not members of this select group would probably learn better under more traditional methods of instruction. Movement education seems to make provision for *their* unique differences.

Some movement educators have made physical education seem only an accessory to academic learning. The emphasis in movement education on greater student involvement in the process of self-directed learning is laudable. Graduates with a fine array of sports skills but with no insight whatever into how they were acquired or how they can be adjusted to meet new requirements could not be counted as successes for any system of physical education. To conclude that "learning to learn" *is the objective* of physical education does *not* necessarily seem to follow from this observation. In a similar sense neither does the assumption that the disposition and ability to solve motor problems will generalize to other kinds of tasks. The dualism of physical and mental has been a haunting and troublesome problem for physical education. There seems to be a real danger in trying to meet this old problem by justifying physical education in terms of any hypothetical connection with cognitive tasks. In making this kind of claim whatever we might gain is more than offset by the fact that we have made movement a means and not an end.

Sequences of good movement problems are difficult to produce. The problems used in movement education are crucial elements in the teacher's relationship to the student. Problem-solving can easily degenerate into trial and error puzzle-solving. When this happens the teacher is placed in an "I know the answer but won't tell you," relationship to the student. This can be disastrous for the lesson. The series of problems within a lesson must be linked together in such a coherent way that both teacher and student know exactly at what problem they are working, what the task demands are, and thus, within what limits a good solution must lie. Such clarity of sequence and definition of problem elements are difficult to produce and maintain under the best of circumstances. Both extensive planning and exquisite improvisation are required.

It is sometimes difficult to know when to terminate exploration. Children cannot discover all things regarding movement with a reasonable economy of time and effort. This is especially true of complex movement patterns such as those associated with sports skills. If exploring and experimenting persist in situations where they are less than likely to produce genuine discovery, they quickly become exploring and experimenting for their own sake. This is a profitless enterprise that quickly leads to a breakdown in class morale. Furthermore, all children want to have a sense of mastering something. When the problems are diffuse and the standards of success unclear, the sense of mastery is often lost.

The kinesthetic element to which much attention is directed in movement education is not always the best focus for the learner. Focusing upon that part of feedback from movement which is available to conscious centers is of limited value in learning a complex skill. As any golfer knows, kinesthesis is inaccurate and can often mislead. The acquisition of motor skills is the gradual placement of control into automatic circuits to which consciousness is no longer adjunct. Any continuing stress on awareness defeats this process. In the final analysis, skill, from the learner's standpoint, is concerned with results in the environment and not process in the performer.

Movement education makes free use of problems in movement drawn from sports skills but usually without the implements (or velocities and forces) that are involved in the sports skills. This produces a situation in which skill is mimed. Because mime is consciously produced this leads to the sort of performance that is not at all realistic. It follows that the kinesthetic element of mime bears little relation to feedback from the real event. Recent movement education texts published in England refer to this as "danciness" and strongly caution against mimed sports movements (37, 44). In the absence of real forces and velocities the student can acquire a much distorted notion of sports movement. The missing element is what Munrow artfully calls ". . . the really shattering degree of tension evoked during impact in some striking skills, or at take-off in a long jump" (37: 195).

The range of ability and past experience to be found in a typical class often creates irritating problems for the teacher. Foremost among these is the tendency of a few quick learners to dominate the pattern of class response irrespective of the teacher's effort to provide a set for internal direction. Although imitation is in itself a skill cultivated in movement education it cannot be allowed to substitute for personal search and evaluation.

Another common difficulty is that some children tend to persevere with the first solution that produces any positive reinforcement. Failure to press on to successively superior solutions works against the basic intent of movement education. Thus, some children need *constant* encouragement to move ahead. Other children will move too fast, avoiding the necessary business of refinement and mastery.

Finally, for children whose past experience has been limited to traditional teaching methods in physical education, the initial experience with movement education is often confusing and unsatisfactory. The teacher's behavior is not consonant with their powerful expectation for direction. Teachers in schools having considerable mobility in the student population find this to be a continuing and disruptive problem.

CONCLUSIONS

Weighing the strengths of movement education in the one hand and the problems that bedevil it in the other, what sort of balance is struck? I am convinced of the special significance of movement education in the lower grades. It will probably prove especially useful with the retarded, the physically handicapped, and children with perceptual-motor impairment. Movement education might well be excellent as a remedial procedure with awkward, inhibited, and unsure adults, much as it is already used in college programs. With children and adults movement education can provide special help in the crucial problem of building confidence and a sense of command over the moving self. Certain teaching strategies closely identified with movement education such as problem-solving and the use of directed observation and techniques that can be used with profit in any kind of teaching system. *Beyond these points I am unconvinced that movement education will bring the millennium in physical education.*

It is apparent that there will be a severe temptation for some physical educators to accept movement education without critical appraisal. Movement education, as it has been defined here, requires careful matching with students, teachers, and programs, systematic planning for implementation, and thorough evaluation if the end result is to strengthen rather than weaken existing programs.

The over-all impact of movement education on American physical education could be beneficent. So long as its supporters are not driven to harden their position into a pedagogical "hang-up" we can look forward to a fruitful synthesis that blends the best parts of the old with the new.

REFERENCES

1. Andrews, Gladys, Sanborn, Jeanette, and Schneider, Elsa, *Physical Education for Today's Boys and Girls* (Boston: Allyn & Bacon, Inc., 1961).
2. Barrett, Kate Ross, *Exploration* (Madison, Wisc.: College Printing and Typing Co., Inc., 1965).
3. Bartenieff, Irmgard, and Davis, Martha Ann, *Effort-Shape Analysis of Movement* (New York: Unpublished Manuscript, 1965).
4. Battig, William F., "Facilitation and Interference," in Edward A. Bilodeau (ed.), *Acquisition of Skill* (New York: Academic Press, 1966).
5. Bilbrough, A., and Jones, P., *Physical Education in the Primary School* (London: University of London Press, Ltd., 1963).
6. Board of Education, *Syllabus of Physical Training for Schools* (London: H.M.S.O., 1933).
7. Broer, Marion, *Efficiency of Human Movement* (Philadelphia: W. B. Saunders Co., 1966).
8. Brown, Camille, and Cassidy, Rosalind, *Theory in Physical Education* (Philadelphia: Lea & Febiger, 1963).
9. Cratty, Bryant J., *Movement Behavior and Motor Learning* (Philadelphia: Lea & Febiger, 1967).
10. ———, "A Three Level Theory of Perceptual-Motor Behavior." *Quest*, Monograph VI (May, 1966), pp. 3–10.
11. ———, *A Program of Developmental Physical Education Activities for Educationally Handicapped Pupils* (Los Angeles: Los Angeles City Schools, 1966).
12. Cullen F. Patricia, and Huelster, Laura J., *Basic Instruction in Physical Education for Women* (Urbana: Stipes Publishing Company, 1962).
13. Dance Notation Bureau—Center for Movement Research and Analysis, *The Effort-Shape Training Program* (New York: Dance Notation Bureau, 1966).
14. Detroit Public Schools, *Exploration of Basic Movements in Physical Education* (Detroit: The Board of Education of the City of Detroit, 1960).
15. Diem, Liselott, *Who Can* (Frankfort A/M., Germ.: Wilhelm Limpert, 1964).
16. Fitts, Paul M., "Perceptual-Motor Skill Learning," in Arthur W. Melton (ed.), *Categories of Human Learning* (New York: Academic Press, 1964).
17. Fleishman, Edwin A., "Human Abilities and the Acquisition of Skill," in Edward A. Bilodeau (ed.), *Acquisition of Skill* (New York: Academic Press, 1966).

18. ———, "Human Abilities and Verbal Learning," in Robert M. Gagne (ed.), *Learning and Individual Differences* (Columbus, Ohio: Charles E. Merrill, 1966).

19. Garland, Iris, *Effectiveness of Problem Solving Method in Learning Swimming.* Unpublished Master's thesis, UCLA, 1960.

20. Hackett, Layne C., and Jenson, Robert B., "Exploring Movement Experiences." *JOHPER*, XXXVI (1965), 28–29.

21. Halsey, Elizabeth, *Inquiry and Invention on Physical Education* (Philadelphia: Lea & Febiger, 1964).

22. ———, and Porter, Lorena, *Physical Education for Children* (New York: Holt, Rinehart and Winston, Inc., 1963).

23. Hunt, Valerie, "Movement Behavior: A Model for Action." *Quest*, Monograph II (April, 1964), pp. 69–91.

24. Huelster, Laura J., "A Course in Movement Fundamentals for College Women," *JOHPER*, XXXI (1960), 24–25.

25. Knapp, B., *Skill in Sport* (London: Routledge & Kegan Paul, Ltd., 1963).

26. Laban, Rudolf, *The Mastery of Movement* (London: MacDonald and Evans, Ltd., 1960).

27. ———, *Modern Educational Dance* (London: MacDonald and Evans, Ltd., 1948).

28. ———, and Lawrence, F. C., *Effort* (London: MacDonald and Evans, Ltd., 1947).

29. Locke, Lawrence F., "The Movement Movement." *JOHPER*, XXXVII (1966), 27–28, 73.

30. London County Council, *Movement Education for Infants* (London: Inner London Education Authority, 1963).

31. Ludwig, Elizabeth, *Six Lessons on Basic Movement Education.* Unpublished manuscript, University of Wisconsin at Milwaukee, Department of Physical Education for Women. n.d.

32. Ministry of Education, *Moving and Growing*, Part I of Physical Education in the Primary School (London: H.M.S.O., 1952).

33. ———, *Planning the Programme*, Part II of Physical Education in the Primary School (London: H.M.S.O., 1953).

34. Morison, Ruth, *Educational Gymnastics for Secondary Schools* (Liverpool: The Author, 1960).

35. ———, *Educational Gymnastics* (Liverpool: The Author, 1956).

36. Mosston, Muska, *Teaching Physical Education* (Columbus, Ohio: Charles E. Merrill, 1966).

37. Munrow, A. D., *Pure and Applied Gymnastics* (London: Edward Arnold, Ltd., 1963).

38. National Association for Physical Education of College Women, *Competence for Action*, 1960 Workshop Report (Washington, D.C.: AAHPER, 1960).

39. ———, *Purposeful Action*, 1956 Workshop Report (Washington, D.C.: AAHPER, 1956).

40. Pallett, G. Doreen, *Modern Educational Gymnastics* (London: Pergamon Press, 1956).

41. Plattsburgh City School District, *Program of Movement Education for the Plattsburgh Elementary Schools* (Plattsburgh, N.Y.: Board of Education City School District, Unpublished application for ESEA Title III Operational Grant, 1966).

42. Pontiac School District, *Perceptual-Motor Activities* (Pontiac, Mich.: Board of Education School District of the City of Pontiac, 1966).

43. Preston, Valerie, *A Handbook for Modern Educational Dance* (London: MacDonald and Evans Ltd., 1963).

44. Randall, Marjorie, *Basic Movement* (London: G. Bell and Sons, Ltd., 1961).

45. Russell, Joan, *Creative Dance in the Primary School* (London: MacDonald & Evans, Ltd., 1965).

46. Souder, Marjorie A., and Hill, Phyllis, J., *Basic Movement* (New York: Ronald Press, 1963).

47. Wisconsin Department of Public Instruction, *A Guide to Curriculum Building in Physical Education*, Curriculum Bulletin No. 28 (Madison, Wisc.: Department of Public Instruction, 1963).

Selected Supplementary References Concerning Movement Education

Articles
Broer, Marion, "Movement Education: Wherein the Disagreement?" *Quest*, Monograph II (April, 1964), pp. 19–24.

Brown, Margaret C., "The English Method of Education in Movement Gymnastics." *The Reporter* (New Jersey AAHPER), XXXIX (1966), 9–10, 18–19.

Crabbe, M. T., "Laban's Influence Upon Physical Education in England." *The New Era in Home and School*, XL (1959), 103–4.

Ludwig, Elizabeth, "Basic Movement Education in England." *JOHPER*, XXXII (1961), 18–19.

Meredith-Jones, Betty, "Understanding Movement." *JOHPER*, XXVI (1955), 14, 59.

Books
Lamb, Warren, *Posture and Gesture* (London: Gerald Duckworth Co., Ltd., 1965).

Mosston, Muska, *Developmental Movement* (Columbus, Ohio: Charles E. Merrill Books, Inc., 1965).

Nixon, John E., and Jewett, Ann E., *Physical Education Curriculum* (New York: Ronald Press, 1964).

Randall, Martin, *Modern Ideas on Physical Education* (London: G. Bell and Sons, Ltd., 1960).

————, and Waine, W. K., *Objectives of the Physical Education Lesson* (London: G. Bell and Sons, Ltd., 1963).

Swain, M. O. B., and LeMaistre, E. H., *Fundamentals of Physical Education* (Sydney, Australia: Ian Novak, 1964).